W9-BNY-262

New Practical Mathematics

For Metalworking Trainees

By Roberta Laine

NATIONAL TOOLING AND MACHINING ASSOCIATION
TEXTBOOK SERIES

1357 Rockside Road • Cleveland, OH 44134 • 800.248.6862 • www.ntma.org

© Copyright 2001

NATIONAL TOOLING AND MACHINING ASSOCIATION
9300 Livingston Rd.
Ft. Washington, MD 20744-4998

ALL RIGHTS RESERVED

NTMA Catalog Number 5055

ISBN 0-910399-05-0

Library of Congress
Catalog Card Number
83-62514

ACKNOWLEDGEMENTS

I wish to acknowledge and thank those who supported me in my efforts to write the **New Practical Mathematics for Metalworking Trainees** textbook. Some people provided encouragement and awe, some provided expertise, and some took care of details, while I channeled my energies on this book. My family Don, Kristi and DT listened patiently to me. My friend Patty Brueggemann encouraged and inspired me. Barry Graff, Kathy Hass, and Carlson Tool employees lent expertise to this project. And, of course, my many students throughout the years who provided the backdrop for my growth and pursuit of the topics.

Last, a very special thanks for the editorial and production support from the National Tooling and Machining Association. Without their cooperative support, this project would not have been completed successfully.

FOREWORD

Practical Mathematics for Metalworking Trainees was originally developed for pre-apprentice training programs conducted by the National Tooling and Machining Association (NTMA). Since 1964, tens of thousands of students have trained through these programs. These skilled craftspeople are the backbone of America's precision custom manufacturing workforce. Across the nation the Practical Mathematics text has been successfully incorporated into numerous training programs in various fields of education. The unique material enables the trainee to gain an intensive, practical, working knowledge of arithmetic, algebra, geometry, trigonometry and metrics.

NTMA is now proud to present the *New Practical Mathematics for Metalworking Trainees*. This text is revised and expanded to include the challenges of solving the more comprehensive problems relevant to precision custom manufacturing. These problems represent the types of problems that face the trainee in an actual shop situation.

The author, Roberta Laine, is the Dean of Trades and Computer Technologies at Moraine Park Technical College in Fond du Lac, Wisconsin. Ms. Laine has a Bachelor of Science Degree from the University of Wisconsin in both math and education, as well as in German and Russian. In addition, she has a Master of Science Degree in computer education. For 16 years she taught math to students in the fields of machining, tool & die, machine repair and nursing at Moraine Park Technical College.

Roberta emphasizes, "To keep in mind that mathematics is first and foremost a thought process. Consider this text a springboard from which your thought processes can flourish." She states, "While I present occupationally specific application of mathematics as a tool for the metalworker, try to expand upon the concepts and broaden your perspective of math. I truly hope you discover the life there is in mathematics."

TRIGONOMETRY

APPENDIX

GLOSSARY

TABLES

EVALUATION EXERCISE

UNIT 1

EVALUATION EXERCISE

Skilled machinists and tool operators must master certain mathematical concepts. This Evaluation Exercise will help you identify areas of basic mathematics that represent both your strengths and weaknesses. After evaluating this exercise, your instructor will help you build a strong base that will include arithmetic, algebra, geometry, trigonometry, and applications, enabling you to have a successful career in the metalworking industry.

OBJECTIVE

After completing this exercise you will:

- Determine your current skill level in basic math without the aid of a calculator.

CONCEPT APPLICATIONS

I. Arithmetic

Do not use a calculator for the exercises in this section.

Add, subtract, multiply, and divide whole numbers.

1. 56,934	2. 1,672,543	3. 6,843,291	4. 2,874,963
89,332	384,657	−6,731,897	−1,429,389
97,968	2,988,785		
75,593	363,592		
33,897	459,678		

5. 385
  × 8

6.   976
  × 27

7. $6{,}489 \div 3 =$ _____

8. $6{,}321 \div 7 =$ _____

Add, subtract, multiply, and divide shop fractions. (Don't convert to decimals.)

9. $\dfrac{3}{8} + \dfrac{1}{16} =$

10. $\dfrac{13}{32} - \dfrac{1}{8} =$

11. $\dfrac{1}{8} \times \dfrac{3}{8} =$

12. $\dfrac{3}{8} \div \dfrac{1}{8} =$

Add, subtract, multiply, and divide decimal fractions.

13. $16.3 + 12.09 + 5 =$

14. $19.8 - 12.31 =$

15. $15.7 \times 1.1 =$

16. $0.951 \div 0.3 =$

Convert between shop fractions and decimal fractions.

17. $\dfrac{3}{4} =$ _____

18. $\dfrac{3}{32} =$ _____

19. $0.125 =$ _____

20. $\dfrac{7}{8} =$ _____

21. $2.875 =$ _____

22. $0.0625 =$ _____

23. Circle the smallest drill size.

$$\dfrac{1}{8} \qquad \dfrac{3}{32} \qquad \dfrac{1}{2} \qquad \dfrac{5}{8} \qquad \dfrac{7}{64} \qquad \dfrac{23}{64} \qquad \dfrac{1}{32} \qquad \dfrac{9}{16}$$

Solve the following percent problems.

24. 6 is what percent of 20? _____

25. 8 is 2% of what number? _____

26. What is 16% of 90? _____

II. Algebra

Add, subtract, multiply, or divide the following. Do not use a calculator for the exercises in this section.

27. $-3 \times -4 =$

28. $-15 + 12 - (-10) =$

29. $-22 \div -2 =$

30. $(8 + -7) \times -2 =$

Solve the following equations.

31. $3X = 18$; $X =$ _____

32. $Y + 3 = 21$; $Y =$ _____

33. $5J + 7 = 42$; $J =$ _____

34. $6Q - 5 + 2Q = 19$; $Q =$ _____

III. Geometry

Determine the missing dimensions in the following. Do not use a calculator for the exercises in this section.

35.

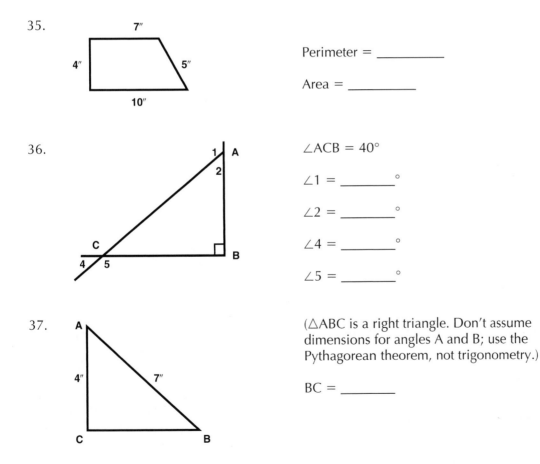

Perimeter = _____

Area = _____

36.

∠ACB = 40°

∠1 = _____ °

∠2 = _____ °

∠4 = _____ °

∠5 = _____ °

37.

(△ABC is a right triangle. Don't assume dimensions for angles A and B; use the Pythagorean theorem, not trigonometry.)

BC = _____

38. Determine the circumference (perimeter) of a 6-inch-diameter disk. Use 3.14 for pi. Circumference = _____ inches.

IV Trigonometry

Determine the missing dimensions.

39.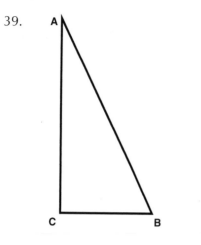

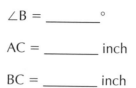

∠A = 25°; ∠C = 90°; AB = 4.500 inch

Use the trigonometry tables at the back of the book to complete this exercise. Use three decimal places in your answers.

∠B = _____ °

AC = _____ inch

BC = _____ inch

Determine the missing dimensions.

40.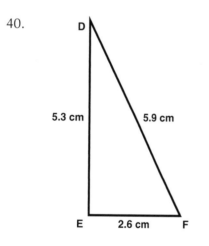

△DEF is a right triangle.

DE = 5.3 cm; EF = 2.6 cm; DF = 5.9 cm
Use the trigonometry tables at the back of the book to complete this exercise. Round angles to the nearest minute.

∠D = _____ ° _____ ′

∠E = _____ °

∠F = _____ ° _____ ′

ARITHMETIC

INTRODUCTION

A machinist's skills include the ability to measure. Measurements are seldom accurate enough when expressed in whole units. Most measurements in metalworking involve the use of decimal fractions and shop fractions. Measurements are used for job layout, reading prints, reading a scale, and numerous other tasks in the shop. Shop fractions allow us to measure objects as well. This unit covers the basic meaning and use of fractions.

OBJECTIVES

After completing this unit, you will be able to:

- Define a fraction.
- Distinguish between shop fractions and other fractions.
- Express a fraction in different but equal forms.
- Order fractions from smallest to largest.
- Read a fractional scale.

WHAT IS A FRACTION?

A *fraction* is a part of a whole number. Any unit can be divided into a number of equal parts. For example, a foot-long scale can be divided into 12 equal parts called *inches*. Each inch is 1/12 of a foot. Five inches is 5/12 of a foot.

```
      1 part              2 parts            3 parts
      ┌─┐            ┌──────────┐      ┌──────────────┐
   ┌──┴─┴──────────────────────────────────────────────┐
   │   1   2   3   4   5   6   7   8   9   10  11  12   │
   └────────────────────────────────────────────────────┘
   ├────────────── 1 foot  =  12 inches ───────────────┤
```

The indicated sections can be related to the total number of parts and expressed with a fraction such as

$$\frac{1}{12} \qquad \frac{2}{12} \qquad \frac{3}{12} \qquad \text{and so on.}$$

A **common fraction** consists of a **numerator** and a **denominator.** It is written as

$$\frac{\text{numerator}}{\text{denominator}} = \frac{1 \text{ part}}{12 \text{ parts}} = \frac{1 \text{ inch}}{12 \text{ inches}} = \frac{1}{12}$$

NOTE:

A common fraction consists of two parts: the numerator and denominator.

The numerator (top number) represents the indicated number of equal parts of the whole.

The denominator (bottom number) represents the total number of equal parts that make up one whole unit.

DEFINITIONS AND TERMS

A number expressed in the form 1/16, 3/7, 1/3, and so on is called a **common fraction.**

If the numerator is less than the denominator, such as 3/4, the common fraction is called a **proper fraction** and has a value less than one whole unit.

If the numerator is greater than the denominator, such as 5/4, the common fraction is called an **improper fraction,** and has a value greater than one whole unit.

If the numerator is equal to the denominator, such as 8/8, the fraction is equal to one.

If the numerator equals one, such as 1/16, the fraction is called a **unit fraction.**

NOTE:

Shop fractions are those fractions most commonly found in shop use, such as

$$\frac{1}{2} \qquad \frac{1}{4} \qquad \frac{1}{8} \qquad \frac{1}{16} \qquad \frac{1}{32} \qquad \frac{1}{64}$$

Each fraction is 1/2 the value of the previous fraction, beginning with the fraction 1/2.

REDUCE A FRACTION

Fractions such as 112/224 are hard to grasp quickly. However, the reduced form of this fraction, 1/2, is quickly understood and is preferred for everyday use. Fractions can be reduced if both the numerator and denominator have a common factor. For example, 6/8 can be reduced because 2 is a common factor of both 6 and 8. 6/8 can be written as 3/4, which is usually more easily understood.

Numbers are divisible by 2 if they are even (ending in 0, 2, 4, 6, etc.).

Numbers are divisible by 3 if the sum of the integers is divisible by 3. For example, 117 is divisible by 3 because 1 + 1 + 7 = 9 which is divisible by 3.

Numbers are divisible by 5 if they end in a 5 or 0.

Numbers are divisible by 10 if they end in a 0.

See your instructor for other "tests of divisibility."

Many hand-held calculators reduce fractions. If your calculator has an $\boxed{a^b/_c}$ key, it will probably perform this function for you. Do some experimenting with it, discuss it with your partner, or ask your instructor.

Write a common fraction to express the shaded part of each of the following figures.

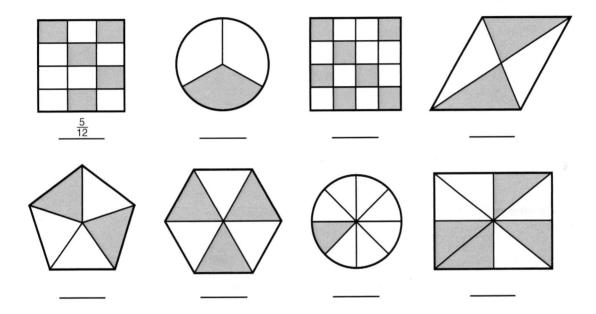

$\frac{5}{12}$

_____   _____   _____   _____

_____   _____   _____   _____

Draw and shade a representation of 11/8 here. Be creative! This circle might help get you started.

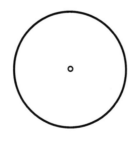

CONSIDER: Divide a square in two. Shade one of the halves.

Divide the square in two again.

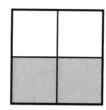

Divide it two more times.

The shaded area represents 1/2 in the first drawing, 2/4 in the second drawing, and 8/16 in the last drawing.

Therefore, 1/2, 2/4, and 8/16 are **equal fractions** or **equivalent fractions.** 4/8 is also an equal fraction or equivalent fraction to this set. Can you think of others?

REDUCE FRACTIONS

1/2 is said to be in **lowest terms.** Measurements given with fractions in lowest terms are easier to use and understand. One process for reducing fractions to lowest terms is to divide both the numerator and denominator by the largest possible number that will go into both numbers evenly.

Examples

$$\frac{8}{16} = \frac{8 \div 8}{16 \div 8} = \frac{1}{2}$$

$$\frac{20}{32} = \frac{20 \div 4}{32 \div 4} = \frac{5}{8}$$

WHOLE NUMBERS WRITTEN AS FRACTIONS

Whole numbers can be written as fractions by inserting the number 1 as the denominator, keeping the whole number as the numerator.

Examples

$$3 = \frac{3}{1} \qquad 7 = \frac{7}{1} \qquad 24 = \frac{24}{1}$$

NOTE:

If the numerator and the denominator are the same number, the fraction is equal to 1.

Examples

$$\frac{5}{5} = 1 \qquad \frac{8}{8} = 1 \qquad \frac{16}{16} = 1$$

MIXED NUMBERS

A **mixed number** is a whole number added to a fraction, hence, the term "mixed." An example of a mixed number is 7 1/8.

Example

$$4 + \frac{1}{8} = 4\frac{1}{8}$$

CHANGING IMPROPER FRACTIONS TO MIXED NUMBERS

Step 1   Divide the numerator by the denominator.

Step 2   If there is a remainder, write it over the denominator as a proper fraction.

Step 3   Reduce the fraction to its lowest terms.

Examples

$$\frac{19}{8} \rightarrow 8\overline{)19} \quad \begin{array}{c} 2 + \text{Remainder } 3 \\ \underline{16} \\ 3 \end{array} \quad = \quad 2\frac{3}{8}$$

$$\frac{5}{2} \rightarrow 2\overline{)5} \quad \begin{array}{c} 2 + \text{Remainder } 1 \\ \underline{4} \\ 1 \end{array} \quad = \quad 2\frac{1}{2}$$

CHANGE MIXED NUMBERS TO IMPROPER FRACTIONS

Step 1   Multiply the whole number times the denominator.

Step 2   Add the numerator to this result.

Step 3   Write the sum as the numerator and use the original denominator.

Examples

$$6\frac{7}{8} = (6 \times 8) + 7 = \frac{55}{8}$$

$$2\frac{1}{4} = (2 \times 4) + 1 = \frac{9}{4}$$

ARRANGE FRACTIONS IN ORDER

Step 1   To arrange fractions in order, write all the fractions as **equivalent fractions** with common denominators and compare their values.

Step 2   Write the fractions in order, based on their values.

Examples

$$\frac{1}{3} \quad \frac{1}{6} \quad \frac{3}{4} \quad \frac{3}{15} \quad \text{become} \quad \frac{20}{60} \quad \frac{10}{60} \quad \frac{45}{60} \quad \frac{12}{60}$$

arranged in order, from smallest to largest: $\frac{10}{60} \quad \frac{12}{60} \quad \frac{20}{60} \quad \frac{45}{60}$

or

$$\frac{1}{6} \quad \frac{3}{15} \quad \frac{1}{3} \quad \frac{3}{4}$$

READING A STEEL SCALE

The **steel scale** is the basic measuring instrument used to check dimensions expressed as common fractions. Reading the graduations on the steel scale is one of the first practical skills a metalworking student acquires. The illustration (an enlarged scale) shows a scale with the top scale graduated in 64ths of an inch and the bottom scale in 32nds of an inch.

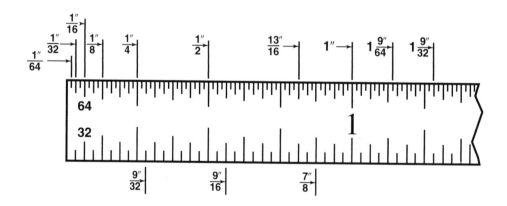

The smallest division on the fractional scale is 1/64 of an inch. The above scale illustrates the relative size of shop fractions. Each multiple of a shop fraction is marked with an etched line of varying length. The shortest marks indicate 1/64 inch, the longest represent 1/2 inch, and the whole unit is indicated by a whole number. A scale such as this one can be used to determine equivalent fractions.

PRACTICE

Using a steel scale, measure at least five objects found in your classroom. With your partner, discuss which objects are appropriate for a steel scale, which are not appropriate for a steel scale, and why or why not. Record each measurement below and make a comparison with your partner's work. Also, discuss why and how you chose the degree of measurement you used (1/2, 1/4, or 1/8 of an inch, etc.).

CONCEPT APPLICATIONS

1. Write three shop fractions and three non-shop fractions.

   Shop fractions: Non-shop fractions:

   _____, _____, _____,   _____, _____, _____

2. Using both terms "numerator" and "denominator," explain the difference between shop fractions and non-shop fractions to your partner.

3. Write equivalent fractions following the boxed example.

   $\boxed{\dfrac{3}{4} = \dfrac{6}{8}}$ $\dfrac{3}{8} = \dfrac{}{32}$ $\dfrac{3}{8} = \dfrac{}{64}$ $\dfrac{1}{16} = \dfrac{}{32}$

   $\dfrac{7}{16} = \dfrac{}{32}$ $\dfrac{5}{8} = \dfrac{}{16}$ $\dfrac{1}{2} = \dfrac{}{16}$ $\dfrac{5}{16} = \dfrac{}{64}$

   $\dfrac{1}{4} = \dfrac{}{64}$ $\dfrac{1}{8} = \dfrac{}{64}$ $\dfrac{1}{32} = \dfrac{}{64}$ $\dfrac{15}{16} = \dfrac{}{64}$

4. Reduce each fraction to **lowest terms,** following the boxed example.

   $\boxed{\dfrac{8}{16} = \dfrac{1}{2}}$ $\dfrac{12}{32} =$ $\dfrac{2}{16} =$ $\dfrac{30}{32} =$

   $\dfrac{6}{8} =$ $\dfrac{6}{16} =$ $\dfrac{32}{32} =$ $\dfrac{64}{64} =$

   $\dfrac{4}{32} =$ $\dfrac{2}{4} =$ $\dfrac{16}{32} =$ $\dfrac{4}{16} =$

5. Change these mixed numbers to improper fractions, following the boxed example. Do any need to be reduced? _____ Under what circumstances might an improper fraction need to be reduced? _____

$$\boxed{2\frac{1}{2} = \frac{5}{2}}$$ $3\frac{1}{4} = \frac{}{4}$ $9\frac{1}{2} = \frac{}{2}$ $1\frac{7}{16} = \frac{}{16}$

$4\frac{1}{2} = \frac{}{2}$ $4\frac{1}{16} = \frac{}{16}$ $4\frac{3}{8} = \frac{}{8}$ $8\frac{3}{8} = \frac{}{8}$

$5\frac{1}{4} = \frac{}{4}$ $2\frac{3}{8} = \frac{}{8}$ $10\frac{3}{16} = \frac{}{16}$ $10\frac{1}{8} = \frac{}{8}$

6. Change each improper fraction to a mixed number, following the boxed example. Reduce as necessary.

$$\boxed{\frac{12}{8} = 1\frac{1}{2}}$$ $\frac{9}{2} =$ $\frac{25}{4} =$ $\frac{5}{2} =$

$\frac{9}{4} =$ $\frac{19}{16} =$ $\frac{13}{8} =$ $\frac{25}{8} =$

$\frac{30}{16} =$ $\frac{40}{32} =$ $\frac{50}{8} =$ $\frac{100}{16} =$

7. Arrange the following fractions in order from smallest to largest.

$\frac{17}{64}$, $\frac{2}{4}$, $\frac{5}{2}$, $\frac{3}{1}$, $\frac{8}{8}$, $\frac{11}{16}$, $\frac{7}{32}$

_____, _____, _____, _____, _____, _____, _____,

8. Using a steel scale, measure the thickness of this text. _____ Is a steel scale the best instrument for measuring the thickness of this text?_____ What might be better?_____ Can you think of an instrument that would not work for measuring the thickness of this text?_____

9. Determine the following dimensions and record them below this enlarged scale. Note the different increments. Record a–h to the nearest 1/32 inch and i–p to the nearest 1/64 inch.

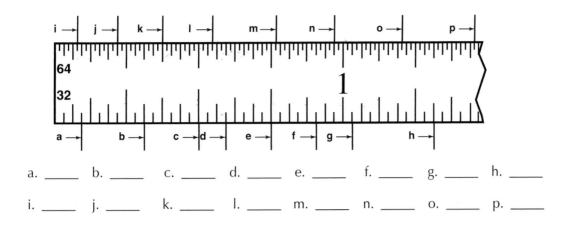

a. _____   b. _____   c. _____   d. _____   e. _____   f. _____   g. _____   h. _____

i. _____   j. _____   k. _____   l. _____   m. _____   n. _____   o. _____   p. _____

ARITHMETIC OPERATIONS ON FRACTIONS

INTRODUCTION

Often fractional measurements need to be added, subtracted, multiplied, and/or divided. This unit covers the four arithmetic operations and the procedures used in each operation. Additional concepts, such as expressing measurements in the same unit (feet, millimeters, pounds, etc.) are also covered to enhance the arithmetic operations.

OBJECTIVES

After completing this unit, you will be able to:

- Determine which operations require a common denominator.
- Find a common denominator.
- Add fractions and mixed numbers with and without common denominators.
- Subtract fractions and mixed numbers with and without common denominators.
- Multiply fractions and mixed numbers.
- Divide fractions and mixed numbers.
- Use a calculator with fractional capability.
- Apply these arithmetic operations to story problems.

ADDING LIKE FRACTIONS

Fractions having the same denominator are called **like fractions.**

Like fractions can be added by using the following process:

> *Step 1*   Add the numerators.
>
> *Step 2*   Write this sum over the like denominator.
>
> *Step 3*   Reduce the fraction to lowest terms if possible.

Example

If the like fractions are mixed numbers,

    Step 4   Add the whole numbers and combine with the reduced fraction obtained from steps 1–3 above. *This may require carrying.*

Example

$$\frac{5}{8} + \frac{1}{8} = \frac{5+1}{8} \text{ (Add numerators and write over the like denominator.)} = \frac{6}{8} = \frac{3}{4} \text{ (Reduce when possible.)}$$

Example

$$1\frac{3}{8} + 2\frac{1}{8} = 3 + \frac{4}{8} = 3 + \frac{1}{2} = 3\frac{1}{2}$$

SUBTRACTING LIKE FRACTIONS

Fractions having the same denominator are called **like fractions.**

Like fractions can be subtracted by using the following process:

    Step 1   Subtract the numerators.

    Step 2   Write this difference over the like denominator.

    Step 3   Reduce the fraction to lowest terms if possible.

If the like fractions are mixed numbers.

    Step 4   Subtract the fractions, borrowing from the whole numbers if necessary.

    Step 5   Subtract the whole numbers and combine with the reduced fraction.
      or
    Step 4   Rewrite the mixed number as an improper fraction and subtract, reducing and rewriting as a mixed number if necessary.

Example

$$2\frac{1}{8} - 1\frac{3}{8} = 1\frac{9}{8} - 1\frac{3}{8} = \frac{6}{8} = \frac{3}{4}$$

      or

$$2\frac{1}{8} - 1\frac{3}{8} = \frac{17}{8} - \frac{11}{8} = \frac{6}{8} = \frac{3}{4}$$

ADDING AND SUBTRACTING UNLIKE FRACTIONS

Fractions having different denominators are called **unlike fractions.**

Unlike fractions can be added or subtracted by using the following process:

    Step 1   Rewrite as like fraction by finding the common denominator.

    Step 2   Follow the steps for like fractions.

MULTIPLICATION OF FRACTIONS

Fractions and mixed numbers can be multiplied by using the following process:

Step 1   Write any mixed numbers as improper fractions.

Step 2   Multiply the numerators and write as a numerator.

Step 3   Multiply the denominators and write as a denominator.

Step 4   Reduce and write the result as a fraction or mixed number as appropriate.

Examples

Proper Fractions:

$$\frac{5}{8} \times \frac{1}{4} = \frac{5 \times 1}{8 \times 4} = \frac{5}{32}$$

Mixed Numbers:

$$2\frac{3}{4} \times 1\frac{5}{8} = \frac{11}{4} \times \frac{13}{8} = \frac{143}{32} = 4\frac{15}{32}$$

A shortcut to multiplying fractions with a common factor in a numerator and denominator is called **cancelling** or reducing.

Example

$$\frac{3}{8} \times \frac{2}{5} = \frac{3}{{}_4\cancel{8}} \times \frac{\cancel{2}^1}{5} = \frac{3}{20}$$

The problem 3/8 × 2/5 has common factor of 2 in the numerator and denominator. It can be written as 3/8 × 2/5 = 3/20. The advantages of cancelling are that the cancelled numbers are smaller and easier to work with and the final step of reducing the answer is eliminated.

DIVISION OF FRACTIONS

Since dividing a number by 2 gives the same result as multiplying it by 1/2, we can exchange multiplication and division, using reciprocals.*

Fractions and mixed numbers can be divided by using the following process:

Step 1   Write any mixed numbers as improper fractions.

Step 2   Invert the divisor[†] (write its reciprocal*) and change the operation sign to multiplication.

Step 3   Multiply as above.

Examples

Proper Fractions

$$\frac{13}{16} \div 2 = \frac{13}{16} \times \frac{1}{2} = \frac{13}{32}$$

Mixed Numbers

$$1\frac{3}{8} \div 2 = \frac{11}{8} \div 2 = \frac{11}{8} \times \frac{1}{2} = \frac{11}{16}$$

---

* Note: The *reciprocal* is the result of inverting or flipping the fraction. A number times its reciprocal always equals 1.

† Note: The *divisor* is the second fraction.

USING A CALCULATOR

Many calculators today are capable of performing operations on fractions. One common way of indicating this capability is a key with an $a^b/_c$ symbol on it. This key communicates to the calculator that you are working with a fraction.

Example

2 3/8 + 7 1/16 may be entered into your calculator this way: 2 $a^b/_c$ 3 $a^b/_c$ 8 + 7 $a^b/_c$ 1 $a^b/_c$ 16. The display may look quite different from others, but it is read as 9 7/16. Explore and experiment with this useful key. Work with a partner and compare answers and displays if you have different calculators.

CONCEPT APPLICATIONS

Add, subtract, multiply, or divide the following, as indicated. Try doing some of the operations below with and without the calculator.

1. $\dfrac{7}{8} + \dfrac{5}{8} =$

2. $\dfrac{7}{16} - \dfrac{3}{16} =$

3. $\dfrac{1}{4} \times \dfrac{1}{8} =$

4. $1\dfrac{3}{8} \div \dfrac{3}{16} =$

5. $1\dfrac{7}{8} + \dfrac{3}{16} =$

6. $\dfrac{8}{4} - \dfrac{7}{8} =$

7. $\dfrac{1}{8} \times \dfrac{16}{1} =$

8. $\dfrac{3}{16} \div \dfrac{3}{4} =$

9. $15\dfrac{1}{4} \div 1\dfrac{1}{2} =$

10. $1\dfrac{1}{4} \times 3 =$

Solve the following. Keep in mind that *division* involves separating one unit into smaller units and *multiplication* is the reverse. *Addition* involves combining quantities, while *subtraction* means deducting one quantity from another.

11. Distance A = _____

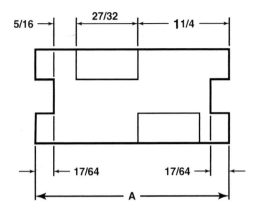

12. Distance C = _____

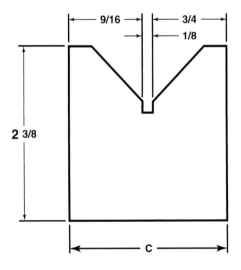

13. A collar has an inside diameter of 4 3/8 inches and a wall thickness of 3/32 inches. What is the outside diameter (OD)?_____

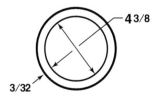

14. D = _____

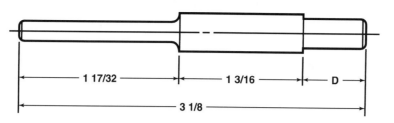

Sketch drawings of the following when appropriate. To build your math vocabulary and explore thought processes, discuss these exercises with your partner.

15. Find the difference between 30 and 21 9/32.

16. A section of a part that is 5 1/8 inches thick must be machined to 4 19/32 inches. How much material is to be removed?

17. A bar of metal weighs 2 3/8 pounds for each foot of length. How much will one piece weigh if it is 7 feet long?

18. What will the piece weigh if it is 7 feet 6 inches long?

19. How much will the piece weigh if it is 7 feet 8 inches long?

20. If a bar of metal weighs 2 1/4 pounds per foot, how long must it be to weigh 36 pounds?

21. There are 75 kilos of bolts in a bin. If each bolt weighs 3/8 of a kilo, how many bolts are there in the bin?

22. Determine distance A and the center-to-center distance between any two holes on the print below.

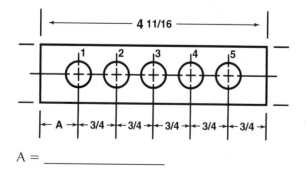

A = _____

Center-to-center distance of any two holes = _____

23. Just-in-time inventory requires 3,600 pieces per day. How many hours are required to produce these parts if each part takes 8 1/2 seconds to produce?

24. The outside diameter of a steel pipe is 3 1/2 inches. If the wall thickness is 9/32 inches what is the ID measurement? _____ What mathematical processes did you use to arrive at your answer?

25–26. Complete the following chart.

	25.	26.
Total length		4 1/2 feet
Total weight	16 pounds	16 pounds
Weight/foot	2 3/8 pounds/foot	

DECIMAL AND METRIC SYSTEMS

INTRODUCTION

Babylonian clay tablets dating to the twentieth century BC reveal fractions written as powers of 60. Later, this same base-60 system was used by the ancient Greeks. Many people worked to bring about the use of the decimal point in the 1500s and early 1600s, but it did not become popular until John Napier used it about 1615. François Viete made a plea in 1579 to use tenths, hundredths, thousandths, etc. rather than multiples of 60, clearing the way for today's decimal system.

The metric measuring system is the most widely used system of measurement throughout the world. It is easy to understand and is convenient to use. The metric system is a decimal system based on the meter (measurement) and the kilogram (weight). Though this system is not widely used in the United States, the number of metalworking-related trades and technical fields using the metric system are increasing. As a matter of fact, some industries in this country specify dimensions *only* in metrics on engineering drawings.

Not only are these systems different than a system based on multiples of 60, but they also differ from the shop fractions discussed in the previous units. This unit introduces the modern decimal system, the metric system, and their basic conversion methods.

OBJECTIVES

After completing this unit, you will be able to:

- Express decimals as words and fractions.
- Express fractions as decimals.
- Compare values of decimals.
- Round decimals.
- Read a decimal scale.
- Convert inches to metric measurements.
- Convert metric measurements to inches.
- Read a metric scale.

THE DECIMAL SYSTEM

The **decimal system** is a set of numbers taken from our general set of fractions. Specifically, it consists of those fractions that contain a denominator of 10, 100, 1,000, and so on.

Fraction form:	$\dfrac{1}{10}$	$\dfrac{1}{100}$	$\dfrac{1}{1,000}$	$\dfrac{1}{10,000}$
Equivalent decimal form:	0.1	0.01	0.001	0.0001

The denominators in the fractions are increasing multiples of 10, while the decimals are decreasing multiples of 10. This is equivalent to the notation of dollars and cents.

The decimal system is based on a unique set of common fractions that have denominators of 10, 100, 1,000, etc., and this set of fractions is called **decimals.**

Examples

$\dfrac{1}{10}$ of a dollar = 10 cents = $0.10 $\dfrac{1}{100}$ of a dollar = 1 cent = $0.01

Therefore, 0.1 has 10 times the value of the next number, 0.01. Agreements have been made that allow us to abbreviate or simplify the form of these fractions. To understand the concept of writing these numbers, we must first examine the following chart which shows how place value is assigned to each digit. Always begin with the identification of the "ones" or "units" place. The decimal point is located to the right of the unit.

Fractional numbers can be written both as decimal fractions and common fractions. Refer to the chart below as a reference.

PLACE VALUE CHART

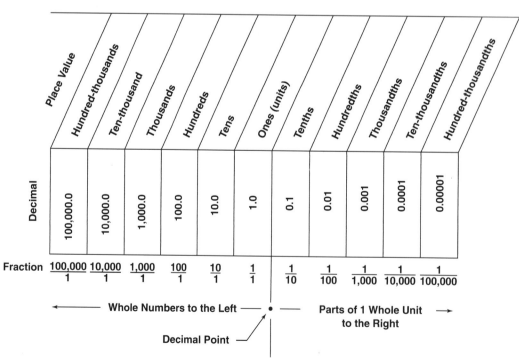

Place Value	Hundred-thousands	Ten-thousand	Thousands	Hundreds	Tens	Ones (units)	Tenths	Hundredths	Thousandths	Ten-thousandths	Hundred-thousandths
Decimal	100,000.0	10,000.0	1,000.0	100.0	10.0	1.0	0.1	0.01	0.001	0.0001	0.00001
Fraction	$\dfrac{100,000}{1}$	$\dfrac{10,000}{1}$	$\dfrac{1,000}{1}$	$\dfrac{100}{1}$	$\dfrac{10}{1}$	$\dfrac{1}{1}$	$\dfrac{1}{10}$	$\dfrac{1}{100}$	$\dfrac{1}{1,000}$	$\dfrac{1}{10,000}$	$\dfrac{1}{100,000}$

← —— Whole Numbers to the Left —— • —— Parts of 1 Whole Unit →
to the Right

Decimal Point

READING DECIMALS

To read decimals, read the whole number to the left of the decimal, say the word "and" at the decimal point, and then read the decimal portion of the number to the right of the decimal point, stating its place value.

Examples

       0.12 is read as twelve-hundredths or one hundred twenty thousandths

       3.106 is read as three and one hundred six thousandths

       0.5 is read as five-tenths or five hundred thousandths

Problems

       Speak or write the following decimals in words.

       a. 0.45   b. 9.02   c. 372.253   d. 0.9   e. 0.0009

Solutions

       a. Forty-five hundredths or four hundred fifty-thousandths*

       b. Nine and two hundredths or nine and twenty-thousandths*

       c. Three hundred seventy-two and two hundred fifty-three thousandths

       d. Nine tenths or nine hundred thousandths*

       e. Nine ten-thousandths or nine tenths*

WRITING DECIMALS AS FRACTIONS

To write decimals as fractions, write the whole number and annex a fraction that represents the decimal and its place value. Reduce if necessary.

Examples

       0.4 is written as 4/10 which can be reduced to 2/5

       7.12 is written as 7 12/100 which can be reduced to 7 3/25

Problems

       Write fractions or mixed numbers for the following.

       a. 0.6   b. 25.001   c. 300.32

Solutions

       a. 6/10 = 3/5   b. 25 1/1000   c. 300 32/100 = 300 8/25

---

* Note: In the metal working trade, the decimal point is often moved to the right of the thousandths digit.

WRITING FRACTIONS AS DECIMALS

To write fractions as decimals, perform the division (numerator divided by denominator) and carry the answer to the desired number of decimal places.

Examples

3/4 is divided as $3 \div 4 = 0.75$ 7/8 is divided as $7 \div 8 = 0.875$

DID YOU KNOW?

$0.25 = \dfrac{1}{4}$ $0.125 = \dfrac{1}{8}$ $0.0625 = \dfrac{1}{16}$

$0.025 = \dfrac{1}{40}$ $0.0125 = \dfrac{1}{80}$ $0.00625 = \dfrac{1}{160}$

COMPARING DECIMAL VALUES

To compare decimal values, add zeros to the numbers so that each has the same number of decimal places.

Examples

To order 0.9, 0.12 and 0.568 in increasing order, annex zeros.

0.9   0.12   0.568   become   0.900   0.120   0.568

Now these decimal values can be easily compared and placed in increasing order as:

0.120   0.568   0.900

ROUNDING DECIMALS

To round a decimal, determine the value to which it should be rounded and consider the digit to the *immediate right*. If the digit is 5 or larger, round the value up one number (increase the digit to the next higher number) and drop all remaining digits. If the digit to the *immediate right* is smaller than 5, drop it and any remaining digits.

Examples

Round to the nearest thousandth.

1.1248 becomes 1.125   1.1244 becomes 1.124   1.12449 becomes 1.124

READING A DECIMAL STEEL SCALE

The enlarged scale below is a decimal-inch scale. The top scale is graduated in hundredths of an inch (0.01 inch). The bottom scale is graduated in fiftieths of an inch (0.02 inch). The scale is divided into staggered graduations of halves, tenths, and fiftieths.

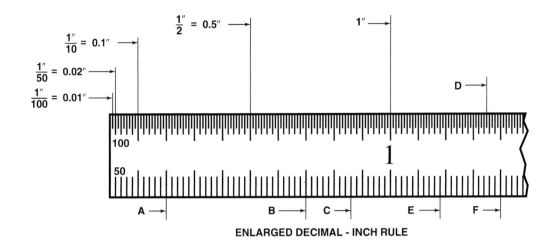

ENLARGED DECIMAL - INCH RULE

Record measurements A–F found on the scale above.

A = _____   B = _____   C = _____   D = _____   E = _____   F = _____

THE METRIC SYSTEM

The basic unit of length in the **Metric System** is the meter. A meter is equal to 39.37 inches. Smaller units of Metric measurements are the centimeter and the more commonly used millimeter. There are 100 centimeters in a meter; therefore, one centimeter measures 39.37 inches divided by 100, or 0.3937 inches. For the more commonly used millimeter, every meter contains 1000 millimeters. A millimeter measures 39.37 inches divided by 1000, or 0.03937 inches. Conversely, there are 25.4 millimeters in an inch, which can be calculated by dividing 1 by 0.03937 inches.

INCH/METRIC EQUIVALENT VALUES

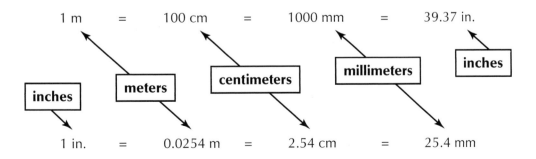

CONVERTING BETWEEN INCHES AND MILLIMETERS

The most common metric conversions required in shop applications are to change inches to millimeters and millimeters to inches. There are 25.4 millimeters (mm) in every inch. To convert inches to millimeters, multiply the number of inches by 25.4. To convert millimeters to inches, divide the number of inches by 25.4. Remember that the multiplication process will result in a larger number, and the division process will result in a smaller number. Use this as a guideline when deciding whether to multiply or divide.

Examples

To convert from inches to millimeters, multiply the number of inches by 25.4:

Inches $\times$ 25.4 = Millimeters (mm)

1.3 inches $\times$ 25.4 = 33.02 mm

To convert from millimeters to inches, divide the number of millimeters by 25.4:

Millimeters $\div$ 25.4 = Inches

50 mm $\div$ 25.4 = 1.969 inches

READING A METRIC STEEL SCALE

The enlarged scale below is a metric scale. The top scale is graduated in half-millimeters (0.5 mm). The bottom scale is graduate in millimeters (1 mm).

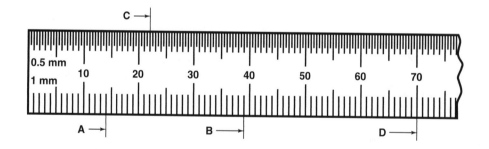

Record measurements A–D found on the scale above.

A = _____   B = _____   C = _____   D = _____

FRACTION-DECIMAL-MILLIMETER EQUIVALENT CHART

Fraction				Decimal	Millimeters	Fraction				Decimal	Millimeters
8ths	16ths	32nds	64ths			8ths	16ths	32nds	64ths		
			1	0.015625	0.396875				33	0.515625	13.096875
		1		0.031250	0.793760			17		0.531250	13.493750
			3	0.046875	1.190625				35	0.546875	13.890625
	1			0.062500	1.587500		9			0.562500	14.287500
			5	0.078125	0.984375				37	0.578125	14.684375
		3		0.093750	2.381250			19		0.593750	15.081250
			7	0.109375	2.778125				39	0.609375	15.478125
1				0.125000	3.175000	5				0.625000	15.875000
			9	0.140625	3.571875				41	0.640625	16.271875
		5		0.156250	3.968750			21		0.656250	16.668750
			11	0.171875	4.365625				43	0.671875	17.065625
	3			0.187500	4.762500		11			0.687500	17.462500
			13	0.203125	5.159375				45	0.703125	17.859375
		7		0.218750	5.556250			23		0.718750	18.256250
			15	0.234375	5.953125				47	0.734375	18.653125
2				0.250000	6.350000	6				0.750000	19.050000
			17	0.265625	6.746875				49	0.765625	19.446875
		9		0.281250	7.143750			25		0.781250	19.843750
			19	0.296875	7.540625				51	0.793875	20.240625
	5			0.312500	7.937500		13			0.812500	20.637500
			21	0.328125	8.334375				53	0.828125	21.034375
		11		0.343750	8.731250			27		0.843750	21.431250
			23	0.359375	9.128125				55	0.859375	21.828125
3				0.375000	9.525000	7				0.875000	22.225000
			25	0.390625	9.921875				57	0.890625	22.621875
		13		0.406250	10.318750			29		0.906250	23.018750
			27	0.421875	10.715625				59	0.921875	23.415625
	7			0.437500	11.112500		15			0.937500	23.812500
			29	0.453125	11.509375				61	0.953125	24.209375
		15		0.468750	11.906250			31		0.968750	24.606250
			31	0.484375	12.303125				63	0.984375	25.003125
4				0.500000	12.700000	8	16	32	64	1.000000	25.400000

Note: Table is exact; all figures beyond the six places given are zeros.
Basis: 1 inch = 25.4 millimeters provides exact six-place values.

CONCEPT APPLICATIONS

1. Speak or read each decimal in "shop" form.

   a. 0.011 _____

   b. 0.12 _____

   c. 0.3 _____

   d. 35.07 _____

   e. 0.2185 _____

2. Write the following in decimal form.

   a. Thirty-two ten thousandths _____

   b. Three and three-tenths _____

3. Write the following decimals as fractions. Reduce when possible.

   a. 2.123 _____   b. 6.057 _____   c. 1.1 _____

   d. 8.16 _____   e. 12.65 _____

4. Write the following fractions as decimals. Round each answer to three decimal places.

   a. $\dfrac{3}{8}$ = _____   b. $\dfrac{5}{7}$ = _____   c. $\dfrac{5}{16}$ = _____

   d. $2\dfrac{1}{6}$ = _____   e. $\dfrac{303}{1000}$ = _____

5. Round the following as indicated.

   a. 3.1234 (three places) _____

   b. 0.67 (one place) _____

   c. 0.675 (two places) _____

   d. 5.4449 (three places) _____

   e. 2.1654565 (four places) _____

6. Read measurements a–g on this enlarged decimal scale.

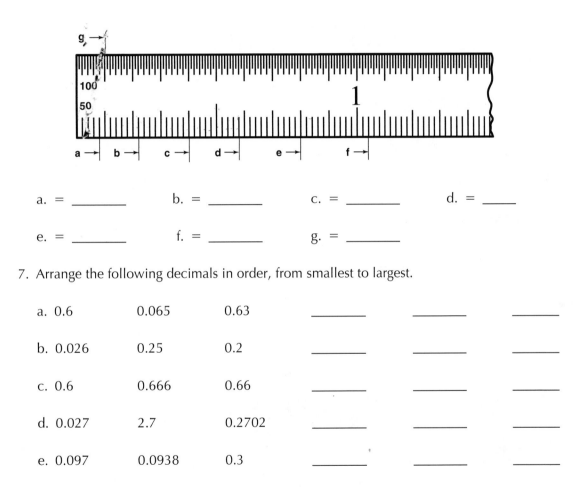

   a. = _____   b. = _____   c. = _____   d. = _____

   e. = _____   f. = _____   g. = _____

7. Arrange the following decimals in order, from smallest to largest.

   a. 0.6   0.065   0.63   _____   _____   _____

   b. 0.026   0.25   0.2   _____   _____   _____

   c. 0.6   0.666   0.66   _____   _____   _____

   d. 0.027   2.7   0.2702   _____   _____   _____

   e. 0.097   0.0938   0.3   _____   _____   _____

8. Refer to the chart below and give decimal or fractional equivalents. Round decimals to three places and reduce the fractions.

Fraction	Decimal
1/9	
	0.675
3/16	
	9.876

Convert the following measurements.

9. 26 inches to mm _____

10. 12 inches to mm _____

11. 78.5 inches to mm _____

12. 1.001 inches to mm _____

13. 56 mm to inches _____

14. 330.708 mm to inches _____

15. 0.127 mm to inches _____

16. 10.16 mm to inches _____

17. Read measurements a–g on this enlarged metric scale.

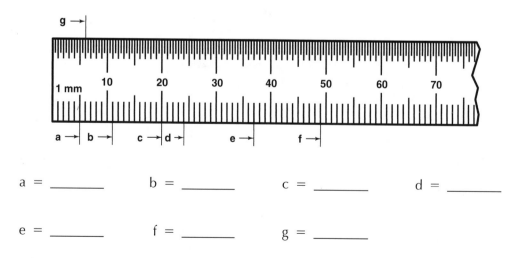

a = _____   b = _____   c = _____   d = _____

e = _____   f = _____   g = _____

36

OPERATIONS ON DECIMALS

INTRODUCTION

Often decimal measurements need to be added, subtracted, multiplied, and/or divided. This unit covers the four arithmetic operations and the procedures used in each operation. Additional concepts, such as expressing measurements in the same unit (feet, millimeters, pounds, etc.), are also covered to supplement the sections on the basic arithmetic operations.

OBJECTIVES

After completing this unit, you will be able to:

- Add decimals.
- Subtract decimals.
- Multiply decimals.
- Divide decimals.
- Apply these arithmetic operations to story problems.

ADDING AND SUBTRACTING DECIMALS

It is necessary to preserve **place value** of the individual digits when adding or subtracting decimals. This preservation requires that the tenths place of one number be aligned or grouped with the tenths place of the other number(s). Similarly, hundredths need to be aligned or grouped together, etc. This rule is usually stated as "line up the decimal points."

Consider how your bank account balance would be affected if you or your banker did not align place values. A $100 deposit to your initial account balance of $515.88 should result in a balance of $615.88, NOT $516.88! Similarly, a withdrawal of $100 from the initial $515.88 should result in a new balance of $415.88, not $514.88! It is understood that the decimal point is placed to the immediate right of $100—the number cannot be written correctly with the decimal placed elsewhere.

In subtraction only, it may be advantageous to add zeros to a number. For example, 0.02-0.003 may be rewritten as 0.020–0.003 in order to have the same number of decimal places.

Write example vertically.

	Correct	Incorrect
	$515.88	$515.88
	+ 100	+ 100
	$615.88	$516.88

MULTIPLYING DECIMALS

Multiply the numbers as if they were whole numbers. To place the decimal point, determine the *total* number of digits to the right of the decimal points in the problem. Place the decimal point in the answer so that the same number of digits are placed to the right of the decimal point.

Examples

21.5	1 digit to the right of the decimal point
× 5	0 digits to the right of the decimal point
107.5	1 digit to the right of the decimal point

21.238	3 digits to the right of the decimal point
× 1.3	1 digit to the right of the decimal point
27.6094	4 digits to the right of the decimal point

DIVIDING DECIMALS

First, let us define some basic terms. The **dividend** is the number to be divided; the **divisor** is the number by which the dividend is to be divided. The **quotient** is the result. The **remainder** is the final undivided part after division that is less than the divisor. Division of decimals is done exactly like division of whole numbers—once the decimal point has been eliminated from the divisor. The elimination of the decimal point from the divisor involves counting the number of digits to the right of the decimal point in the divisor and moving the decimal point, the same number of places to the right so that the divisor no longer has a decimal point. The decimal point is then moved to the right the same number of places in the dividend. The decimal point in the quotient is located directly above this new location. Zeroes may need to be added to the dividend to move the decimal point the necessary number of places. Division of numbers with a decimal in the dividend does not require any special action.

Examples

```
   0.26
5)1.30      divisor is 5              (Note: no action necessary because the
   10       quotient is 0.26          divisor doesn't have any digits
   30       dividend is 1.30 or 1.3   to the right of the decimal.)
   30       remainder is zero
    0
```

38

$$\text{step 1} \rightarrow 3.6 \overline{\smash{)}17.2\wedge 8} \leftarrow \text{step 2}$$

$$\begin{array}{r} 4.8 \\ 36\overline{\smash{)}172.8} \\ \underline{144} \\ 28\ 8 \\ \underline{28\ 8} \\ 0 \end{array}$$

(Note: Move the decimal point one place to the right on both the dividend and the divisor. The new place of the decimal point is denoted by the "$\wedge$" mark.)

$$.06 \overline{\smash{)}36.} \rightarrow \begin{array}{r} 600. \\ 6\overline{\smash{)}3600.} \end{array}$$

(Note: zeros need to be added to the dividend to match the number of places the decimal point has been moved to the right in the divisor.)

USING A CALCULATOR

Electronic calculators automatically apply the above rules. There is no special key or action required. The first example is entered as 17.2 ÷ 3.6 =. The calculator applies the rules and gives the result as 4.8.

DID YOU KNOW

When you use a calculator, observe how it rewrites calculation of .50+. Did you notice that it eliminated the zero? Also, notice that it inserted zero as a whole number.

CONCEPT APPLICATIONS

Add, subtract, multiply, or divide the following. Try at least one of each type without using a calculator to refresh your skills.

1. 2.503 + 0.056 + 3.1 =

2. 0.625 + 0.125 + 0.3125 + 0.0625 =

3. 0.0001 + 0.001 + 0.01 =

4. 8 − 0.8940 =

5. 2.125 − 2.105 =

6. 0.001 − 0.0001 =

7. $14.3 + 8.31 - 9.7 =$

8. $4.25 \times 0.5 =$

9. $0.5 \times 4.25 =$

10. $0.25 \times 0.25 =$

11. $1.00 \div 8 =$

12. $1.00 \div 16 =$

13. $0.42 \div 0.2 =$

14. Did the numbers in Problem 2 need the zeroes to the left of the decimal?

15. Why are the solutions to Problems 8 and 9 the same? We usually think the answer in a multiplication problem will be larger. Why aren't these answers larger than 4.25? When does multiplication give a larger answer? A smaller answer?

16. Rewrite Problems 11 and 12 as fractions. Don't use the zeros.

17. We usually think the answer in a division problem will be smaller. Why is the solution to Problem 13 larger?

18. Refer to the drawing at the right for the following.

X = _____

Y = _____

Z = _____

W = _____

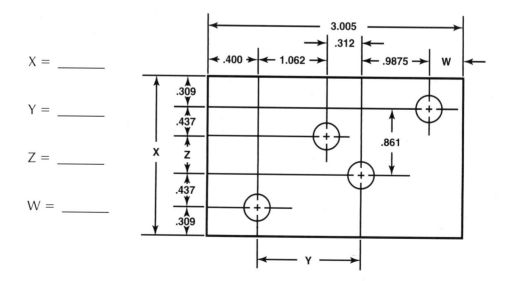

19. Refer to the drawing at the right for the following.

Note: "Typical" means that there is another dimension of equal measure.

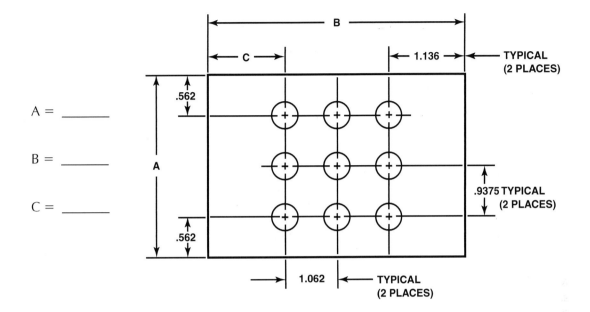

A = _____

B = _____

C = _____

20. Refer to the drawing below for the following.

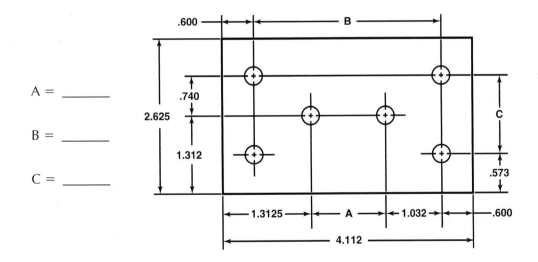

A = _____

B = _____

C = _____

21. Refer to the drawing below for the following.

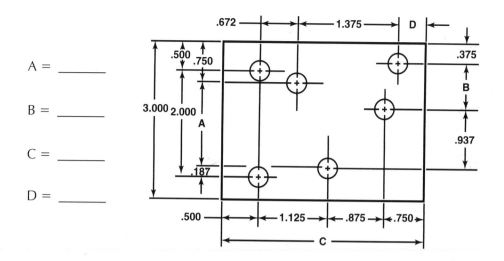

A = _____

B = _____

C = _____

D = _____

The circumference of a circle (the distance around it) is found by multiplying pi (π, approximately 3.14) by the diameter. Scientific calculators have π programmed as a number with several decimal places. In most cases, a key with the π symbol appears on the keyboard. Determine the following circumferences. First use 3.14 for π, and then use a more accurate approximation for π by using the π key on your calculator.

	Diameter	Circumference (π as 3.14)	Circumference (π key from the calculator)
22.	4.25 in.		
23.	88.88 cm		
24.	5963.00 mm		

Note how the circumferences vary as the diameter increases!

Complete the following, drawing sketches when appropriate. Remember that determining a total is likely to involve addition or multiplication, and separating a total into parts involves subtraction or division.

25. How much stock is required to make 500 parts, each 3.250 inches long?

26. If it takes 25 tons of pressure to shear a 1-square-inch cross section of mild steel, how many tons of pressure will it require to shear 23.937 square inches?

27. What is the center-to-center distance between each of eight equally spaced holes if the center-to-center distance between the first and eighth hole is 3.0062 cm? Sketch a part with eight equally spaced holes here.

28. How many parts 1.76 inches long can be made from a 60-foot length of stock? Don't consider its width.

29. If it takes 0.067 kilo to produce a plastic part, how many parts can be produced from 100 kilos of plastic?

30. A metal strip is 39.96 inches long. How many parts each 2.125 inches long can be made from the strip if 0.095 inch waste is allowed for each part?

31. One kind of sheet metal stock has a thickness of 0.0375 cm. How many sheets of this stock are in a pile 15-cm high?

32. An assembly consists of four parts weighing 348 pounds, 360 pounds, 50 pounds, and 242 pounds. Four of these assemblies are to be delivered in the shop's truck, which has a capacity of 2 tons. How many trips will be required?

33. A mechanic can assemble four machines every six hours. How many machines can 48 mechanics assemble in a month of 20 eight-hour days?

34. If it takes 45 seconds to cut through a section of 3-inch-diameter bar stock, how long will it take to cut 12 pieces, each 3 inches long, from a 48-inch length of bar stock? Did you need to know that the bar stock has a 3-inch diameter? Why did you need to know its length?

35. What is the cost of a bar of stock, that weighs 118 pounds and costs $69.50 per hundred-weight?

36. Joe's Production Stamping Company must produce 150,000 metal mousetrap bases. The shop rate for production machining is $30.50 per hour. (a) With a jig costing $300, parts can be produced at a rate of one part every 15 seconds. (b) An alternative is to spend $2,800 for a jig and produce 300 parts per hour. Calculate the following for both alternatives a and b.

	(a)	(b)
Total time required		
Total labor cost		
Total cost		
Cost per part		

37. Which of the alternatives is more economical? _____

38. What is the total savings in choosing the economical alternative? _____

39. Rewrite the problem in a more easily understood manner. It might be a chart, a comparison of each factor, or something completely different.

DID YOU KNOW?

π is a Greek letter representing the approximate number of diameters contained in a given circle's circumference. It has intrigued mathematicians for centuries and has been calculated to billions of decimal places. The speed and accuracy of this calculation is one of the tests the U.S. Defense Department's computers must pass. There are sites on the Internet which display the value of π to thousands of decimal places. The University of Tokyo is one of the leading institutions researching pi.

UNIT

6

TOLERANCES, CLEARANCE, AND INTERFERENCE

INTRODUCTION

Tolerances provide the amount of accuracy required to machine parts. Since it is impossible to duplicate an exact measure or dimension, the tolerance is a realistic guide that limits how far a dimension is allowed to vary from a basic dimension and still be acceptable. The acceptable tolerance range has a great influence on the cost of the final product. Dimensions with larger tolerances are easier to machine and, therefore, can be made faster and cheaper than parts with narrower tolerances.

OBJECTIVES

After completing this unit, you will be able to:

- Identify unilateral dimensions.
- Identify bilateral dimensions.
- Identify the basic dimension.
- Determine maximum dimensions.
- Determine minimum dimensions.
- Determine allowable tolerance.
- Determine mean dimensions.
- Determine maximum clearance.
- Determine minimum clearance.
- Determine maximum interference.
- Determine minimum interference.

DEFINITIONS

Measure: An indication of comparative size.

Tolerance: A determination of an acceptable range of measurement.

Basic dimension: A dimension without tolerance.

Example

In 2.132 ± 0.005, 2.132 is the basic dimension.

Unilateral tolerance: A measure that is either added to OR subtracted from a basic dimension, but not both.

Examples

$$2.312 \begin{array}{l} + 0.000 \\ - 0.003 \end{array} \qquad 2.312 \begin{array}{l} + 0.012 \\ - 0.000 \end{array}$$

Bilateral tolerance: A measure that is added to AND subtracted from a basic dimension to establish maximum and minimum limits; the measure added may be unequal to the measure subtracted from the basic dimension.

Examples

$$2.132 \pm 0.005 \qquad 2.132 \begin{array}{l} + 0.001 \\ - 0.003 \end{array}$$

Maximum dimension: A measure used to identify the largest acceptable dimension.

Example

The maximum dimension for 2.132 ± 0.005 is 2.132 + 0.005 = 2.137 inches.

Minimum dimension: A measure used to identify the smallest acceptable dimension.

Example

The minimum dimension for 2.132 ± 0.005 is 2.132 − 0.005 = 2.127 inches.

Total tolerance, allowable tolerance: The range of acceptable variance.

Example

The total tolerance for 2.132 ± 0.005 is 0.005 + 0.005 = 0.010 inch.

Mean dimension: The dimension that is halfway between the maximum and minimum dimensions (the average of the maximum and minimum dimensions).

Example

$$+ 0.000$$
The mean dimension for $2.312 - 0.004$ is 2.310, halfway between 2.312 (the maximum dimension) and 2.308 (the minimum dimension).

Maximum clearance: The largest amount of gap between two mating parts.

Example

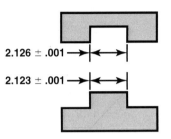

2.126 ± .001

2.123 ± .001

The maximum clearance for these mating parts is

```
  2.127      (2.126 + 0.001) (maximum dimension)
- 2.122      (2.123 − 0.001) (minimum dimension)
  0.005
```

Minimum clearance: The smallest amount of gap between two mating parts. (See drawing above.)

Example

The minimum clearance for these mating parts is

```
  .1245      (.125 − .0005) (minimum dimension)
- .1240      (.1235 + .0005) (maximum dimension)
  .0005
```

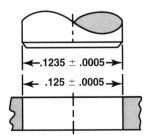

.1235 ± .0005

.125 ± .0005

Maximum interference: The largest amount of overlap between two mating parts. (This involves a press fit.)

Example

The maximum interference for these mating parts is

    0.1255   (0.125 + 0.0005) (maximum dimension)
  − 0.1230   (0.1235 − 0.0005) (minimum dimension)
    0.0025

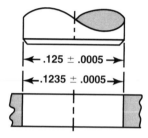

Minimum interference: The smallest amount of overlap between two mating parts (This involves a press fit.) (See drawing above.)

EXAMPLE:

The minimum interference for these mating parts is

    0.1245   (0.125 − 0.0005) (minimum dimension)
  − 0.1240   (0.1235 + 0.0005) (maximum dimension)
    0.0005

- -

NOTE:

In part, the success of a machinist depends on the ability to work with measures. While measures are given in both fractional and decimal form, decimal measures are more common today. *It is impossible to duplicate an exact measure.* The amount of accuracy depends on the instrument used, the machine used and the machining method used to produce the part, the conditions of production, and the person responsible for using each. However, it is generally possible to produce a product with dimensions within an acceptable range. The amount that a measure can vary and still be acceptable is referred to as the tolerance for the dimension. While this unit dwells on measurements of length, tolerance is used in other measurements. For example, an angle can be stated as 15° ± 2°. The same principles apply to this measurement: the acceptable range is 13°–17°.

- -

Which dimensioning method will allow less variation in determining the correct reference point (edge X) of the part sketched below: the method on the left or on the right? _____

Why? _____

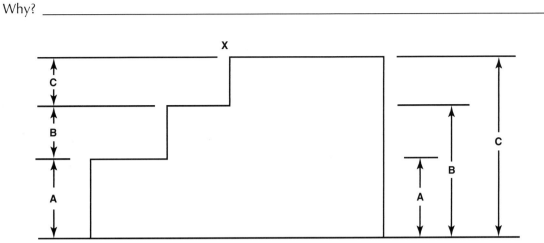

CONCEPT APPLICATIONS

1–30. Complete the chart below. Use a check mark to indicate if each dimension is unilateral (Uni) or bilateral (Bi), and state the basic dimension (Ba), the maximum dimension (Max), the minimum dimension (Min), the mean dimension (Mean), and the total tolerance (T). Refer to the first three examples.

	Bi	Uni	Ba	Max	Min	Mean	Total Tolerance
2.312 ± 0.005	✓		2.312	2.317	2.307	2.312	0.010
$0.875 \begin{smallmatrix} + 0.000 \\ - 0.010 \end{smallmatrix}$		✓	0.875	0.875	0.865	0.870	0.010
$1.250 \begin{smallmatrix} + 0.001 \\ - 0.002 \end{smallmatrix}$	✓		1.250	1.251	1.248	1.2495	0.003
0.625 ± 0.004							
0.4375 ± 0.0015							
$0.1875 \begin{smallmatrix} + 0.000 \\ - 0.003 \end{smallmatrix}$							
$0.1875 \begin{smallmatrix} + 0.002 \\ - 0.003 \end{smallmatrix}$							
$0.500 \begin{smallmatrix} + 0.0025 \\ - 0.000 \end{smallmatrix}$							

31. Determine the maximum clearance in the drawing below.

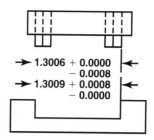

32. Determine the minimum clearance in the same drawing.

33. Determine the maximum interference in the drawing below.

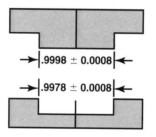

34. Determine the minimum interference in the same drawing.

35. With a partner, design two mating parts such that the maximum clearance = 0.002 inch and the minimum clearance = 0.001 inch.

36. With a partner, design two mating parts such that the maximum interference = 0.0002 inch and the minimum interference = 0.0001 inch.

INTRODUCTION

Percent is a form of comparison expressed as parts per hundred. When a percent is written as a fraction, the denominator is 100. **Percentages,** or a part of a whole expressed in hundredths, are used in industry to express the total quantity of the form of a ratio. Shrinkage of plastic materials is calculated by percentage; in statistical process control (SPC), the number of parts scrapped is indicated by percentage; and heat treating metal results in a percentage of shrinkage. These are just a few of the many examples of percentage calculations in the metalworking trade.

OBJECTIVES

After completing this unit, you will be able to:

- Convert between decimals, fractions and percents.
- Solve percentage problems.

UNDERSTANDING WHAT A PERCENT IS

Percent always refers to a number of parts out of 100. It never refers to any total quantity other than 100. (Notice that the % symbol is a rearranged form of the number "100" and is used as a shorthand for 100.) Therefore, 50% is 50/100 or 1/2 (reduced) or 0.5 (as a decimal). These are the three forms of writing percentage. In the square below, 50 of the 100 squares are shaded so we say 50/100 or 50% of the squares are shaded.

Examples

$$1\% = 1/100 = 0.01^*$$

$$40\% = 40/100 = 0.40$$

* Refer back to Unit 4 to review how to convert fractions to decimals, if necessary.

CHANGING A PERCENT TO A FRACTION

Write the percent as a fraction with a denominator of 100. Reduce to lowest possible terms.

Examples

$$35\% = 35/100 = 7/20 \text{ (reduced)}$$

$$99\% = 99/100$$

CHANGING A PERCENT TO A DECIMAL

Write the percent as a fraction. Divide the numerator by the denominator (100 in every case). The resulting decimal is equivalent to the original percent.

NOTE:

When dividing by 100, many use the decimal point shift shortcut of just moving the decimal point two places to the left, inserting zeros if necessary. Thus, 44 divided by 100 = 0.44; 4 divided by 100 = 0.04 when the zero is inserted.

Examples

$$21\% = 21/100 = 0.21$$

$$3.5\% = 3.5/100 = 0.035$$

CHANGING A DECIMAL TO A PERCENT

Multiply the decimal by 100. Add the percent symbol.

NOTE:

> When multiplying by 100, many use the decimal point shift shortcut of moving the decimal point two places to the right.

Examples

$$0.875 \times 100 = 87.5\%$$

$$0.3 \times 100 = 30\%$$

CHANGING A FRACTION TO A PERCENT

Divide the numerator by the denominator. Change this resulting decimal to a percent as outlined above.

Examples

$$3/5 = 0.6; \qquad 0.6 \times 100 = 60\%$$

$$1/3 = 0.33333; \qquad 0.33333 \times 100 = 33.333\%$$

Refer to Unit 4 to review how to change a fraction to a decimal.

SOLVING PERCENTAGE PROBLEMS

Several methods are used to solve percentage problems. To eliminate confusion, only one method will be presented in this text. This method involves comparing the part with the whole, and setting that comparison (or ratio) equal to the percent that must be written as a fraction with a denominator of 100. This is a called a *proportion*.

$$\frac{Part}{Whole} = \frac{\%}{100}$$

Refer to Unit 13 for more information on proportions.

This method of solution does not use the % key on calculators.

Examples

Problem	Setup		Solution
6 is what percent of 40?	$\frac{Part}{Whole} = \frac{\%}{100}$	$\frac{6}{40} = \frac{\%}{100}$	$(6 \times 100) \div (40) = 15\%$
What is 12% of 60?	$\frac{Part}{Whole} = \frac{\%}{100}$	$\frac{X}{60} = \frac{12}{100}$	$(60 \times 12) \div (100) = 7.2$
57 is 8% of what number?	$\frac{Part}{Whole} = \frac{\%}{100}$	$\frac{57}{X} = \frac{8}{100}$	$(57 \times 100) \div (8) = 712.5$

This formula can also be worded as: $$\frac{Change}{Original} = \frac{\%}{100}$$

Examples

Problem

A worker's weekly hours were increased from 40 to 45. What percent increase is this?

Setup

$$\frac{Change}{Original} = \frac{\%}{100} \qquad \frac{5\,^*}{40} = \frac{\%}{100}$$

Solution

$$(5 \times 100) \div (40) = 12.5\%$$

*Note: The change in hours is 5 hours.

Problem

A major software firm went public with its stock in 1986. Each share of stock cost $21 at that time. By 1993 each share of stock had risen in value to $778.50. What percent increase is this?

Setup

$$\frac{Change}{Original} = \frac{\%}{100} \qquad \frac{757.5\,^*}{21} = \frac{\%}{100}$$

Solution

$$(757.5 \times 100) \div (21) = 3,607\% \text{ increase}$$

*Note: This is the change in value.

CONCEPT APPLICATIONS

1–18. Complete the chart below, converting between percent, decimal and fraction forms.

Percent	Decimal	Fraction
50%		
	0.75	
		3/8
		4/5
	0.225	
10%		
	0.13	
		2/3
16%		

Answer the following, using proportions throughout.

19. What is 12% of 70?

20. 35 is 18% of what number?

21. 25 is what percent of 75?

22. 25 is what percent of 20? (Why is your answer over 100%?)

23. A 6 inch by 1 inch block of tool steel is to be hardened and will shrink 2% in both directions. What are the new dimensions?

24. Iron undergoes approximately 1.5% shrinkage as it cools. What are the dimensions of a cube of iron in a 1-cm cube form, when shrunk, if it shrinks evenly without distorting the cube?

25. Heating above 230°C (445°F) causes a shrinkage of approximately 4–5%. What range of lengths can be expected from a part that was 15.5 cm long before heating? State the dimensions to the nearest tenth of a centimeter.

26. Because of concessions, wages dropped from $9.50/hour to $9.30/hour. What percent decrease is this?

27. A worker's hours were increased from 40 hours/week to 50 hours/week. What percent increase is this?

28. An employee's wages were increased 75¢/hour, which represented a 5% raise. What were the employee's original wages?

29. What are this employee's new wages? (Do the new wages equal 105% of the original wages?)

30. If your present wages are $12.25/hour, would you prefer a 6% raise or a 75¢/hour-raise?

31. If an alloy is 67% copper and 33% zinc, how many pounds (to the nearest tenth) of each metal will there be in a casting weighing 90 pounds?

32. If the horsepower of an engine is increased 5% to 525 hp, what was the original horsepower? Hint: 525 hp is 105% of the original power.

At times, we hear that 99.9% correct is good enough—and all we can expect. Answer the following question about 99.9% correct.

33. Approximately 2,000 airplanes land at each of the major US airports daily. If 99.9% of the landings are perfect, how many landings are too long or too short?

SIGNED NUMBERS

INTRODUCTION

Signed numbers have many practical uses, from finances to Computer Numerical Control (CNC) programming. The positive and negative signs refer to both value and location. An overdraft of $2.30 is represented as -2.3 while a movement of 2.3 inch to the left or down in a CNC program is also represented as -2.3. Other trades and professions use the same symbolism, making it universal. The machinist needs to know the system of signed numbers and to be ready to use them on a daily basis.

OBJECTIVES

After completing this unit, you will be able to:

- Simplify double negatives.
- Add, subtract, multiply and divide signed numbers.
- Determine locations on a coordinate system.
- Use a calculator to perform arithmetic operations on signed numbers.

SIMPLIFYING DOUBLE NEGATIVES

When two negatives appear together, we say one "cancels" the other, resulting in a positive statement.

Examples

Consider this sentence. "Tests are not unimportant." The first negative, "not" is canceled by the second, "un." The resulting positive statement is "Tests are important." Similarly, "The wise student is not irresponsible about planning study time" should be rewritten as a positive statement "The wise student is responsible about planning study time."

We apply this to numbers by making two consecutive negatives into a positive. For example, $-(-5) = +5$. And $7-(-1) = 7 + 1$ or 8.

NOTE:

    The parentheses around a number are simply there to serve as mathematical punctuation, separating arithmetic operations from signed numbers.

ADDING SIGNED NUMBERS

The first step in adding two signed numbers is to determine if the signs are the same or different. If the signs are the same, the numbers are added together and the result has the same sign. However, if the two signed numbers have different signs, the numbers are subtracted. The result has the sign of the "larger" number, based on absolute value.*

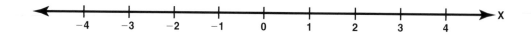

Examples

    A deposit of $15 followed by a deposit of $8 results in a balance of $23. This follows the rule of adding two signed numbers with the same sign ⇒ (+15) + (+8). A withdrawal of $8 from a balance of $15 results in a new balance of $7 ⇒ (−8) + (+15).

    On the *x*-axis, a move of 1.125 inch to the right (+, or positive direction) from an initial location +3.250 inch results in a new *x* location of +4.375 inch ⇒ (+1.125) + (+3.250). A move of 1.125 inch to the left (−) from a location of +3.250 inch results in an *x* location of +2.125 inch ⇒ (−1.125) + (3.250).

    If there is more than one move, continue adding or subtracting from the previous location. If the *x* coordinate at the start is +4.25 inch, and the first move to the right is (+) 0.125 inch, and the second move to the left (−) is 1.000 inch, the resulting location ⇒ +4.25 + 0.125 + (−1.000) = +3.375 inch.

SUBTRACTING SIGNED NUMBERS

Subtraction of signed numbers is generally converted to addition by the use of *two consecutive* sign changes. This recalls what was said above about two negative statements resulting in a positive one. As long as two consecutive sign changes are made, the resulting statement is equivalent to the original. Once the subtraction has been changed to addition, the rules for addition apply. Subtraction of signed numbers is harder to relate to everyday life. Consider these examples.

---

* **Note:** Absolute value refers to the actual value of a number, not its positiveness or negativeness. It represents the distance the number is located from zero on a number line. It is written as | |. | −4 | = 4 and | +4 | = 4 because each number is located 4 units from zero on a number line.

Examples

13 − (−5) is rewritten with two consecutive sign changes as 13 + (+5) = 18.

−13 − (−5) is rewritten with two consecutive sign changes as −13 + (+5) = −8.

A bank account balance is $12.   (+12)
The opposite of a $7 withdrawal is made.   − (−7)
The resulting balance is $19.   12 − (−7) = 12 + (+7) = 19.

A bank account balance is an overdraft of $12.   (−12)
The opposite of a $7 deposit is made.   − (+7)
The resulting balance is −$19.   −12 − (+7) = −12 + (−7) = −19.

MULTIPLYING SIGNED NUMBERS

To multiply two or more signed numbers, multiply the numbers. Determine the sign using the following guidelines. If there is an *even* number of negative signs, the result is positive. If there is an *odd* number of negative signs, the result is negative. The number of positive signs does not influence the sign of the result, only the number of negative signs.

Examples

(−3) × (+4) × (−2) = +24 (an even number of negative signs)

(+8) × (−1) = −8 (an odd number of negative signs)

Three $5 withdrawals from a bank is written as 3 × (−5) = −15.

DIVIDING SIGNED NUMBERS

To divide signed numbers, divide the numbers. Determine the sign using the following guidelines. If there is an *even* number of negative signs, the result is positive. If there is an *odd* number of negative signs, the result is negative. The number of positive signs does not influence the sign of the result, only the number of negative signs.

Examples

(+15) ÷ (−3) = −5 (an odd number of negative signs)

(−15) ÷ (−3) = +5 (an even number of negative signs)

USING A CALCULATOR

Most calculators have a "signed number" key similar to $\boxed{+/-}$ that allows the user to perform arithmetic operations on signed numbers. The key used for subtraction is not the same as this signed number key. Generally, calculators use the algebraic entry system. However, using the signed number key is often done in reverse order and the negative sign of a number is entered after the number itself. To enter −6 using $\boxed{+/-}$, press 6 *then* press $\boxed{+/-}$. The $\boxed{+/-}$ key can be used at any time to change the sign of a number.

Examples

(−4) × (−6) + (−5) may be entered as 4$\boxed{+/-}$ × 6$\boxed{+/-}$ + 5$\boxed{+/-}$ = and the answer is 19. The positive sign is understood.

(−4) × (+6) + (−5) may be entered as 4$\boxed{+/-}$ × 6 + 5$\boxed{+/-}$ = and the answer is −29. The signed key does not need to be used for (+6) as it is understood.

CONCEPT APPLICATIONS

Add, subtract, multiply, or divide the following. Try solving some of the problems below with a calculator and some without a calculator. Practice changing the signs for subtraction.

1. −12 + (+8) =

2. 13 + (−5) =

3. (−3) + (−4) + 6 + (−5) + (−4) =

4. −8 + (−9) =

5. 4 − (−4) =

6. −4 − (−4) =

7. 11 − (+6) =

8. −11 − (+6) =

9. (3) × (−2) × (−1) =

10. (+5) × (+6) × (−3) =

11. (−8) × 6 =

12. (−0.8) × (1.36) =

13. (−16) ÷ 8 =

14. $12 \div (-4) =$

15. $-0.25 \div (-2) =$

16. $-1 \div 8 =$

17. Rewrite this example, using temperature instead of money.

   A bank account balance is $12 (+12). The opposite of a $7 withdrawal $(-(-7))$ is made. The resulting balance is $19 $((+12) - (-7))$ or $((+12) + (+7)) = +19$.

Answer the following questions about the coordinate system below.

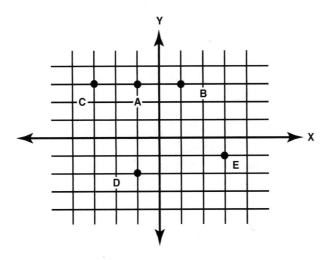

18. Draw a tooling path from point A to point B. Represent the horizontal movement numerically.

19. Draw a tooling path from point A to point C. Represent the horizontal movement numerically.

20. Draw a tooling path from point D to point E. Represent the horizontal movement numerically.

France is said to be the center of mathematical development in the 1600's. Two famous French mathematicians, Pierre de Fermat and René Descartes, each working independently, developed the idea of using two perpendicular number lines to identify the location of objects on a flat surface. The grid system used in problems 18-20 is called a Cartesian coordinate system, in honor of Descartes.

POWERS AND ROOTS

INTRODUCTION

Powers and roots represent a shortcut for multiplication and division. Powers and roots are commonly used in the machine trade to find area, volume, and dimensions with formulas. The most common powers and roots used are squares and square roots. This unit focuses on these two as well as their applications to the machining trade.

The symbol used today for a square root ($\sqrt{}$) was first introduced in 1525 by the German mathematician, Christoff Rudolff. Square roots of some numbers are called irrational numbers, that is, numbers that cannot be written as fractions. Calculators generally display square roots as decimals without regard to whether a number is rational or irrational.

The Pythagoreans were an elite group of Greek religious and scientific thinkers who followed a man named Pythagoras. It is sometimes said their most significant contribution to mathematics was the Pythagorean theorem. This theorem was not discovered by the Pythagoreans; it was only proven by them. This theorem also uses squares and square roots.

OBJECTIVES

After completing this unit, you will be able to:

- Use a scientific calculator to determine powers and roots of numbers.
- Solve problems using powers and roots.
- Solve problems using the Pythagorean theorem.

DEFINING THE PROCESSES

Determining the power of a number is a shortcut for multiplication in which a number is multiplied by itself numerous times. This is commonly referred to as "raising a number to a power."

Determining the root of a number is a shortcut for division in which a number is evenly divided by a second number multiple times, resulting in a value equal to the second number.

USING A CALCULATOR TO DETERMINE THE POWER OF A NUMBER

Scientific calculators have two methods for determining a power of a number. If the power is 2 or 3, there may be calculator keys identified as $\boxed{x^2}$ and $\boxed{x^3}$. 7^2 is entered into the calculator by pressing 7 and then the $\boxed{x^2}$ key. The answer, 49, should appear.

If the power is not 2 or 3, the exponent key, $\boxed{y^x}$, needs to be used. The correct way to use this key for finding 8^4 is to press 8, then the $\boxed{y^x}$ key, followed by 4 and the $\boxed{=}$ key. 4,096 should appear. In general, the base is entered first (8 in this case), then the exponent key ($\boxed{y^x}$), the exponent (4), and finally, the = key.

Examples

The fifth power of 4 is written as 4^5 and is a shortcut for $4 \times 4 \times 4 \times 4 \times 4 = 1,024$.

The second power of 10 (commonly called "the square of 10" or "10 squared") is written as $10^2 = 10 \times 10 = 100$.

The third power of 6 (commonly called "the cube of 6" or "6 cubed") is written as 6^3 and is shortcut for $6 \times 6 \times 6 = 216$.

USING A CALCULATOR TO DETERMINE ROOTS

Scientific calculators have two methods for determining a root of a number. If the root is 2 or 3, there may be keys identified as $\boxed{\sqrt[2]{x}}$ and $\boxed{\sqrt[3]{x}}$. To find $\sqrt[2]{49}$ (the square root of 49), enter 49 and then press the $\boxed{\sqrt[2]{x}}$ key. The display should show 7. With some calculators, the $\boxed{\sqrt[2]{x}}$ key needs to be pressed first, and then 49.

If the root is not 2 or 3, the root key, $\boxed{\sqrt[x]{y}}$, needs to be used. The correct way to use this key for finding the $\sqrt[4]{4,096}$ press 4,096, then the $\boxed{\sqrt[x]{y}}$ key followed by 4 and the = key. The display should show 8. In general, the *radicand* (the quantity under the radical sign) is entered first (4,096 in this case), then the root key ($\boxed{\sqrt[x]{y}}$), the root (4) and finally, the = key. If your calculator has the $\boxed{y^{\frac{1}{x}}}$ key, enter 4,096, then press the $\boxed{y^{\frac{1}{x}}}$ key, 4, and the $\boxed{=}$ key. The display should show 8. $\boxed{y^{\frac{1}{x}}}$ This key is the inverse root key.

Examples

The second root (called "the square root") of 25 is 5 because $5 \times 5 = 25$. It is written as $\sqrt{25} = 5$.

The square root of 9 is 3 because $3 \times 3 = 9$. It is written as $\sqrt{9}$.

The cube root of 64 is 4 because $4 \times 4 \times 4 = 64$. It is written as $\sqrt[3]{64}$.

The fourth root of 256 is 4 because $4 \times 4 \times 4 \times 4 = 256$. It is written as $\sqrt[4]{256} = 4$.

THE PYTHAGOREAN THEOREM

The Pythagorean theorem is one of the most useful and practical theorems in mathematics. It can be applied to many trades including the metalworking. The theorem states that the sum of the squares of the two legs of a right triangle is equal to the square of the hypotenuse. The Pythagorean theorem can be stated as $a^2 + b^2 = c^2$, where a^2 and b^2 are the squares of the legs of the triangle and c^2 is the square of the hypotenuse.

VOCABULARY

A **right triangle** is any triangle with an angle of 90°.

The **leg** of a right triangle is a side that forms the right angle. Each right triangle has two legs.

The **hypotenuse** of a right triangle is the third and longest side. It is directly across from the right angle.

REQUIREMENTS FOR THE PYTHAGOREAN THEOREM

1. It must be a right triangle.

2. Two sides must be known.

EXPLANATION

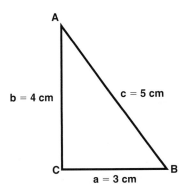

Uppercase letters refer to angles and lowercase letters refer to line segments.

In the right triangle above, legs a and b are equal to 3 cm and 4 cm, respectively. The hypotenuse is 5 cm.

The primary use of the Pythagorean theorem is to determine missing dimensions of a right triangle.

1. If the legs are known, square each, add to find the sum and then find the square root of that sum. This is the length of the hypotenuse.

2. If the hypotenuse is known, square it, subtract the square of the known leg, and then find the square root of that difference. This is the length of the missing leg.

The algebra involved in this process is contained in a later section of this text.

The theorem's secondary use is to determine if a triangle is a right triangle. A triangle is a right triangle if and only if the theorem works.

Examples

1. Determine the length of a hypotenuse, given the two legs.

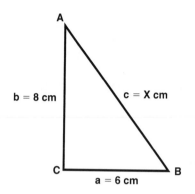

To find the hypotenuse, c, in this right triangle, we need to add the squares of the two legs. This is $8^2 + 6^2 = 64 + 36 = 100$. 100 represents the square of the hypotenuse, c^2. The square root of 100 is 10. Therefore, the hypotenuse of the triangle, c, is 10 cm.

2. Determine the length of one leg, given the hypotenuse and the other leg.

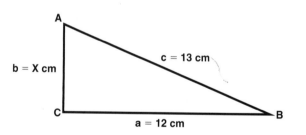

To find leg b, in this right triangle, we need to subtract the square of the known leg from the square of the hypotenuse. This is $13^2 - 12^2 = 169 - 144 = 25.25$ represents the square of leg b^2. The square root of 25 is 5. Thus, b = 5 cm.

3. Determine if a triangle is a right triangle.

This has practical applications to home improvement projects as well as the metalworking trades.

Is a 16 ft × 20 ft deck with a diagonal measurement of 24.5 ft "square"? Draw a sketch here.

The diagonal should represent the hypotenuse of a right triangle if it is square. Is $16^2 + 20^2 = 24.5^2$? No, $256 + 400 \neq 622.3$. Therefore, the deck is NOT square.

CONCEPT APPLICATIONS

Using a calculator, determine the square roots of the following. Round to three decimal places if necessary.

1. $\sqrt{99} =$

2. $\sqrt{121} =$

3. $\sqrt{12.1} =$

4. $\sqrt{0.5} =$

5. $\sqrt{0.0625} =$

I WONDER . . .

Is $\sqrt{121}$ similar to $\sqrt{12.1}$? Is $\sqrt{121}$ similar to $\sqrt{1.21}$? Why would this be? Can you predict the pattern?

What is 0.0625 as a fraction? Does it make sense that $\sqrt{1/16} = 1/4$?

Notice that the square root in problems 1–3 is a smaller number than the original number, but the square root in problems 4–5 is a larger number. Can you predict a pattern?

Using a calculator, determine the square of each of the following. Round to three decimal places if necessary.

6. $8.1^2 =$

7. $0.12^2 =$

8. $12^2 =$

9. $101^2 =$

10. $3.25^2 =$

I WONDER . . .

Is 0.12^2 similar to 122? Is 0.12^2 similar to 1.2^2? Why? Can you predict the pattern?

How can $(3\ 1/4)^2$ be entered in a scientific calculator? Is there only one way to do this?

Mathematics has its own forms of shorthand. Multiplication is a shorthand for addition because $3 \times 4 = 3 + 3 + 3 + 3$. Powers are shorthand for multiplication because $3^4 = 3 \times 3 \times 3 \times 3$. Can you extend this to division and roots?

Determine if triangles with the following dimensions are right triangles. In each case, if it is NOT a perfect right triangle, correct one dimension to make a right triangle. Sketch each, labeling the sides as legs or hypotenuse.

11. $a = 13, b = 8, c = 15.264$

12. $a = 9, b = 10, c = 13.500$

13. $a = 1.5, b = 2.5, c = \sqrt{8.5}$

Determine the missing dimensions in the following problems. In each case, sketch a drawing and solve. Remember that a and b refer to legs of the triangle and c refers to the hypotenuse. Round to three decimal places if necessary.

14. $a = 9$ inches, $b = 12$ inches, $c = $ _____ inches. Is the hypotenuse known or unknown? _____

Drawing:

15. a = _____ cm, b = 2.6 cm, c = 6.2 cm. Is the hypotenuse known or unknown? _____

Drawing:

16. a = 1.250 inches, b = _____ inches, c = 2.250 inches. Is the hypotenuse known or unknown? _____

Sketch:

I WONDER . . .

It is believed the Pythagoreans were the first to discover irrational numbers in the sixth century BC. Legend has it that Hippasus, a member of the Pythagoreans, was drowned because he relayed this secret to a nonmember of the Pythagoreans. A great deal has been written about the Pythagoreans. They were centered in southern Italy but were influenced by cultural and intellectual currents from beyond their immediate geographical area. They influenced contemporary mathematics, philosophy, and music. You can read more about them in your library or on-line.

UNIT

10

ORDER OF OPERATIONS

INTRODUCTION

The order of operations is a set of rules governing the priority and order of mathematical operations when no indications of order are given. This set of rules is universally accepted and mandates the way in which expressions are evaluated. This unit presents those rules and applications.

OBJECTIVES

After completing this unit, you will be able to:

- Write the order of operations.
- Evaluate expressions using the order of operations.
- Evaluate formulas.
- Apply the order of operations to trade-related formulas.

ORDER OF OPERATIONS

The order of operations states that expressions must be evaluated in the following order:

1. Parentheses

2. Exponents and roots

3. Multiplication and division

4. Addition and subtraction

Mathematical expressions MUST be evaluated from left to right and those listed together above have equal priority. That is, multiplication and division have equal priority and are evaluated as read, from left to right; and addition and subtraction have equal priority and are evaluated as read, from left to right.

Some students find jingles helpful in memorizing rules and use "*Please Excuse My Dear Aunt Sally*" to remember *P*arentheses, *E*xponents, *M*ultiplication, *D*ivision, *A*ddition, and *S*ubtraction.

Examples:

Evaluate each of the following, applying the order of operations.

$3 + 4 \times 5$ The first step is to multiply $4 \times 5 = 20$. Adding $3 + 4$ first is incorrect because it does not follow the order of operations, which clearly states that multiplication must be performed before addition. The next and final step is to add $3 + 20 = 23$.

$6 - 3^2$ The exponent must be evaluated first, resulting in $6 - 9 = -3$.

$12 \div (2 + 2 \times 5)$ The parentheses must be evaluated first, and within the parentheses multiplication is performed first. The result of the operations within the parenthesis is 12. Simplifying the expression, we have $12 \div 12$ which equals 1.

In summary:

$$3 + 4 \times 5 = 3 + 20 \qquad = 23$$

$$6 - 3^2 = 6 - 9 \qquad = -3$$

$$12 \div (2 + 2 \times 5) = 12 \div (2 + 10) = 12 \div 12 = 1$$

EVALUATING FORMULAS

Evaluation of formulas is a process of substituting numerical values for literals or variables in a given formula. If no operation is indicated between factors, multiplication is the understood operation. Once the numerical values are substituted, the expression is evaluated following the order of operations.

Examples:

Evaluate $5y - 4a$ given that $y = 5$ and $a = 6$.

Substituting, $5y - 4a$ becomes $5 \times 5 - 4 \times 6 = 25 - 24$ (Multiplication is performed before subtraction.) $25 - 24 = 1$.

Evaluate $\dfrac{4x - 2y}{a + c}$ given that $x = 3$, $y = 4$, $a = 2$, and $c = 6$.

Substituting, $\dfrac{4x - 2y}{a + c} = \dfrac{4 \times 3 - 2 \times 4}{2 + 6} = \dfrac{12 - 8}{8} = \dfrac{4}{8} = \dfrac{1}{2}$

(In fractions, the numerator and denominator are each simplified before division is performed.)

Evaluate revolutions per minute (rpm) = $\dfrac{CS \times 4}{D}$ given that CS (cutting speed) = 90 and D (diameter) = 0.5.

Substituting, $\dfrac{90 \times 4}{0.5} = \dfrac{360}{0.5} = 720$ rpm

CONCEPT APPLICATIONS

Complete the following, writing down as many steps as possible.

1. Write the order of operations.

   _____

   _____

   _____

   _____

2. Evaluate the following expressions.

   a. $2 \times 3 + 4 - 2 - 5 =$ _____

   b. $2(3 + 4) - 2 - 5 =$ _____

   c. $2 \times 3 + (4 - 2) - 5 =$ _____

   d. $2 \times 3 + 4 - (2 - 5) =$ _____

   e. $2[(3 + 4) - 2] - 5 =$ _____

   f. $3 - 7(8 - 12) =$ _____

   g. $12 - (-3)(-2) + 4^2 =$ _____

   h. $(5 - 3)(5 - 8)(-1)(4.3 - 4.3) =$ _____

   i. $8 + 6 \div 2 - 10 =$ _____

   j. $9 \times 3 + 2 + 1 - 6 \times 4 =$ _____

3. For each of the following answers, write a problem using at least four arithmetic operations that would result in the given answer. Include a decimal in one and a fraction in another.

   a. 7 = _____

   b. 0 = _____

   c. 10 = _____

   d. −3 = _____

   e. 500 = _____

4. Evaluate the following formulas, writing as many steps as possible. Refer to the order of operations throughout.

   a. P = 2L + 2W. Determine P (perimeter) given L (length) = 7 cm and W (width) = 5 cm.

      P = _____ cm

   b. ipm = F × N × rpm. Determine ipm (inches per minute) given F (feed per tooth) = 0.002 inch N (number of teeth in the cutter) = 2 (two-flute end mill) and rpm = 960.

      ipm = _____ inches

   c. sin = opp ÷ hyp. Determine sin (angle's sine) given opp (length of side opposite) = 7.5 cm and hyp (length of hypotenuse) = 10 cm.

      sin = _____

   d. tan = opp ÷ adj. Determine tan (tangent) given opp (length of side opposite) = 20 mm and adj (length of side adjacent) = 10 mm.

      tan = _____

   e. hyp = adj ÷ cos. Determine hyp (hypotenuse) given adj (length of side adjacent) = 4 inches and cos (angle's cosine) = 0.5

      hyp = _____ inches

   f. $d = \dfrac{N + 2}{P}$. Determine d (the outside diameter of a gear) given N (the number of teeth) = 16 and P (the pitch) = 0.25 inch.

      d = _____ inches

I WONDER . . .

Did you notice that the numbers and operations of exercises 2a–2e are the same? In each, there is multiplication between the 2 and 3, addition between the 3 and 4, subtraction between the 4 and 2 and subtraction between the 2 and 5. But notice how the answers vary, depending on the prescribed order of operations!

ALGEBRA

AREA AND VOLUME

INTRODUCTION

Finding the area and volume of geometric shapes are practical examples of applying the order of operations and formula evaluation. This unit introduces basic geometric shapes and the formulas used to find the area or volume of each.

OBJECTIVES

After completing this unit, you will be able to:

- Identify various geometric shapes.
- Substitute given dimensions into formulas.
- Evaluate formulas to determine area and volume.

AREA

Calculating the area of a figure is a means of calculating the number of square regions that can be drawn on that figure. We sometimes speak of square inches, square feet, square centimeters, and so on. The term "area" is used for two-dimensional figures, and for each type of figure (rectangle, triangle, etc.) a formula is used to calculate the area. These formulas are found in this unit and in Appendix A at the back of this book.

NOTE:

If the dimensions of a figure are not given in like (the same) units, you must first convert to like units before trying to calculate the area. For example, finding the area of a 5-inch by 2-foot rectangle isn't just a matter of multiplying 5 × 2. The dimensions need to be converted to like units, that is, such as 5 inches × 24 inches.

Rectangle

area = length × width (rectangle)

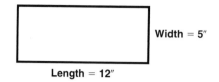

Width = 5″

Length = 12″

In the rectangle drawn above, the area is equal to length times width = 5 × 12 = 60 square inches. To confirm this, draw grid lines to represent 5 inches and 12 inches. These grid lines should mark off 60 squares, each 1 inch × 1 inch or 1 square inch. Therefore, the area is 60 square inches.

I WONDER . . .

Could the formula for the area of a rectangle be written as width × length? The answer is yes because multiplication is *commutative,* that is, the order in which numbers are multiplied doesn't change the result.

Could the formula for the area of a rectangle be written as base × height? The answer is yes, but mathematical convention states it as length × width.

Triangle

area = 1/2 base × height (right triangle)

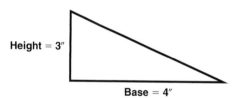

Height = 3″

Base = 4″

In the right triangle drawn above, the area is equal to one-half its base times its height = 1/2 × 4 × 3 = 6 square inches. To confirm this, draw lines to make the triangle part of a rectangle 3 inches × 4 inches. Is it logical that the formula for finding the area of this triangle is 1/2 times the area of the rectangle?

I WONDER . . .

Will this formula work for all triangles? The answer is yes, as long as the true base and true height have been calculated.

---

5 cm

Base = 6 cm

We can find the area of this triangle by first splitting the 6-cm base evenly to obtain right triangles. Using the Pythagorean theorem ($a^2 + b^2 = c^2$), we can calculate the height of the triangle to be $5^2 - 3^2 = height^2$. (Refer to Unit 9 for a discussion of Pythagorean theorem.) The height of the triangle is 4 cm.

We can then apply the formula for finding the area of a triangle, 1/2 base × height. This results in $1/2 \times 6 \times 4 = 12$ square cm.

Circle

area = $\pi \times radius^2$ (circle)

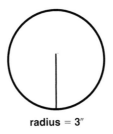

radius = 3″

This formula is often read as "pi r squared" (and leads to math jokes about whether pies are square or round). In the circle drawn above, the area is equal to π times the radius squared or $\pi \times 3^2 = 28.2743$ square inches.

Trapezoid

area = $\dfrac{(Base + base)}{2} \times$ height (trapezoid)

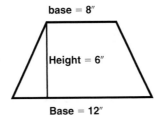

base = 8″

Height = 6″

Base = 12″

In this formula, the bases are averaged and then multipled by the height of the trapezoid. Referring to the trapezoid above, the area is $\dfrac{12 + 8}{2} \times 6 = 10 \times 6 = 60$ square inches. When using a calculator, use parentheses around the 8 and 12 to override the order of operations so the calculator doesn't add 12 and $[(8 \div 2) \times 6]$, leading to an incorrect result of $12 + 24$, or 36.

Another approach to finding the area of a trapezoid is to draw lines and divide the figure into one rectangle in the center and a triangle on each side. Try to visualize rotating and sliding these two triangles to form another rectangle. The formulas previously discussed above can be used on these familiar figures.

Parallelogram

area = base × height (parallelogram)

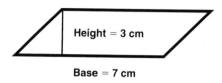

Height = 3 cm

Base = 7 cm

In the parallelogram above, the area = base × height = 7 × 3 = 21 square cm. Notice that once again, the figure can be divided into one rectangle and two triangles, which can be slid together to form a second rectangle.

VOLUME

Calculating the volume of a solid is a means of calculating the number of perfect cubes that could be placed within that solid. It may help to think of those cubes as perfect ice cubes. We sometimes speak of cubic inches, cubic yards, cubic centimeters (cc's), and so on. Volume is used for three-dimensional figures, and each figure has a formula used to calculate its volume. These can be found in this unit and in Appendix A at the back of this book.

Remember that dimensions must be in like (the same) units before calculations are performed! Convert if necessary.

Rectangular Solid

volume = length × width × height (rectangular solid)

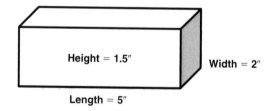

Height = 1.5″ **Width = 2″**

Length = 5″

In the solid drawn above, the volume equals its length × its width times its height = 5 × 2 × 1.5 = 15 cubic inches.

Cylinder

volume = $\pi \times$ radius$^2 \times$ height (cylinder)

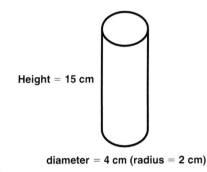

Height = 15 cm

diameter = 4 cm (radius = 2 cm)

In the cylinder above, the volume equals π times radius^2 times height = π times 2^2 times 15 = 188.496 cubic centimeters (cc's). This is actually finding the area of the base and multiplying it times the height.

I WONDER . . .

Can you think of a way to eliminate the multiplication signs in these formulas?

CONCEPT APPLICATIONS

1. Write the five formulas for finding area and the two formulas for finding volume.

Shape	*Formula*
Area	
_____	_____
_____	_____
_____	_____
_____	_____
_____	_____
Volume	
_____	_____
_____	_____

2. Draw rectangles with the following dimensions. Determine the area of each rectangle. Convert to like units.

Dimensions	Drawing	Area

a. L = 1 foot

    W = 5 feet   _____ sq ___

    Formula _____

b. L = 4 inches

    W = 6 inches   _____ sq ___

    Formula _____

c. L = 3 yards

    W = 3 feet   _____ sq ___

    Formula _____

3. Draw right triangles with the following dimensions. Determine the area of each triangle.

Dimensions	Drawing	Area

a. B = 12 inches

    H = 10 inches   _____ sq ___

    Formula _____

b. B = 9 feet

    H = 7 feet   _____ sq ___

    Formula _____

c. B = 5 inches

    H = 1 foot   _____ sq ___

    Formula _____

4. Draw circles with the following dimensions. Determine the area of each. Use the $\boxed{\pi}$ key and round to three decimals.

Dimensions	Drawing	Area

a. Radius = 7 mm

    Formula _____   _____ sq ___

b. Radius = 0.25 miles

    Formula _____   _____ sq ___

c. Diameter = 20 inches; radius = 10 inches

    Formula ___   _____ sq ___

d. Radius = 1 yard = 3 foot = 36 inches

    Formula _____   _____ sq yd

                                               OR

                                         _____ sq ft

                                               OR

                                       _____ sq in

5. Draw trapezoids with the following dimensions. Determine the area of each trapezoid.

         Dimensions   *Drawing*   *Area*

a. b = 2 feet

    B = 3 feet

    H = 1.5 feet   _____ sq ___

    Formula _____

b. b = 6 mm

    B = 8 mm

    H = 5 mm   _____ sq ___

    Formula _____

c. b = 1.5 yards   Draw this trapezoid sideways (vertically).

    B = 2 yards

    H = 1.3 yards   _____ sq ___

    Formula _____

6. Draw parallelograms with the following dimensions. Determine the area of each parallelogram.

Dimensions	Drawing	Area

a. B = 10 cm = 100 mm

H = 6 mm

_____ sq ___

Formula _____

b. B = 5 inches

H = 3.2 inches

_____ sq ___

Formula _____

c. Draw and label a parallelogram with an area of 24 square feet.

d. Draw and label a different parallelogram with an area of 24 square feet.

7. Draw rectangular solids with the following dimensions. Determine the volume of each rectangular solid.

Dimensions	Drawing	Volume

a. L = 20 cm

W = 10 cm

H = 15 cm

_____ cu ___

b. L = 30 ft

W = 10 ft

H = 8 ft

_____ cu ___

8. Draw cylinders with the following dimensions. Determine the volume of each cylinder.

	Dimensions	*Drawing*	*Volume*
a.	r = 1 inch		
	H = 4 inches		_____ cu ___

b. r = 3 mm   Draw this cylinder on its side.

   H = 9 mm   _____ cu ___

c. r = 2 feet

   H = 12 inches   _____ cu ___

9. How many cubic inches are there in 1 cubic foot? Place a drawing here to help visualize the situation.

10. How many cubic feet are there in 1 cubic yard? Make a drawing.

11. How many cubic inches are there in one cubic yard? Make a drawing.

12. A baseless cylinder can be formed two ways from an 8.5 inch × 11 inch sheet of paper (one tall and narrow, the other short and wide). Are the volumes of these two cylinders equal? _____ Justify your answer with a drawing and calculations.

13. Two identical oil pipelines are cylinders of radius 6 inches. Due to environmental concerns, they must be replaced with a single pipeline with the same capacity. If the new pipeline is also cylindrical, what must its radius be? _____

14. Which pizza is a better deal: a 10-inch pizza for $10.00?

OR

a 12-inch pizza for $12.00? _____

UNIT
12

EQUATIONS AND FORMULAS

INTRODUCTION

The methods used to solve equations are the tools used to manipulate and rearrange formulas. These important skills are used by the metalworker when looking up formulas in reference books and for solving triangles with trigonometry. Preliminary skills used in solving simple equations include the addition and subtraction of algebraic terms. This unit covers those operations as well as the solution of simple equations and the rearrangement of formulas.

OBJECTIVES

After completing this unit, you will be able to:

- Add algebraic terms.
- Subtract algebraic terms.
- Solve simple equations.
- Rearrange simple formulas.

ADDING OR SUBTRACTING ALGEBRAIC TERMS

Algebraic terms must be *like terms* (identical in letters and exponents) to be added or subtracted. That is, an x can only be added or subtracted from another x, not a y or an x^2. And the result of that addition or subtraction is the same *like term*. If there is no number (coefficient) in front of the x (variable), the understood coefficient is 1.

Examples

$$3x + 4x - 2x = 5x \qquad 3x + 4x - x = 6x \qquad 12m + m - 6m = 7m$$

Notice that the answer is still "x" or "m" with no exponent. Also, notice how both the second and third examples, contain a term whose coefficient is 1.

Examples

$$3x + 4y = 3x + 4y \qquad 3x - y = 3x - y \qquad 12m + 6j = 12m + 6j$$

In each of these examples, the terms are not *like terms* and therefore cannot be simplified.

SOLVING SIMPLE EQUATIONS

The goal in solving equations is to isolate the variable (letter), resulting in a statement of $x = \_\_$. When this statement is true, the equation is solved. The processes used to solve the equations vary, depending on the operations in the equation. In each situation, the process used is the opposite of the operation in the equation. If the equation contains addition, subtraction is used to solve it. If it contains multiplication, division is used, and so on. However, to keep the equation balanced, it is vital that whatever is done on one side of the equation be done on the other side as well.

Think of an equation as a scale with two balanced sides. If weight is either added or subtracted from only one side, the scale is no longer balanced. However, if equal weight is added to or removed from both sides, the scale remains balanced. This is true when solving equations and must be adhered to throughout the processes.

Examples

$$\begin{array}{r} J + 10 = 21 \\ \underline{- 10 - 10} \\ J = 11 \end{array}$$

10 is subtracted from both sides of the equation to eliminate the $+10$ and to isolate J. The solution to this equation is $J = 11$, which is a true statement.

We know it is a true statement because when we substitute 11 for J in the original equation, $11 + 10$ does equal 21. This is called "checking the solution or answer."

$$\begin{array}{r} m - 12 = 5 \\ \underline{+ 12 + 12} \\ m = 17 \end{array}$$

12 is added to each side of the equation to eliminate the -12 and to isolate m. The solution to this equation is $m = 17$, which is a true statement.

Again, we know this is a true statement by substituting 17 for m in the original equation. $17 - 12$ does equal 5.

$6Q = 18$
$\underline{\div 6 \quad \div 6}$
$Q = 3$

Both sides are divided by 6 to eliminate the multiplication of 6 and to isolate Q. The solution to this equation is Q = 3, which is a true statement.

Verify this solution by checking it into the original equation.

$\dfrac{Y}{8} = \dfrac{3}{4}$

When division is involved, one easy solution is to cross-multiply.* In this case, cross-multiplication would result in the new equation 4Y = 24.

$4Y = 24$
$\underline{\div 4 \quad \div 4}$
$Y = 6$

We then solve this equation by dividing both sides by 4.

The solution to this equation is Y = 6, which is a true statement when substituted into the original equation, $\dfrac{Y}{8} = \dfrac{3}{4}$; $\dfrac{6}{8} = \dfrac{3}{4}$.

Some equations involve more than one process in their solution. A logical sequence of steps for solving multiprocess equations is:

1. Deal with addition and subtraction first, keeping the equation balanced.

2. Deal with multiplication and division next, keeping the equation balanced.

Examples

$8G + 10 = 34$
$\underline{ - 10 - 10}$
$8G = 24$

10 is subtracted from both sides. (Addition and subtraction first.)

$\underline{\div 8 \quad \div 8}$
$G = 3$

Both sides are divided by 8. (Multiplication and division next.)

The solution to this equation is G = 3. If we substitute 3 into the original equation in place of G, we get a true statement, 8 × 3 + 10 = 34. This guarantees a correct solution and it is recommended that you check EVERY solution in this manner.

$7P - 16 = 15.5$
$\underline{ + 16 + 16}$
$7P = 31.5$

16 is added to both sides. (Addition and subtraction first.)

$\underline{\div 7 \quad \div 7}$
$P = 4.5$

Both sides are divided by 7. (Multiplication and division next.)

The solution to this equation is P = 4.5. If we substitute 4.5 into the original equation, we get the true statement, 7 × 4.5 − 16 = 15.5.

In some equations, the variable appears on both sides of the equal sign. A logical sequence of steps for solving this multiprocess equations is:

1. Move all variables to one side of the equal sign. This will involve addition or subtraction.

---

* Note: If there is a missing denominator, it is equal to one and one can be written into the equation. See exercises 33–37

2. Move all constants (numbers) to the other side of the equal sign by:

   a. Dealing with addition and subtraction, keeping the equation balanced.

   b. Dealing with multiplication and division, keeping the equation balanced.

Examples

$$9W + 15 = 3W + 45$$
$$\underline{-\ 3W \qquad\quad -\ 3W}$$
$$6W + 15 = \quad 45$$

Subtract 3W from both sides to get the variables on ONE side.

$$\underline{\quad\quad -\ 15\ -\ 15}$$
$$6W = 30$$

Subtract 15 from each side.

$$\underline{\quad\quad \div\ 6 \quad \div\ 6}$$
$$W = \quad 5$$

Divide both sides by 6.

The solution to this equation is W = 5. Check the solution by substituting 5 for each W in the original equation. $9 \times 5 + 15$ should equal $3 \times 5 + 45$. It is a true statement and you can be assured of the solution.

$$9W + 15 = 13W + 45$$
$$\underline{-\ 9W \qquad\quad\ -\ 9W}$$
$$15 = \quad 4W + 45$$

Subtract 9W from each side to get the variables on ONE side.

$$\underline{-\ 45 \qquad\quad\ -\ 45}$$
$$-\ 30 = \quad 4W$$

Subtract 45 from each side.

$$\underline{\div\ 4 \qquad\quad\ \div\ 4}$$
$$-7.5 = \quad W$$

Divide both sides by 4.

The solution to this equation is W = −7.5. Be sure to check the solution back into the original equation.

REARRANGING FORMULAS

Formulas can be rearranged to solve for, or isolate, any given variable. The processes and sequences used for solving equations are used again.

1. Deal with addition and subtraction first, keeping the formula balanced.

2. Deal with multiplication and division next, keeping the formula balanced.

Examples

   Isolate A in this formula: F = MA

   To isolate A, M needs to be moved to the left side of the equal sign. The correct way to eliminate M (which is multiplied by A) is to divide both sides by M.

$$\frac{F}{M} = \frac{MA}{M}$$ The M's on the right side cancel, or divide to 1.

$\frac{F}{M} = A$ The solution to this rearrangement is $\frac{F}{M} = A$.

Isolate L in this formula for finding the area of a rectangle: $A = LW$

To isolate L, W needs to be moved to the left side of the equal sign. The correct way to eliminate W, which is multiplied by L, is to divide both sides by W.

$\frac{A}{W} = \frac{LW}{W}$ The Ws on the right side cancel, or divide 1.
The solution to this rearrangement is $\frac{A}{W} = L$.

Isolate RPM in this formula, which is used for cutting speeds: $4 \times (SFM) = (d) \times (RPM)$. SFM = surface feet per minute; d = diameter; RPM = revolutions per minute.

To isolate RPM, d must be eliminated by dividing both sides by D.

$\frac{4 \times SFM}{d} = \frac{D \times RPM}{d}$ The d's on the right side cancel, or divide to 1.
The solution to this rearrangement is $\frac{4 \times (SFM)}{d} = RPM$.

CONCEPT APPLICATIONS

Simplify the following expressions using addition or subtraction of like terms.

1. $4K + K - 3K$ _____

2. $-2M - 10M + 6M$ _____

3. $6.2Q + Q$ _____

4. $7j - 11j + 3F$ _____

Solve the following equations. Check your solution into the original equation. Show your work.

5. $X + 22 = -5$ $X =$ _____

6. $3J = -6$ $J =$ _____

7. $m + 2.25 = 6$ $m =$ _____

8. $D + 2.25 = -6$ $D =$ _____

9. $8T = 21$ $T =$ _____

10. $6 = C - 15$ $C =$ _____

The following equations are multistep equations. Refer to the outlined steps in this unit. Show your work here.

11. $12Y + 4 = 64$ $Y =$ _____   12. $5n + 2 = 22$ $n =$ _____

13. $4.2P + 2 = 44$ $P =$ _____   14. $10X - 4 = 46$ $X =$ _____

15. $3X + 12 = 5X$ $X =$ _____   16. $0.5R + 6 = 6.5R$ $R =$ _____

17. $3G + 4G - 2G = 30$ $G =$ _____   18. $10j - 2 = 3j + 12$ $j =$ _____

19. $3B - 3 = B + 3$ $B =$ _____   20. $-4c - 2 = -6c - 10$ $c =$ _____

21. $21 + 4k = 10k - 21$ $k =$ _____   22. $4.2q + 3.1 = 2.1q + 7.3$ $q =$ _____

23. $\dfrac{2}{3} = \dfrac{8}{6x}$ $x =$ _____   24. $\dfrac{V}{20} = \dfrac{2.5}{5}$ $V =$ _____

25. $\dfrac{3y}{5} = \dfrac{9}{1}$ $y =$ _____   26. $\dfrac{5}{w} = \dfrac{3}{6}$ $w =$ _____

Rearrange the following formulas, solving for the indicated variable.

27. $d = rt$ $r = \underline{\hspace{1cm}}$ 28. $d = rt$ $t = \underline{\hspace{1cm}}$

29. $A = 0.5BH$ $B = \underline{\hspace{1cm}}$ 30. $A = 0.5BH$ $H = \underline{\hspace{1cm}}$

31. $A = \pi r^2$ $r^2 = \underline{\hspace{1cm}}$ 32. $A = \pi r^2$ $\pi = \underline{\hspace{1cm}}$

33. $A = \dfrac{BH}{2}$ $B = \underline{\hspace{1cm}}$ 34. $A = \dfrac{BH}{2}$ $H = \underline{\hspace{1cm}}$

35. $\sin = \dfrac{opp}{hyp}$ $opp = \underline{\hspace{1cm}}$ 36. $\sin = \dfrac{opp}{hyp}$ $hyp = \underline{\hspace{1cm}}$

37. $C = \dfrac{F - 32}{1.8}$ $F = \underline{\hspace{1cm}}$ 38. $Y = mx + b$ $b = \underline{\hspace{1cm}}$

39. $V = LWH$ $L = \underline{\hspace{1cm}}$ 40. $V = \pi r^2 h$ $h = \underline{\hspace{1cm}}$

I WONDER . . .

Did you notice any relationship between exercises 29 and 30 and exercises 33 and 34? What formula is used in these four exercises? Does it matter if we divide by 2 or multiply by 1/2?

UNIT
13

RATIOS AND PROPORTIONS

INTRODUCTION

Ratios and proportions are used often in solving typical shop problems, such as cutting speeds, gears, and cutting fluids. Ratios are used to establish the original comparison between two quantities and proportions are used to carry this comparison to a new setting.

OBJECTIVES

After completing this unit, you will be able to:

- Set up like quantities in ratio form.
- Express problems in ratio form.
- Reduce ratios to lowest terms.
- Set up proportions.
- Solve proportions.
- Use proportions to solve problems.

DEFINITIONS

Ratio

A ratio is a comparison between two like (similar or identical) terms and is usually written as a fraction such as 1/4 or as 1:4. It is read as "one to four." Terms must be converted to like units in order to make a meaningful comparison.

Example

> An ant weighs approximately 0.5 grams. It can lift approximately 1 ounce or 30 grams. The ratio representing an ant's weight to the weight it can lift is 0.5/30 = 1/60 and can be written as 1/60 or 1:60. While the 1/2-gram ant can lift 1 ounce, these units must be converted to like units in order to have a meaningful comparison. (See the note at the beginning of Unit 11 for a review of "like terms.")

Proportion

A **proportion** is made up of two fractions. The first represents the original comparison and the second represents the new setting that reflects the same ratio.

$\frac{3}{4}$ is an example of a ratio. $\frac{X}{8}$ is another ratio. If they refer to the same setting, they become an equation: $\frac{3}{4} = \frac{X}{8}$. This equation is called a proportion and can be solved as before.

Example

> If the 0.5-gram ant above can lift 30 grams, how much should a 300-pound Olympic champion be able to lift? $\frac{0.5}{30} = \frac{300}{X}$.
>
> One simple procedure used to solve this proportion is cross-multiplication. This was used in Unit 7 on percents and Unit 12 on equations. The equation resulting from cross-multiplication is $0.5X = 9,000$. Solving this equation, we get the result of 18,000 pounds, an unrealistic weight for humans to lift. Olympic champions lift less than 450 pounds! If one's weight determines the amount one can lift, humans fall short of ants in terms of strength.
>
> Notice that the first ratio has like units: grams. The second ratio also has like units: pounds. The comparison between the ratios is important, not the units within each ratio.

There are two types of proportion: Direct and Indirect (or Inverse).

Direct Proportion

Direct proportion is the term used to describe situations where units being compared are either both increasing or decreasing.

Examples

> An example of direct proportion is a gas and oil mixture. As the amount of gas increases, so does the amount of oil used in that mixture. If the ratio of oil to gas is 1 to 15 (original comparison) and the amount of gas used is 20 ounces (new setting), the amount of oil needed can be found using a proportion.
>
> $\frac{1}{15} = \frac{X}{20}$ Using cross-multiplication, $15X = 20$. $X = 1.333$ or 1.3 ounces of oil. Both numerators represent oil and both denominators represent gas.
>
> Be sure to check the answer. Is 1.3 ounces of oil a logical answer?
>
> Another example of direct proportion is time and production. If a machine can produce 700 parts per hour, how many hours will it take to produce 900 parts? The proportion that describes this situation is $\frac{700^*}{900} = \frac{1}{X}$. Cross-multiplication results in the following equation: $700X = 900$ and then $X = 1.286$ hours or about 1 hour and 17 minutes. Note that in this proportion, both the numerator and denominator of the first ratio represent parts, whereas the numerator and denominator in the second ratio represent the time, in hours.

---

* Ratios have like terms or units.

Be sure to check the answer. Is 1 hour 17 minutes a logical answer?

A lifelike example of direct proportion is the following. If 7.5 ounces of dough are used to make a 5-inch pizza, how many ounces are used for a 20-inch pizza?

Using like terms, the proportion can be set up as $\frac{5}{20} \overset{*}{=} \frac{7.5}{X}$. Cross-multiplication yields an equation of 5X = 150 and X = 30 ounces of dough.

Be sure to check the answer. Is 30 ounces of dough a logical answer?

Indirect Proportion

Indirect proportion is the term used to describe situations where units being compared do not BOTH increase or decrease. As one INCREASES, the other DECREASES.

Examples

A typical example of indirect proportion in the machine trade is the calculation of pulleys, gear speeds and teeth. If two gears are in mesh, the larger gear turns slower. That is, as the number of teeth INCREASES, the speed DECREASES.

If a 20-tooth gear rotates at 100 revolutions per minute (rpm) and is in mesh with another gear, how many teeth are required on that gear for it to rotate at 200 rpm?

The ratio describing rpm is $\frac{100}{200}\overset{*}{}$. But, if we set up the other half of the proportion as $\frac{20}{X}$, we get a proportion of $\frac{100}{200} = \frac{20}{X}$ which gives us the answer 40. However, we know the answer cannot be greater than 20 teeth. To accomplish this, indirect proportion requires that the second fraction of the proportion is inverted.[†] So, our proportion looks like this:

$$\frac{100}{200} = \frac{X}{20}.$$

Using cross-multiplication, the resulting equation is 200X = 2,000 and X = 10 teeth, which is a logical answer.

A second example of indirect proportion is workers and time. As the number of workers on a job INCREASES, the length of time needed to accomplish the task should DECREASE.

If 10 workers can complete a production job in 2 hours, how long should it take 15 workers? $\frac{10}{15}\overset{*}{=} \frac{X}{2}$ is the correct form of the proportion, with the second fraction inverted.

Cross-multiplying results in a new equation, 15X = 20 and X = 1.3 hours, a logical solution.

---

* Ratios have like terms or units.
† Other formulas can be used to determine teeth and rpms for gears. This is one accepted method and affords practice with proportion.

CONCEPT APPLICATIONS

Write the following comparisons as ratios in reduced form. Be sure each compares like units.

1. 2 hours of travel to 5 hours of work _____

2. 3 yards to 3 feet _____

3. 7 parts solution to 14 parts water _____

Solve the following proportions. First identify if each is an example of direct or indirect proportion, then write the proportion, solve it, and check the answer.

4. If a cutting mixture requires 1 pint of cutting compound for every 5 gallons of water, how many pints are required for a 40-gallon tank? (There are 8 pints in 1 gallon.)

   Direct or indirect? _____

   Pints of compound = _____ (Is this a logical answer?)

5. If 8 workers complete a project in 12 days, how many days will be needed for 6 workers?

   Direct or indirect? _____

   Number of days = _____ (Is this a logical answer?)

6. A gear with 16 teeth is driving a gear with 64 teeth. If the driven gear is required to rotate at 160 rpm, what is the required rpm of the driver?

   Direct or indirect? _____

   rpm = _____ (Is this a logical answer?)

7. Corresponding sides of similar triangles are directly proportional. These two triangles are similar. Determine the missing dimensions. (Write the given ratio and solve for one side at a time.)

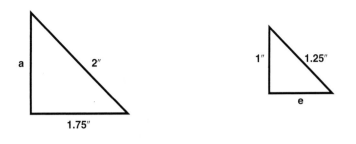

Direct or indirect? _____

a = _____ (Is this a logical answer?)

c = _____ (Is this a logical answer?)

8. A 6-inch-diameter pulley is rotating at 1200 rpm. If it is connected to an 8-inch pulley, what will be the rpm of the 8-inch pulley?

Direct or indirect? _____

rpm = _____ (Is this a logical answer?)

9. If 40 feet of wire weigh 4 3/4 pounds, what is the weight of 7 feet of wire?

Direct or indirect? _____

pounds = _____ (Is this a logical answer?)

10. A fan motor is running at 1,750 rpm and is fitted with a 2 1/2-inch pulley. If the motor is attached to a 7 1/2-inch pulley, what is the rpm of the fan?

Direct or indirect? _____

rpm = _____ (Is this a logical answer?)

11. On a drawing with a scale of 1/4 to 1, the machinist measures a line that is 1 5/8 inches, what is its actual length?

Direct or indirect? _____

inches = _____ (Is this a logical answer?)

12. If a machinist can drill and tap 10 holes in 46 minutes, how many holes can the machinist drill in an 8-hour shift?

Direct or indirect? _____

holes = _____ (Is this a logical answer?)

13. It is required to reduce the speed of a pulley to a ratio of 6.4 to 2. If the driven pulley is 3.25 inches in diameter, what is the required size of the driver?

Direct or indirect? _____

inches = _____ (Is this a logical answer?)

14. Determine the missing dimensions on the two similar triangles.

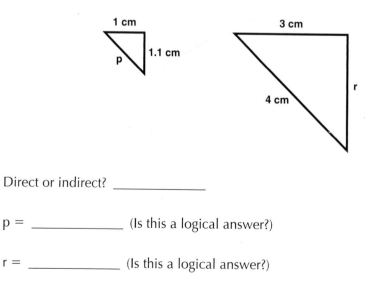

Direct or indirect? _____

p = _____ (Is this a logical answer?)

r = _____ (Is this a logical answer?)

15. If 16 ounces of dough are used to make a 14-inch pizza, how many ounces are used for a 20-inch pizza?

Direct or indirect? _____

ounces = _____ (Is it logical?)

I WONDER . . .

Refer back to the example on page 99 regarding pizza dough. Will the answer always be the same if the ounces and pizza diameter have a difference of 2.5? Try 100 ounces and a 97.5-inch pizza. Try even larger numbers. Try small numbers. What conclusion can you draw?

GEOMETRY

UNIT
14
ANGLES AND LINES

INTRODUCTION

Establishing points, lines, planes, and angles are tasks the metalworker is repeatedly called upon to perform. Many hand and mechanical devices have been created to help with these tasks, such as protractors, squares, indexing heads, and sine bars. Even though so much of this work is done on computers today, the skilled metalworker has a solid knowledge of geometry, which is the study of the functional relationships between points, lines, planes, and angles.

OBJECTIVES

After completing this unit, you will be able to:

- Recognize the definitions of basic geometric terms such as *point, line, plane,* and *angle.*
- Use basic geometric symbols and terms interchangeably.
- Identify parallel, perpendicular, and oblique lines and planes.
- Identify equivalent angles.
- Identify types and measures of angles.
- Convert between degree, minute, second form, and decimal degree form of angle measure.
- Add, subtract, multiply, and divide angles in either form.
- Determine missing dimensions on prints using geometric principles.

Mathematics uses symbols to replace words in sentences. Some of the basic geometric symbols are given below. Memorizing these symbols will help you to better understand this unit.

GEOMETRY SYMBOLS

Angle	∠	Arc	⌒
Parallel	∥	Pi	π
Perpendicular	⊥	Circle	⊙
Triangle	△	Radius	**R,r**
Right Triangle	◿	Circumference	**C**
Right Angle	∟	Line	**A ↔ B**
Degree	°	Therefore	∴
Minute	′	Intersection	∩
Second	″	Point	●
Greater Than	>	Plane	▱
Less Than	<	Oblique Lines	×

DEFINITIONS

Point

A point is a location or position on a line or in a plane. This location or position is indicated with a dot (●) and a capital letter.

Example:

Points A, B, and C all fall along this line segment.

Line

Two points establish the location of a line. In this book, the word *line* means a *straight line* unless otherwise indicated. Lines extend indefinitely in both directions indicated by the arrowheads pointing in opposite directions and are indicated with two capital letters at the ends of a segment of a line or one small letter in the middle of a line.

Lines can be parallel. *Parallel lines* never intersect.

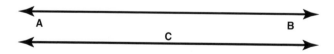

Lines AB and c are parallel: AB ∥ c

Lines can intersect. Perpendicular lines and oblique lines are two types of intersecting lines. *Perpendicular lines* intersect at 90° angles (right angles). *Oblique lines* intersect at angles other than 90°.

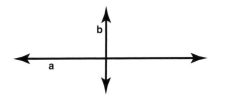 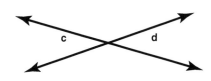

a is perpendicular to b: a ⊥ b

c and d are oblique lines, intersecting at an angle other than 90°

Propositions Regarding Lines

1. A straight line has 180° on each side.

2. If two or more lines are perpendicular to the same line, they are parallel.

3. If one of two parallel lines is perpendicular to the third line, the other parallel line is also perpendicular to the third line.

Planes

A *plane* is an imaginary flat surface extending infinitely in all directions.

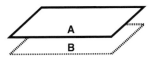

Parallel planes do not intersect.

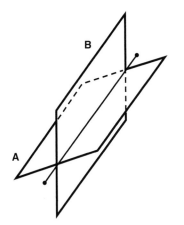

Plane A is parallel to plane B.

Intersecting planes can be *perpendicular* or *oblique*. *Intersecting planes* intersect in a straight line and intersecting perpendicular planes form 90° angles (right angles).

Planes A and B intersect in a straight line.

109

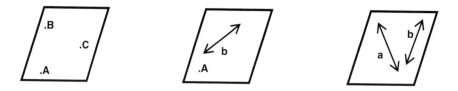

The position of a plane can be established by (1) three points or (2) a line and one point or (3) two lines.

Angles

Angles are formed by two intersecting lines. The point of intersection is called the *vertex*. The lines form the sides of the angles. Angles are named by three capital letters ($\angle$ ABC), a single capital letter ($\angle$ B), a small letter written inside the angle ($\angle$ b), or a number ($\angle$ 2).

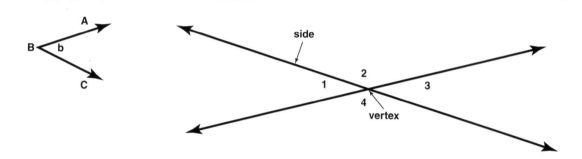

The measure of $\angle$ 1 and $\angle$ 3 = 30° each. The measure of $\angle$ 2 and $\angle$ 4 = 150° each.

When two lines intersect, they form two pairs of equal *vertical* or *opposite* angles. In the drawing above, $\angle$ 1 and $\angle$ 3 form a pair of vertical angles. $\angle$ 2 and $\angle$ 4 form another pair of vertical angles, ∴ (therefore), $\angle$ 1 = $\angle$ 3 and $\angle$ 2 = $\angle$ 4.

When two parallel lines are intersected by a third line (called a transversal), equal pairs of *alternate interior angles* are formed. Refer to the diagram below.

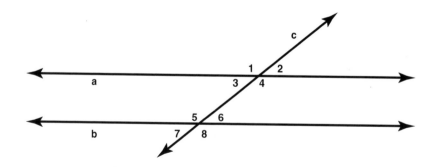

a ∥ b, $\angle$ 3 and $\angle$ 6 are *alternate interior angles* because they alternate on sides of transversal c and they are interior to lines a and b. ∴ $\angle$ 3 = $\angle$ 6.

$\angle$ 4 and $\angle$ 5 are also *alternate interior angles* and ∴ $\angle$ 4 = $\angle$ 5.

When two parallel lines are intersected by a third line (called a transversal), equal pairs of *alternate exterior angles* are formed. Refer to the previous diagram.

a ∥ b, ∠ 1 and ∠ 8 are *alternate exterior angles* because they alternate on sides of transversal c and they are exterior to lines a and b. ∴∠ 1 = ∠ 8.

∠ 7 and ∠ 2 are also *alternate exterior angles* and ∴ ∠ 7 = ∠ 2.

Corresponding angles are also formed when two parallel lines are intersected by a transversal. Refer to the previous diagram. Statements of logic, when applied to *alternate interior* and *alternate exterior angles,* lead to the same conclusions as statements of *corresponding angles.*

∠ 1 corresponds to ∠ 5, ∠ 2 corresponds to ∠ 6, ∠ 3 corresponds to ∠ 7 and ∠ 4 corresponds to ∠ 8. The angles in each pair of corresponding angles are equal.

Propositions Regarding Angles

1. If two angles have their corresponding sides parallel, the angles are equal.

2. If two angles have their corresponding sides perpendicular, the angles are equal.

Classification of Angles by Measure

Acute angles have measures less than 90°.

Right angles have a measure of exactly 90°.

Obtuse angles have measures between 90° and 180°.

Straight angles have a measure of exactly 180°. (Straight lines have exactly 180° on each side.)

Reflex angles have measures between 180° and 360°.

A revolution or *circle* measures exactly 360°.

Complementary angles are two angles whose sum is exactly 90°.

Supplementary angles are two angles whose sum is exactly 180°.

There are 60 seconds (60″) in 1 minute and 60 minutes (60′) in 1 degree and 360° in one circle. 60″ = 1′. 60′ = 1°. 360° = ⊙.

Forms of Expressing Angles

Angles can be expressed in decimal form or in degree-minute-second (DMS) form. Decimal form is based on a base-10 number system and DMS form is on a base-60 system. Both forms are used in today's metalworking trade, sometimes interchangeably. Most scientific calculators have keys programmed to switch between the two forms. However, to better understand the two systems, study the following table.

Degree Minute Second	Decimal
12° 30′	12.5°
12° 30′30″	12.50833°
12° 17′ 44″	12.29556°

The procedure used to convert from degree-minute-second form to decimal degrees is:

1. Divide the number of seconds by 60. (There are 60 seconds in 1 minute.)

2. Add the decimal from step 1 to the number of minutes.

3. Divide this sum by 60. (There are 60 minutes in 1 degree.)

4. Add the decimal from step 3 to the number of degrees.

5. Record this result as the equivalent form of the angle.

OR

Use a calculator.* A common method is to enter the angle as a decimal. For example, 20°14′15″ is entered as 20.1415. [Many models require two digits for minutes (′) and two digits for seconds (″). Thus, 3°3′3″ is entered as 3.0303.] Press the key indicating decimal degrees ($\boxed{DD}$). The display should read 20.2375 OR use the $\boxed{° ′ ″}$ button, pressing it after each unit: 20 $\boxed{° ′ ″}$ 14 $\boxed{° ′ ″}$15$\boxed{° ′ ″}$. The display should read 20.2375.

The procedure used to convert from decimal degrees to DMS form is:

1. Multiply the decimal portion by 60. (There are 60 minutes in 1 degree.)

2. Record the whole number of minutes.

3. Subtract the whole number of minutes from the result in step 1.

4. Multiply this difference by 60. (There are 60 seconds in 1 minute.)

5. Round the result from step 4 to the nearest whole second.

OR

---

* The method used to convert between forms on a scientific calculator varies by manufacturer and model. Ask your instructor for help or refer to the owner's manual for your calculator if necessary.

Use a calculator.* A common method is to enter the decimal form and then press a key indicating DMS. 20.2375 should convert to 20°14'15".

Perform Arithmetic Operations on Angles in Degree-Minute-Second Form

Angles can be added, subtracted, multiplied, and divided in the DMS form. In addition,[†] each unit is added separately and the sum is rewritten so that there are no more than 59" and no more than 59' in the final sum. Study the example below.

Example 1

$$43° \ 15' \ 25''$$
$$+\underline{12° \ 50' \ 50''}$$
$$55° \ 65' \ 75'' = 55° \ 66' \ 15'' = 56° \ 6' \ 15''$$

In subtraction,[†] each unit is subtracted separately. Borrowing is done in a base-60 system rather than the familiar base-10 system. Study the examples below.

Example 1

$$65° \ 43' \ 20''$$
$$-\underline{14° \ 14' \ 14''}$$
$$51° \ 29' \ \ \ 6''$$

Example 2

$$124° \ 25' \ 32'' = 124° \ 24' \ 92'' = 123° \ 84' \ 92''$$
$$-\underline{\ \ 79° \ 30' \ 40''} \ \ -\underline{\ 79° \ 30' \ 40''} \ \ -\underline{\ 79° \ 30' \ 40''}$$
$$52'' \ \ \ \ \ 44° \ 54' \ 52''$$

Multiplication[†] is done in a similar fashion. After completing the multiplication, any number of seconds greater than 59 is converted to minutes, and any number of minutes greater than 59 is converted to degrees. Study the example below.

Example 1

$$55° \ 18' \ 15''$$
$$\underline{\ \ \ \ \ \ \ \ \ \ \ \times 4}$$
$$220° \ 72' \ 60'' = 220° \ 73' \ 0'' = 221° \ 13' \ 0''$$

When dividing[†] an angle, the operations are performed in reverse order. First the degrees are divided, then the minutes, and finally the seconds. It may be necessary to convert de-

---

† Most scientific calculators will perform these arithmetic functions after the angles are converted to decimal form as outlined on previous page. See your instructor for specific directions for your calculator.

grees to minutes and minutes to seconds as in the second and third examples below. Study these examples.

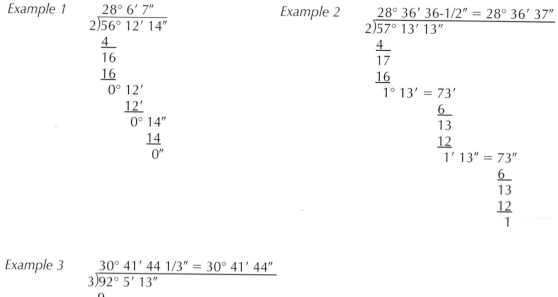

Example 1

$$28° 6' 7''$$
$$2\overline{)56° 12' 14''}$$
$$\underline{4}$$
$$16$$
$$\underline{16}$$
$$0° 12'$$
$$\underline{12'}$$
$$0° 14''$$
$$\underline{14}$$
$$0''$$

Example 2

$$28° 36' 36\text{-}1/2'' = 28° 36' 37''$$
$$2\overline{)57° 13' 13''}$$
$$\underline{4}$$
$$17$$
$$\underline{16}$$
$$1° 13' = 73'$$
$$\underline{6}$$
$$13$$
$$\underline{12}$$
$$1' 13'' = 73''$$
$$\underline{6}$$
$$13$$
$$\underline{12}$$
$$1$$

Example 3

$$30° 41' 44\ 1/3'' = 30° 41' 44''$$
$$3\overline{)92° 5' 13''}$$
$$\underline{9}$$
$$2° 5' = 125'$$
$$\underline{12}$$
$$5$$
$$\underline{3}$$
$$2' 13'' = 133''$$
$$\underline{12}$$
$$13$$
$$\underline{12}$$
$$1''$$

CONCEPT APPLICATIONS

Refer to the drawing below for Exercises 1–3.

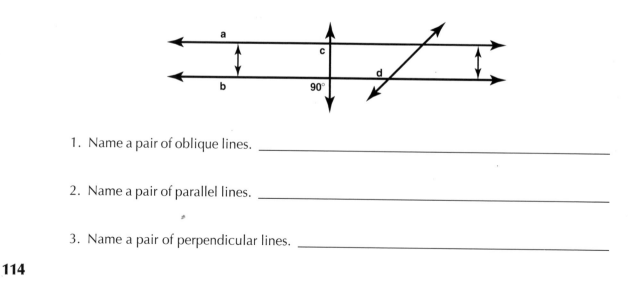

1. Name a pair of oblique lines. _____

2. Name a pair of parallel lines. _____

3. Name a pair of perpendicular lines. _____

114

Write the symbol for each of the following.

4. parallel lines _____   5. perpendicular lines _____

6. minute _____   7. triangle _____

8. degree _____   9. circle _____

10. second _____   11. right angle _____

12. How many seconds are there in 1 minute? _____

13. How many seconds are there in 1 degree? _____

14. How many minutes are there in 1 degree? _____

15. How many minutes are there in 1 circle? _____

Use three letters to name the following angles.

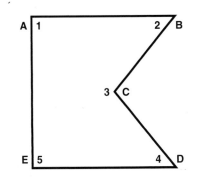

16. ∠ 1 _____

17. ∠ 2 _____

18. ∠ 3 _____

19. ∠ 4 _____

20. ∠ 5 _____

Determine the following angles, using addition, subtraction, multiplication, and division. For each problem, indicate which operation(s) you used.

21. $\angle 1 =$ _____

operation(s) _____

22. $\angle 2 =$ _____

operation(s) _____

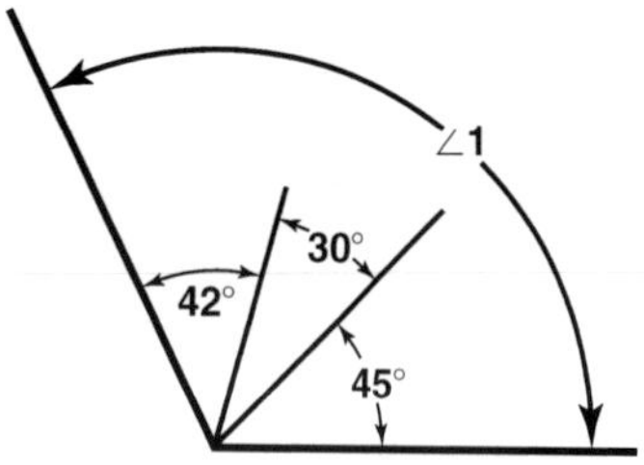

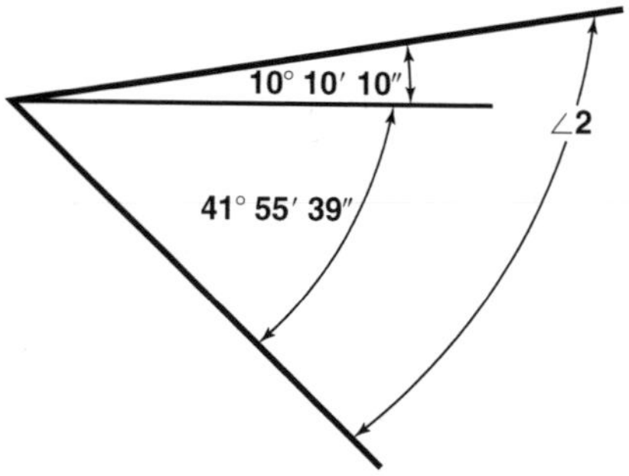

23. $\angle 3 + \angle 4 + \angle 5 =$ _____

operation(s) _____

24. $\angle 1 - \angle 2 =$ _____

operation(s) _____

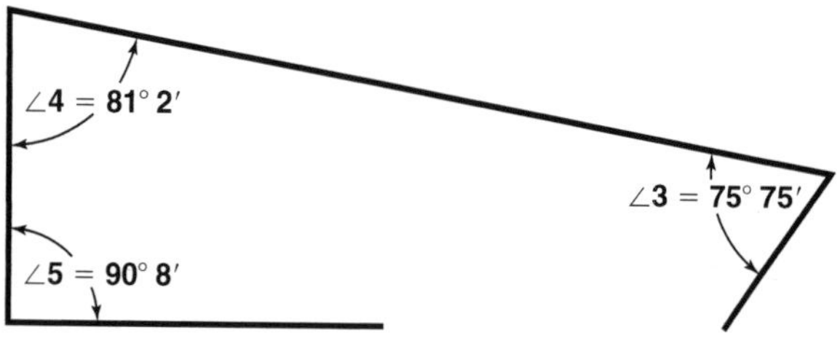

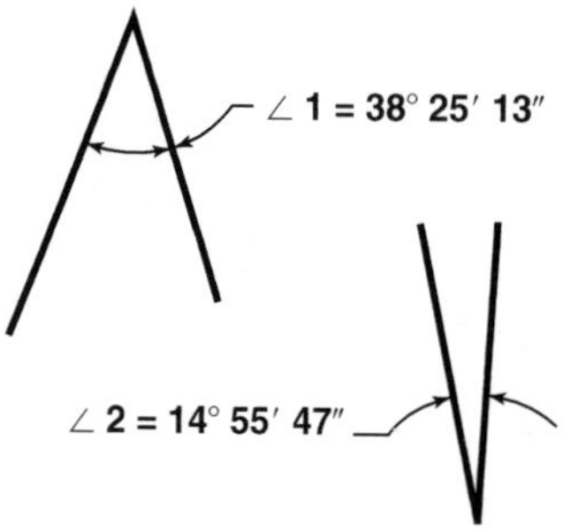

25. ∠ 7 = _____

∠ a = 47° 15′ 2″

operation(s) _____

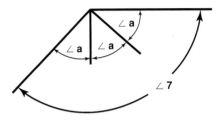

26. ∠ 1 = ∠ 2 = ∠ 3 = ∠ 4 = ∠ 5 = 53°41′

∠ 6 = _____

operation(s) _____

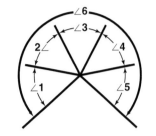

27. ∠ y = _____

operation(s) _____

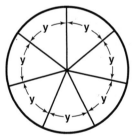

28. ∠ y = _____

operation(s) _____

Refer to the drawing to the left for exercises #27 and #28. Imagine eight equal angles for #28.

29. Determine the measure of ∠ 2 through ∠ 16.
m ∥ n; a ∥ b; ∠ 1 = 110° 10′

_____   _____   _____

_____   _____   _____

_____   _____   _____

_____   _____   _____

_____   _____   _____

Use the same drawing to name:

30. a pair of alternate interior angles _____

31. a pair of alternate exterior angles _____

32. a pair of vertical or opposite angles _____

118

Are the following angles acute, right, obtuse, straight, or reflex?

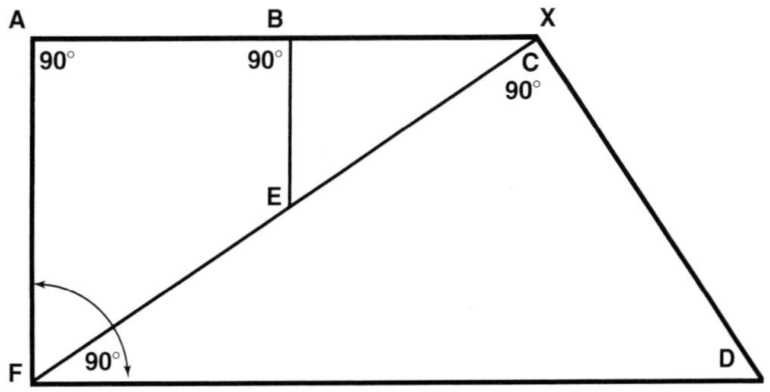

33. ∠ BAF _____

34. ∠ ABC _____

35. ∠ EFD _____

36. ∠ X _____

37. ∠ DCA _____

Express these angles in degrees, minutes, and seconds. (Round to the nearest whole second.)

38. 19.203899° _____   39. 99.3758333° _____

40. 12.5000° _____   41. 8.13555556° _____

Express these angles in decimal form. Round to five decimal places.

42. 270° 14′ _____   43. 270° 14′ 10″

_____

44. 110° 30′30″ _____   45. 1° 1′ 1″ _____

46. Illustrate the three propositions regarding lines here.

47. Illustrate the two propositions regarding angles here.

I WONDER . . .

If a cube is dipped in paint and then rolled on paper, it can create a path that looks like this.

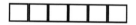

How can the same cube create the path below? _____

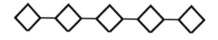

Can you think of other path designs?

INTRODUCTION

The majority of problems in a math course in the metalworking trade involve the solution of triangles. Workers are asked to determine missing angles and/or unknown sides. This unit covers the basic types of triangles and their properties, and forms the ground work to later units, which will cover solutions to various problems involving triangles.

OBJECTIVES

After completing this unit, you will be able to:

- Identify types of triangles.
- State the sum of the angles of any triangle.
- Apply the properties of triangles to determine missing dimensions in triangles.

DEFINITION

A **triangle** is a closed, three-sided figure. All triangles have three angles and the sum of the measures of those angles is always 180°. Can a triangle have an angle greater than 90°? _____ Why or why not? Can a triangle have more than one angle equal to or greater than 90°? _____ Why or why not?

TYPES OF TRIANGLES

Right Triangle

A **right triangle** is a triangle containing one right, 90° angle. Can there be more than one right angle in a right triangle? _____ Why or why not? Is this statement true or false? The two nonright angles of a right triangle are always acute angles. _____

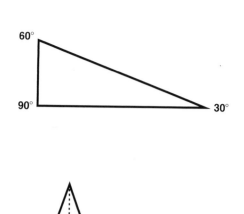

Isosceles Triangle

An **isosceles triangle** is a triangle with one pair of equal sides.

Can an isosceles triangle also be a right triangle? _____ Why or why not? Can an isosceles triangle have more than two equal sides? Why or why not? _____

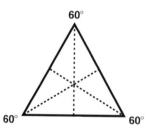

Other Properties of an Isosceles Triangle

1. Angles opposite the equal sides are equal.
2. The altitude divides the triangle into two congruent or identical triangles.

Equilateral Triangle

An **equilateral triangle** has three equals sides.

Other Properties of an Equilateral Triangle

1. The three angles each measure of 60°.
2. The altitudes divide the triangle into pairs of congruent or identical triangles.
3. Each of these congruent triangles is a right triangle.

Scalene Triangle

A **scalene triangle** has no equal sides or angles. Can a right triangle be a scalene triangle? Why or why not?

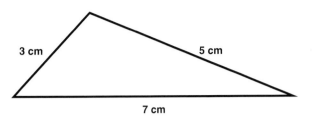

CORRESPONDING PARTS OF TRIANGLES

Corresponding parts of triangles are used to solve triangles. When comparing two triangles, corresponding parts are determined by measure, not by location. The longest side of the first triangle below corresponds with the longest side of the second, the shortest side with the shortest side, and the third side with the third side. Similarly, the largest angle of the first triangle corresponds with the largest angle of the second triangle, the smallest angle corresponds with the smallest angle, and the third angle corresponds with the third angle of the other triangle.

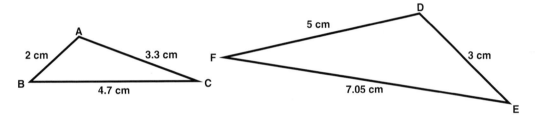

In the example above, side AB corresponds with side DE because they are the shortest sides. Side BC corresponds with side EF because they are the longest sides, and side AC corresponds with DF because they are the third sides.

SIMILAR TRIANGLES

Triangles are similar if corresponding lengths of sides are proportional or if corresponding angles are equal. If the corresponding sides are proportional, the corresponding angles are equal, and if the corresponding angles are equal, the corresponding sides are proportional.

Example

In these triangles, the ratios of corresponding sides are each = 0.66, $\frac{2}{3} = \frac{3.3}{5} = \frac{4.7}{7.05}$. Therefore, the triangles are called similar triangles.

When triangles are similar, their angles are equal. Therefore, $\angle A = \angle D$, $\angle B = \angle E$ and $\angle C = \angle F$. Remember, the pairings are based on measurement of the angles, not on their location.

CONGRUENT TRIANGLES

Two triangles are congruent if they are identical.

CONCEPT APPLICATIONS

Identify each of the following triangles as scalene, right, isosceles, or equilateral.

1. _____

2. _____

3. _____

4. _____

5. _____

6. _____

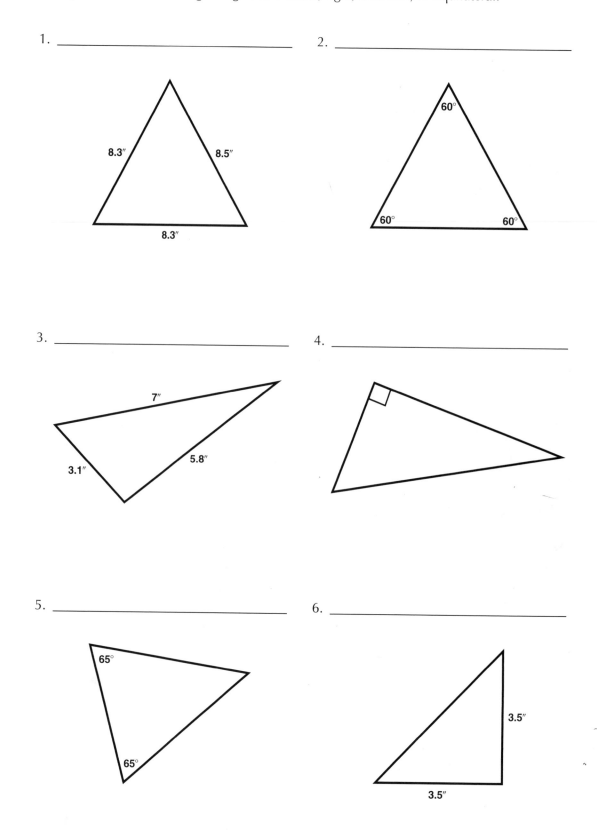

7. _____   8. _____

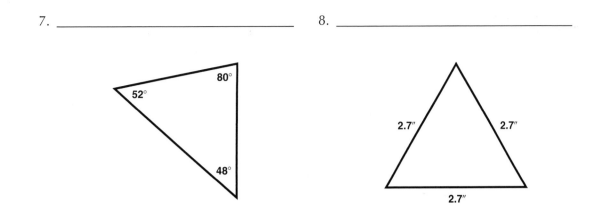

9. Determine each of the missing angles. What type of triangle is this? _____

∠A = _____

∠B = _____

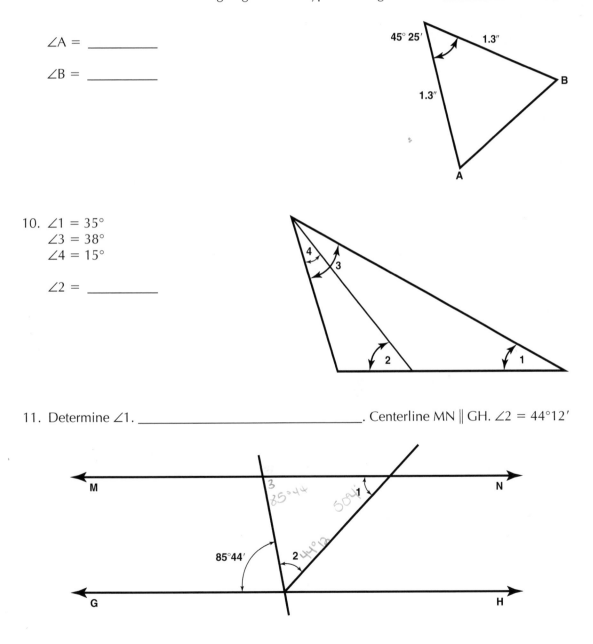

10. ∠1 = 35°
    ∠3 = 38°
    ∠4 = 15°

    ∠2 = _____

11. Determine ∠1. _____. Centerline MN ∥ GH. ∠2 = 44°12′

12. Exploration: On a separate piece of paper, draw any type of triangle. In the interior of the triangle, label one angle A, another B and the third C. Tear the three vertices from the triangle and place them next to each other to form a straight line.

13. What is the sum of the angles of any triangle? _____ How many degrees are there

    on either side of a straight line? _____

14. The two right triangles below are corresponding triangles. Determine the missing dimensions on each. Refer to Unit 13, Ratio and Proportion for methods of solutions.

AB = 2.8"   ∠B = _____   ∠E = _____   BC = _____

DE = 2.0"

DF = 1.9"   ∠D = _____   EF = _____

AC = 1.2"

∠A = 55°

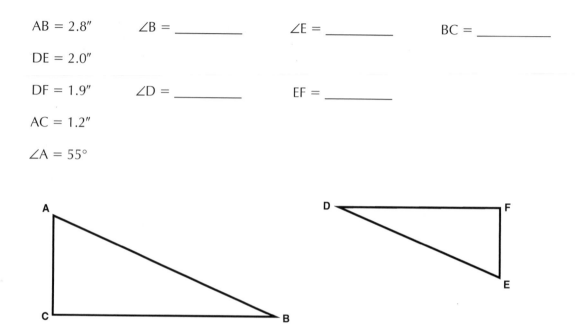

15. Draw an isosceles triangle and two nonisosceles triangles. Write a statement about isosceles triangles.

16. Draw an equilateral triangle and two nonequilateral triangles. Write a statement about equilateral triangles.

17. Are all isosceles triangles equilateral triangles?

18. Are all equilateral triangles isosceles triangles?

I WONDER . . .

Draw any triangle. Extend one side in one direction. Measure this exterior angle. Measure the interior angles at the other two vertices. How does their sum compare with this exterior angle? Try it on another vertex of this triangle or on another triangle. Can you form a hypothesis?

INTRODUCTION

Much of a metalworker's math-related time is spent working with triangles drawn inside polygons. Therefore, it is essential to know the geometry, properties, dimensions, and angles of the original polygons.

OBJECTIVES

After completing this unit, you will be able to:

- Identify regular and irregular polygons.
- Identify types and properties of quadrilaterals.
- Determine the interior and exterior angle of a regular polygon.
- Determine missing dimensions on polygons.

DEFINITIONS

Polygons are many-sided figures. **Regular polygons** have equal sides and angles. An example of a regular polygon is a square with its four equal sides and four right angles. An equilateral triangle is a regular polygon.

Irregular polygons have unequal sides and unequal angles. Scalene triangles and right triangles are examples of irregular polygon.

QUADRILATERALS

Quadrilaterals are four-sided polygons. The term includes both regular and irregular shapes.

SQUARE

A square is a quadrilateral with:

1. Four equal sides
2. Four equal angles of 90°

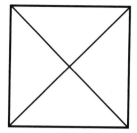

Other Properties of the Square

1. Opposite sides of the square are parallel.
2. The diagonals bisect the 90° angles.
3. The diagonals bisect each other.
4. The diagonals form congruent triangles.
5. The diagonals are perpendicular to each other.
6. The diagonals are equal to each other in length.

Identify eight right angles in the drawing above. There are eight line segments in the drawing. They can be separated into two sets of four equal segments. Identify these two sets.

RECTANGLE

A rectangle is a quadrilateral with:

1. Opposite sides that are equal.
2. Four equal 90° angles.

Other Properties of the Rectangle

1. Opposite sides of the rectangle are parallel.
2. The diagonals are equal.
3. The diagonals bisect each other.
4. The diagonals form pairs of congruent triangles.

Indicate the right angles and equal line segments in this drawing.

PARALLELOGRAM

A parallelogram is any quadrilateral with opposite sides that are parallel.

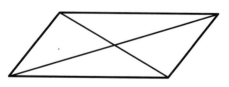

Other Properties of the Parallelogram

1. The opposite sides are equal.
2. The opposite angles are equal.
3. The diagonals are NOT equal.
4. The diagonals bisect each other.
5. The diagonals form pairs of congruent triangles.

Indicate the four pairs of equal line segments and two pairs of congruent triangles in this drawing.

CALCULATING INTERIOR ANGLES

The measure of central angles (angle with its vertex at the center of the polygon) in polygons is calculated differently than vertex angles (angle with its vertex at the intersection of two sides). Each method is outlined below.

CENTRAL ANGLES

The sum of the central angles of any polygon is 360°. If the polygon is irregular, there is no quick method for measuring any single central angle. However, if the polygon is regular, the measure of any central angle is 360 ÷ n, where n = the number of sides of the regular polygon.

Examples

The measure of each central angle in this regular pentagon is 360 ÷ 5 = 72°.

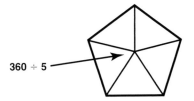

The measure of each central angle of this regular hexagon is 360 ÷ 6 = 60°.

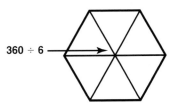

VERTEX ANGLES

The sum of the vertex angles of any polygon is (n − 2) × 180, where n = the number of sides of the polygon. If the polygon is irregular, there is no quick method for measuring a single vertex angle. However, if the polygon is regular, the measurement of a single vertex angle is found to be equal to the sum found using (n − 2) × 180 divided by n, the number of sides of the polygon.

The sum of the eight vertex angles of this octagon is $(8 - 2) \times 180 = 1080°$. If this is a regular octagon, each of the vertex angles is $1080 \div 8 = 135°$. If the octagon is irregular, the sum of the vertex angles is 1080, but there is no quick method for determining how much a single vertex angle measures.

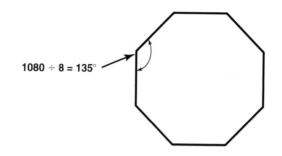

1080 ÷ 8 = 135°

- -

I WONDER . . .

Consider the symmetrical pentagon below. Is it a regular or irregular polygon? _____

Why? _____

Draw a line segment connecting points 1 and 3. Draw a second segment connecting points 1 and 4. How many triangles do you now see in this pentagon? _____ What should the sum of the angles of this many triangles be? _____ Use the formula $(n - 2) \times 180$ to determine the sum of the vertex angles of the pentagon. Does this sum agree with the sum of the angles of the triangles? _____ Will this method work with other polygons? _____ Try it out here. Each time one additional side is added to a polygon, how many degrees are added to the sum of the vertex angles? _____

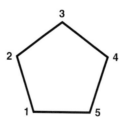

- -

SUMMARY OF FORMULAS

The sum of the central angles of any polygon = 360°.
Each central angle of a regular polygon = 360 ÷ n, where n = number of sides of the polygon.
The sum of the vertex angles of any polygon = (n − 2) × 180, where n = number of sides.
Each vertex angle of a regular polygon = [(n − 2) × 180] ÷ n where n = number of sides.
The exterior angle at any vertex angle equals 360 minus the interior vertex angle. That is, the sum of the interior and exterior angles is 360°. Sketch a drawing that demonstrates this.

CONCEPT APPLICATIONS

Refer to the drawing on the right.

1. ∠2 = 93°, ∠1 = _____

2. ∠1 = 90°, ∠2 = _____

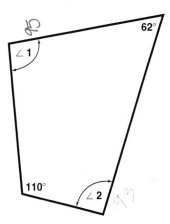

3. Determine ∠2 in the drawing to the right.

∠2 = _____

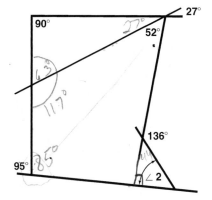

133

Refer to the drawing below. It is a regular polygon.

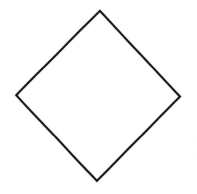

4. What shape is this? _____

5. What is the sum of the measures of the vertex angles? _____

6. What is the measure of each of the vertex angles? _____

Sketch the diagonals on the drawing above.

7. What is the measure of each of the four central angles formed by the diagonals? _____

Draw a 10-sided regular polygon (decagon). Include the diagonals.

8. What is the sum of the central angles? _____

9. What is the sum of the vertex angles? _____

10. What do each of the central angles measure? _____

11. What do each of the vertex angles measure? _____

12. Determine ∠C in this drawing. Remember that the formula for finding a vertex only applies to interior angles. ∠C = _____

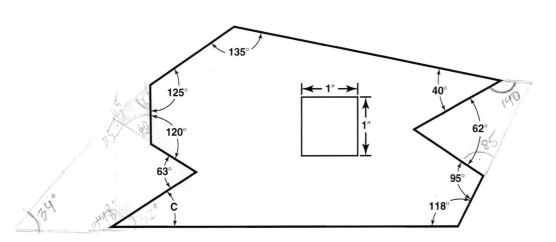

Using colored markers, trace the isosceles triangles in the drawing below.

13. Why are these isosceles triangles? _____

14. Determine ∠D = _____

15. Determine ∠C = _____

16. Determine ∠E = _____

17. Determine ∠F = _____

18. Determine ∠B = _____

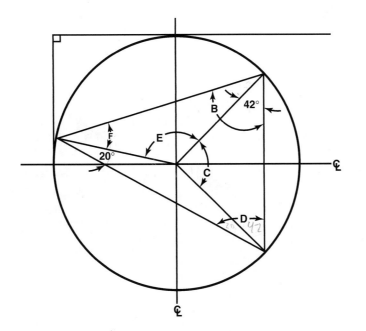

Using colored markers, trace the isosceles triangles in the drawing below.

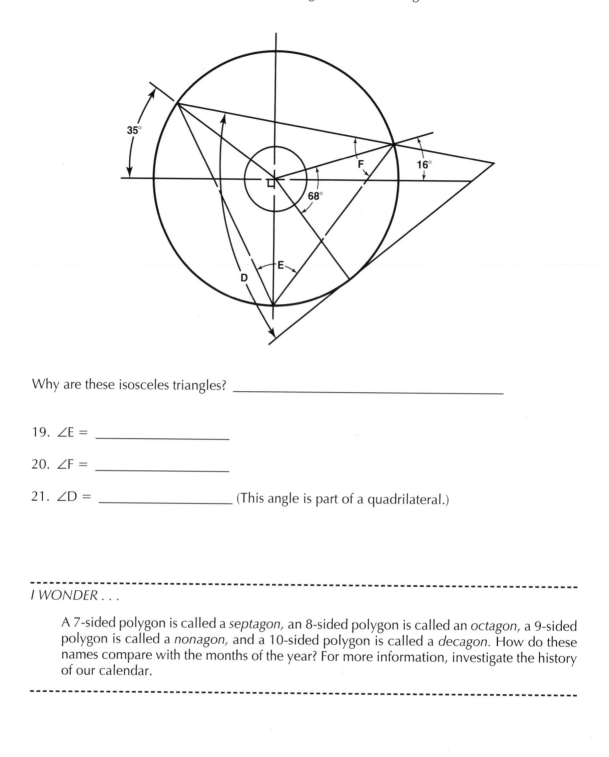

Why are these isosceles triangles? _____

19. ∠E = _____

20. ∠F = _____

21. ∠D = _____ (This angle is part of a quadrilateral.)

I WONDER . . .

A 7-sided polygon is called a *septagon,* an 8-sided polygon is called an *octagon,* a 9-sided polygon is called a *nonagon,* and a 10-sided polygon is called a *decagon.* How do these names compare with the months of the year? For more information, investigate the history of our calendar.

UNIT 17

CIRCLES AND TANGENTS

INTRODUCTION

The metalworker works with radii, diameters, circumferences and tangents, and their measures or locations. Determining the measures and locations of these involves circles. Therefore, a thorough understanding of the circle, its parts, and related formulas is fundamental to the study of geometry.

OBJECTIVES

After completing this unit, you will be able to:

- Identify parts of a circle.
- Calculate the measurement of central angles.
- Calculate the length of arcs.
- Determine missing dimensions involving circles and tangents.

DEFINITIONS

Circle

A *circle* is a set of points equidistant from a fixed point, called the *center*. All circles measure 360°. Each point on the circumference of the circle is equidistant from the center point of the circle. A circle, by definition, is the visible ring. A circle is named by its center point.

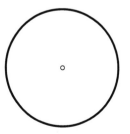

Diameter

A diameter is a special chord that goes through the center of a circle. Its location is determined by three points.

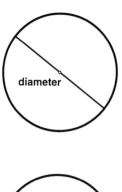

Radius

A radius is a line segment that connects the center to any point on the circle. Its length is always 1/2 the diameter.

Chord

A chord is a line segment that connects any two points on a circle.

Circumference

The circumference is the measure of the distance around the outside of a circle. (In polygons, this distance is referred to as perimeter.) The circumference is always equal to π times the diameter. (π is approximately 3.14.)

Arc

An arc is a curved segment of a circle.

This is arc ABC. It can also be named arc AC (A͡C), but there is possible confusion when only two letters are used. Can you explain why?

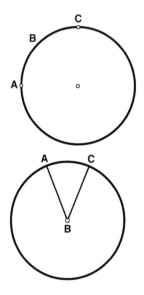

Central Angle

A central angle is formed by two radii. The circle's center is the vertex of the central angle. The sum of the central angles of all circles is 360°. It is not known when the 360° circle began to be used regularly, but the concept of the circle is credited to Hipparchus, a Greek mathematician who lived in the second century BC.

∠ABC is a central angle. It is formed by two radii.

Inscribed Angle

An inscribed angle is an angle formed by two chords that intersect on the circle. Its vertex is on the circle.

DE and EF are chords forming inscribed ∠DEF.

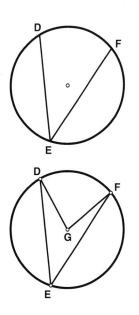

When a central angle and an inscribed angle cut off the same or equal arcs, the inscribed angle always measures exactly 1/2 the central angle.

Inscribed ∠DEF marks off the same arc as central ∠DGF.

∴ ∠DEF = 1/2 ∠DGF.

I WONDER . . .

If point E is moved along the circumference of circle G, will it still be true that ∠DEF = 1/2 ∠DGF?

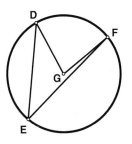

What other locations for point E can you visualize?
Try experimenting with a geometry software program, such as Geometers Sketchpad, to verify your predictions.

Segment

A segment of a circle is the region bounded by an arc and a chord.

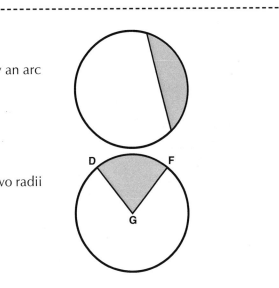

Sector

A sector of a circle is the region bounded by two radii and the arc they cut off.

Tangent

A tangent is a line that intersects a circle at one and only one point, called the *point of tangency* or *tangent point*. The tangent is perpendicular to the radius it intersects.

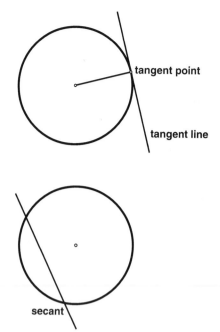

Secant

A secant is a line that intersects a circle at exactly two points. It differs from a chord in that it extends beyond the circle.

Pi

Pi (π) is the Greek letter that represents the ratio of the circumference of a circle to its diameter. That is, the circumference of a circle divided by its diameter always equals pi, which is approximately 3.14.

SUMMARY OF GEOMETRIC TERMS

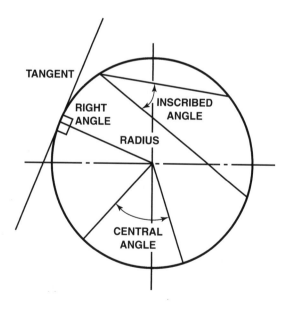

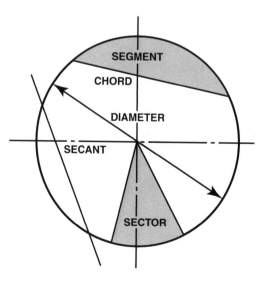

PRINCIPLES

The following principles relate to circles and tangents.

1. If a tangent and radius intersect, they are perpendicular at the point of tangency.
2. If two tangents are drawn to a circle from the same exterior point, the lengths of the corresponding segments from this point to the points of tangency are equal.
3. If two tangents are drawn to a circle from the same exterior point, an extended radius to this exterior point bisects the angle formed by the two tangents.
4. The perpendicular bisector of any chord passes through the center of the circle.
5. If two circles are tangent externally, the length of the line segment joining their center points is equal to the sum of their radii and passes through the point of tangency.
6. If two circles are tangent internally, the length of the segment joining their center points is equal to the difference of their radii and, if extended, will pass through the point of tangency.
7. Equal central angles in a circle subtend equal arcs.
8. Equal chords in a circle subtend equal arcs.
9. If two chords intersect inside a circle, the product of the two segments of one chord equal the product of the two segments of the other chord.

Diagram each of these principles with a study partner. Because these principles are basic to your understanding of geometry, be sure to resolve any questions that arise during your diagramming and discussion.

FORMULAS

1. Circumference = π times the diameter
2. $\dfrac{\angle}{\angle} = \dfrac{\frown}{\frown}$ The ratio of one central angle to another in the same circle is maintained by the arcs. (Read as "angle over angle = arc over arc.")
3. The measure of an inscribed angle, which cuts off the same arc as a central angle, is 1/2 the measure of the central angle.

CONCEPT APPLICATIONS

Identify the parts of the circle shown below.

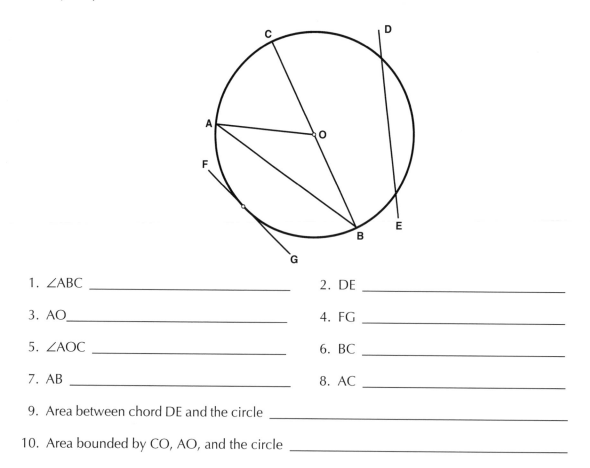

1. ∠ABC _____

2. DE _____

3. AO_____

4. FG _____

5. ∠AOC _____

6. BC _____

7. AB _____

8. AC _____

9. Area between chord DE and the circle _____

10. Area bounded by CO, AO, and the circle _____

Review the formulas in this unit and select an appropriate formula to solve the following problems.

Refer to the drawing to the right. Use the formula for angles and arcs.

∠EOF = 80°, ∠HOP = 140°

11. If $\overset{\frown}{EF}$ = 2.28 cm; $\overset{\frown}{HP}$ = _____ cm

12. If $\overset{\frown}{HP}$ = 3.5 cm; $\overset{\frown}{EF}$ = _____ cm

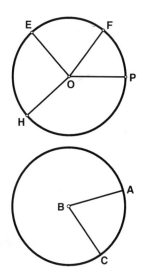

The circumference of circle B = 15.500 inches = πd.
$\overset{\frown}{AC}$ = 3.100 inches.

13. ∠ABC = _____

Refer to the circle N on the right.

14. Central ∠MNO = 40°. M͡O = _____

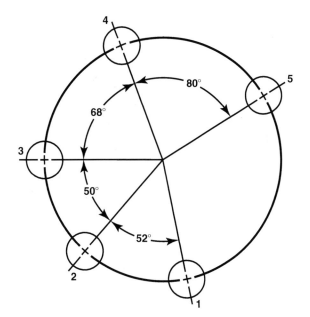

You are required to drill five holes on a bolt circle with a diameter of 3.312 inches. To maintain the angles specified, determine the dimensions of the arc through which the rotary table must be rotated for each hole.

15. Arc 1–2 _____

16. Arc 2–3 _____

17. Arc 3–4 _____

18. Arc 4–5 _____

19. Arc 5–1 _____

20. What should the sum of all five arcs equal? (Answer in words, not numbers.) _____

_____

Solve the following problems, using the principles outlined in this unit. Indicate in each case which principle is illustrated.

Refer to the drawing below.

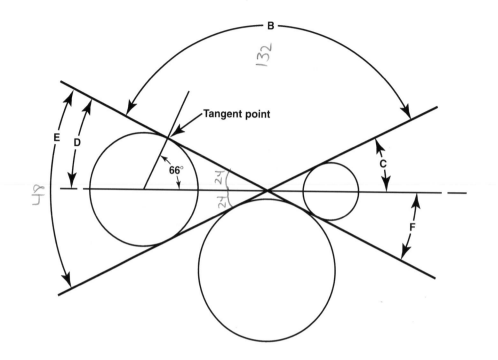

Principle no. _____

21. ∠D = _____

22. ∠E = _____

23. ∠C = _____

24. ∠F = _____

25. ∠B = _____

Refer to the drawing below. There are three tangent points.

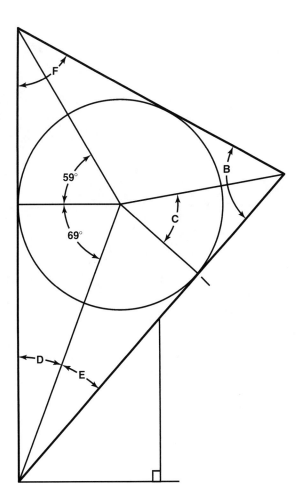

Principle no. _____

26. ∠D = _____

27. ∠E = _____

28. ∠F = _____

29. ∠B = _____

30. ∠C = _____

Refer to the drawing below. There are two tangent points.

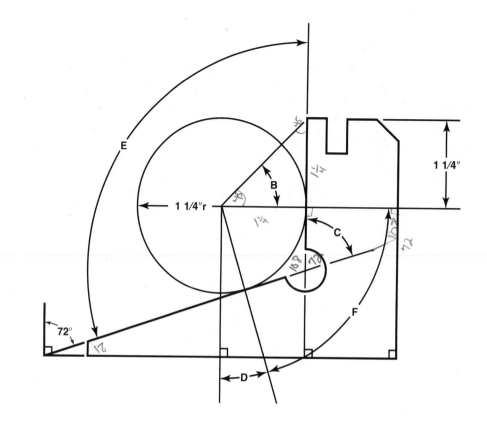

Principle no. _____

31. ∠B = _____

32. ∠C = _____

33. ∠E = _____

34. ∠D = _____

35. ∠F = _____

The machinist is required to visualize the 1.400 inch dimensions below as the radius of an imaginary circle. Construct that circle and determine the following dimensions. Refer to the drawing below.

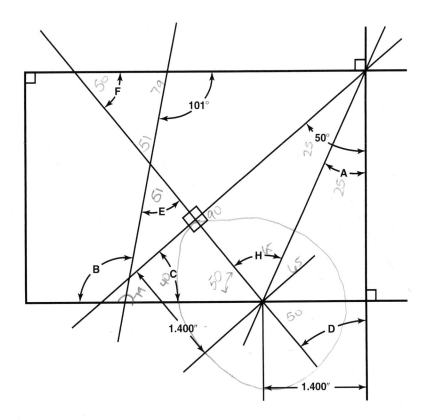

Principle no. _____

36. ∠D = _____

37. ∠A = _____

38. ∠H = _____

39. ∠C = _____

40. ∠B = _____

41. ∠E = _____

42. ∠F = _____

G and F are tangent points; diameter of circle E = 3.250 inches; ∠GEF = 144°; GH = 3.500 inches.

Refer to the drawing below.

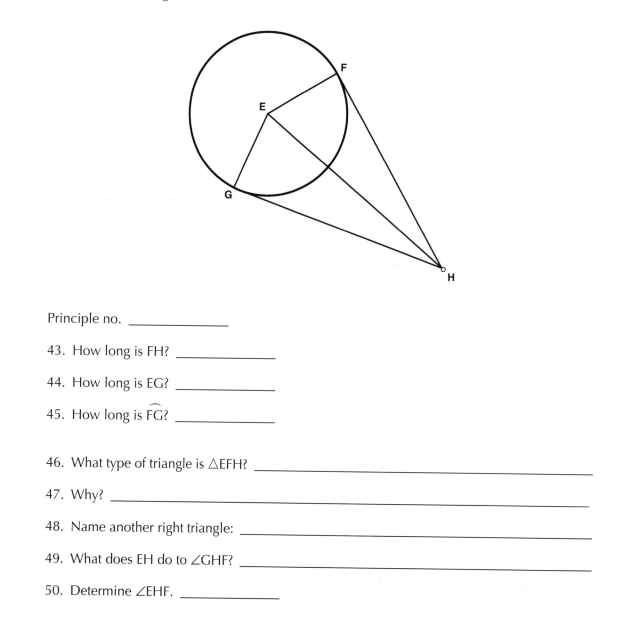

Principle no. _____

43. How long is FH? _____

44. How long is EG? _____

45. How long is F͡G? _____

46. What type of triangle is △EFH? _____

47. Why? _____

48. Name another right triangle: _____

49. What does EH do to ∠GHF? _____

50. Determine ∠EHF. _____

148

PYTHAGOREAN THEOREM

INTRODUCTION

The Pythagorean theorem was introduced in Unit 9. It is a powerful theorem which has daily practical applications in many trades, as was discussed in Unit 9. This unit presents one of many proofs of the theorem and also discusses its applications in the metalworking trade.

OBJECTIVES

After completing this unit, you will be able to:

- Identify right triangles in printed drawings.
- Solve right triangles using the Pythagorean theorem.
- Determine missing dimensions on printed drawings.

THE PYTHAGOREAN THEOREM

Formally, the Pythagorean theorem states that the square of the hypotenuse of a right triangle is equal to the sum of the squares of its other two sides. Simply written, the Pythagorean theorem states that $a^2 + b^2 = c^2$. The legs of the right triangle are designated by a and b, which can be used interchangeably. The hypotenuse is designated by c. In the drawing below, a = 3, b = 4, and c = 5. This is a classic right triangle and is referred to as a "3-4-5 right triangle." (Recall that the Pythagorean theorem only applies to right triangles.)

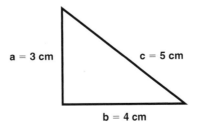

a = 3 cm c = 5 cm
b = 4 cm

Over the course of history, the Pythagorean theorem has been proven in numerous ways. One of the more common proofs is illustrated below. The area of square A (a^2) plus the area of square B (b^2) equals the area of square C (c^2). 9 squares plus 16 squares = 25 squares.

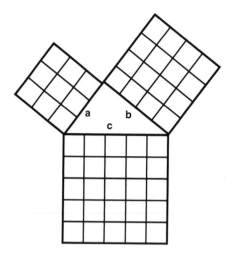

Examples

1. In the right triangle to the right, one leg measures 6 inches and the other leg measures 9 inches. How long is the hypotenuse?

   _____ inches

   We know that $a^2 + b^2 = c^2$

   In this case, $6^2 + 9^2 = c^2$

   $36 + 81 = c^2$

   $117 = c^2$

   $\therefore 10.817'' = c$

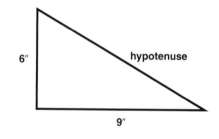

2. The hypotenuse in the triangle to the right measures is 10 cm long. One leg is 5 cm long. How long is the other leg?

_____ cm

We know that $a^2 + b^2 = c^2$. The formula needs to be rearranged.

In this case

$$c^2 - a^2 = b^2$$

$$10^2 - 5^2 = b^2$$

$$75 = b^2$$

$$\therefore \ 8.660 \ cm = b$$

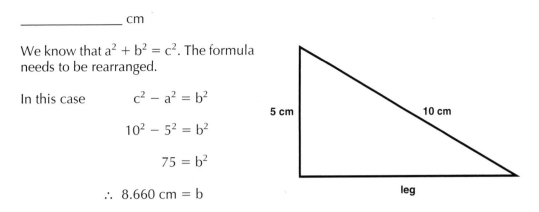

5 cm   10 cm

leg

Always be sure the hypotenuse is the longest side of the right triangle.

On the line below, write your own rule as to when you should use addition with the Pythagorean theorem and when you should use subtraction.

_____

When the Scarecrow in the movie *The Wizard of Oz** got his brain, he said, "The sum of the square roots of any two sides of an isosceles triangle is equal to the square root of the remaining side. Oh, joy, rapture! I've got a brain!"

But, he was wrong! How should he have stated the Pythagorean theorem? _____

_____

_____

* © 1999 Warner Bros.

CONCEPT APPLICATIONS

Solve the following, using the Pythagorean theorem. Round to three decimal places.

Refer to the triangle to the right.

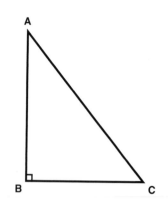

1. Find the length of AB if the length of AC = 3.700 inches and the length of BC = 2.400 inches.

    AB = _____ inches

2. Assume the length of each leg of the right triangle is 2.800 inches.

    AC = _____ inches

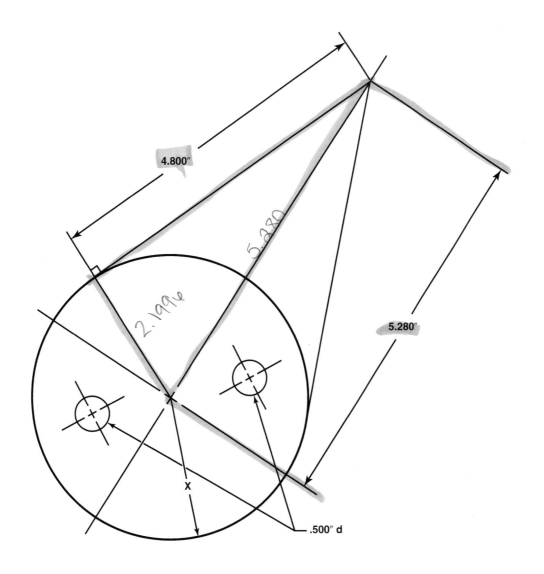

4.800″

5.280

2.1996

5.280″

X

.500″ d

3. Radius X = _____ inches

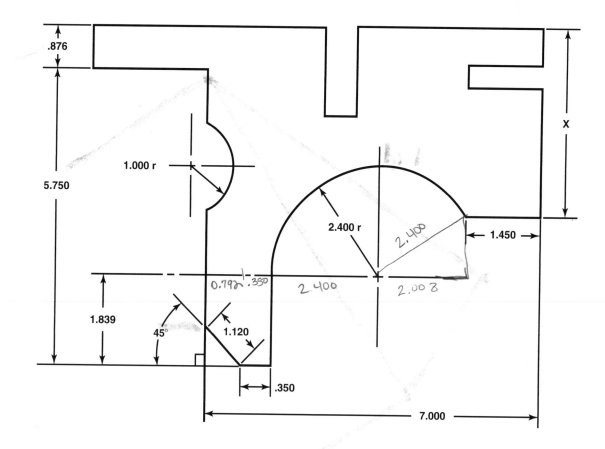

Hints: Use the 45° angle as part of a right triangle. The hypotenuse is given. The 2.400 radius can be rotated to form the hypotenuse of another right triangle.

4. Distance X = _____

This figure is symmetrical about its vertical centerline.

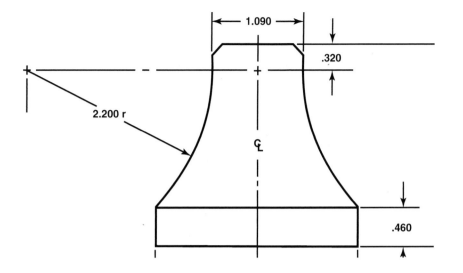

Hint: The 2.200 radius can be rotated.

5. Distance Y = _____

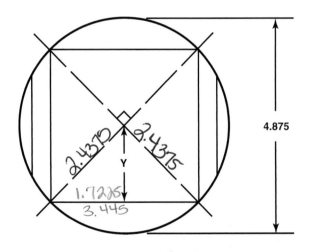

Hint: Y is the perpendicular bisector of one side of the inscribed square.

6. Y = _____

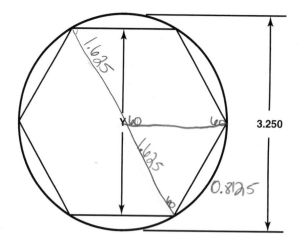

Hint: Y is the distance across the flat sides of the inscribed, regular hexagon.

7. Y = _____

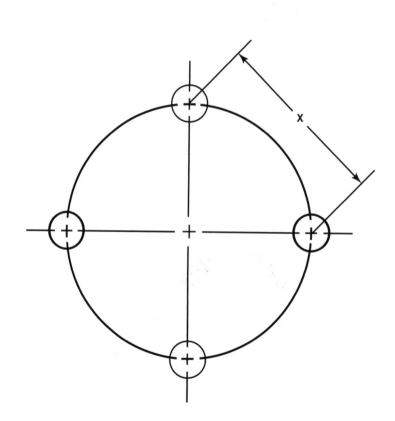

Find the distance between the centers of four equally spaced holes on a 3.500-inch-diameter bolt circle.

8. Distance X = _____ inches

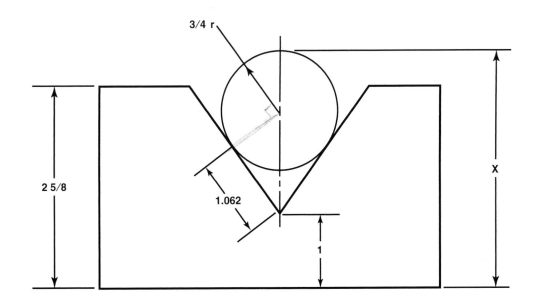

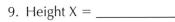

9. Height X = _____

UNIT
19

OTHER GEOMETRIC FORMULAS

INTRODUCTION

While the Pythagorean theorem is perhaps the most important formula in geometry for the metalworker, other formulas are helpful as well. This unit covers three other formulas used in the machine trade.

OBJECTIVES

After completing this unit, you will be able to:

- Determine the diameter of a circle inscribed in a right triangle.
- Determine the diameter of a circle circumscribed about a triangle.
- Determine the projection of a side of a triangle onto its base.

FORMULAS

1. The diameter of a circle inscribed in a right triangle is leg + leg − hypotenuse.
2. The diameter of a circle circumscribed about a triangle is chord × chord ÷ altitude to the third side.
3. The projection of a side of a triangle onto its base is $side^2 + base^2 - remaining\ side^2 \div (2 \times base)$.

Examples

1. If a right triangle has an inscribed circle in it, the diameter of that circle can be found by adding the lengths of the two legs and subtracting the hypotenuse from that sum.

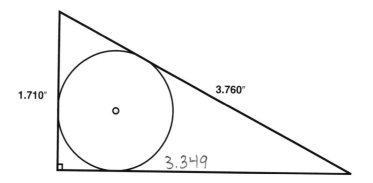

We need all three lengths to use the formula. The missing leg can be found using the Pythagorean theorem and is equal to 3.349 inches.

The formula   diameter = leg + leg − hypotenuse

in this case is   diameter = 1.710 + 3.349 − 3.760 inches

diameter = 1.299 inches.

Therefore, the diameter of this inscribed circle is 1.299 inches.

2. If the circle is circumscribed about a triangle (any type of triangle), the diameter of that circle can be found by multiplying one chord times the other, divided by the altitude drawn to the third chord (side of the triangle).

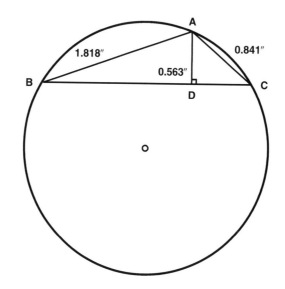

The diameter of this circle = AB × AC ÷ AD.

In this case,   diameter = 1.818 × 0.841 ÷ 0.563 inches

diameter = 2.716 inches

(AD must be an altitude, perpendicular to the base of the triangle.)

3. The projection (or shadow that would be cast) of side AB onto its base (BC) can be stated this way.

projection = $AB^2 + BC^2 - AC^2 \div (2 \times BC)$

$BD = 1.446^2 + 2.813^2 - 2.147^2 \div (2 \times 2.813)$

$BD = 0.959$ inches

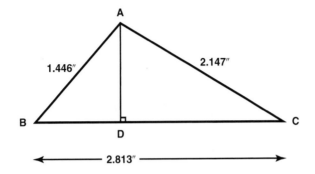

CONCEPT APPLICATIONS

Round to three decimal places.

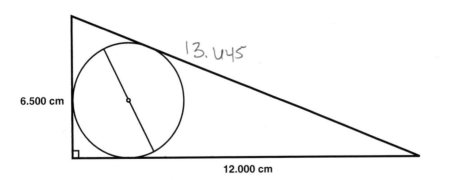

Determine the diameter of the inscribed circle above.

1. Formula _____

2. Hypotenuse _____ cm

3. Diameter _____ cm

161

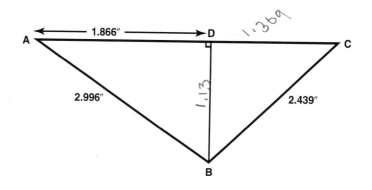

4. Refer to the drawing above. AC = _____ inches.

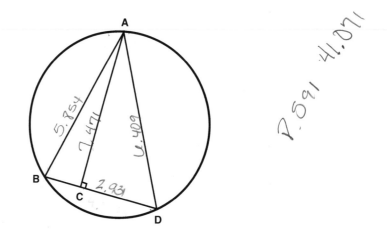

Refer to the drawing above. AB = 5.854 cm, AD = 6.409 cm, and CD = 2.931 cm. Determine the diameter of the circumscribed circle, answering the following.

5. AC = _____ cm

6. Formula for finding the diameter: _____

7. Diameter = _____ cm

Note: Use the same drawing and same given dimensions (but in inches) to answer the following.

8. BD = 4.268 inches. Formula for finding the projection of AB onto BD _____

9. BC = _____ inches.

10. Does this answer "check" when adding BC + CD = BD? _____

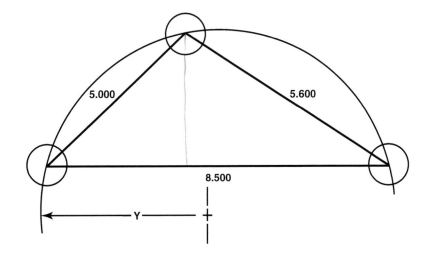

Refer to the drawing above.

11. The projection of 5.000 onto the base = _____.

12. The altitude of the triangle = _____.

13. The diameter of the circle = _____.

14. Y = _____.

$$\frac{(5^2) + (8.500)^2 - (5.600)^2}{}$$

$$\frac{25 + 72.25 - 31.34}{17}$$

$$y = 3.8758$$

TRIGONOMETRY

INTRODUCTION

The word *trigonometry* comes from the Greek words for "triangle" and "measure." It is the branch of mathematics that deals with the sides and angles of triangles, their measurement, and the relationships between them. It is the tool that allows metalworkers to determine angles and the length of sides of both right and nonright triangles.

OBJECTIVES

After completing this unit, you will be able to:

- Identify the hypotenuse and the sides opposite and adjacent in relation to a given acute angle in a right triangle.
- Label the sides as opposite (opp), adjacent (adj), and hypotenuse (hyp) in reference to an acute angle.
- Express the ratios between the sides for each of the six trigonometric functions.
- List the abbreviation for each of the trigonometric functions.
- State the cofunction of an acute angle and trigonometric function.
- State the inverse function of an acute angle and trigonometric function.

GROUND RULES

1. Capital letters are used to indicate angles. The sides opposite each angle are indicated with small letters and/or the abbreviations for opposite (opp), adjacent (adj), and hypotenuse (hyp). Side a is directly across from angle A, side b is directly across from angle B, and so forth.
2. The six trigonometric functions apply only to right triangles for our current purposes.
3. The sides "opposite" and "adjacent" may interchange, depending on which acute angle is the reference angle.
4. Identify the sides in a systematic order. FIRST identify the hypotenuse. It is directly across from the right angle and is always the longest side of a triangle. SECOND, identify the side adjacent. It is next to and forms one side of the acute reference angle chosen. The THIRD side is the side opposite, or across from, the acute reference angle chosen.

In the right triangle below, use acute angle A as the reference angle and label the sides of the triangle, first with letters a, b, and c, then with terms hyp, adj, and opp. When labeling the sides of the triangle, begin with the hypotenuse. In this case, side c is the hyp. The second side to identify is the side adjacent (next to the reference angle). In this triangle, side b is the adj side with reference to angle A. And side a is the side opp angle A.

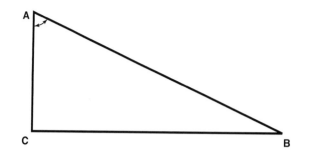

If acute angle B is the reference angle, side c is still the hyp, but side a is now the side adj and side b is now the side opp.

THE TRIGONOMETRIC FUNCTIONS

There are six trigonometric functions, each a ratio between two sides of a right triangle. The functions and their abbreviations are:

$$\text{sine (sin)} = \frac{\text{opp}}{\text{hyp}} \qquad\qquad \text{cosecant (csc)} = \frac{\text{hyp}}{\text{opp}}$$

$$\text{cosine (cos)} = \frac{\text{adj}}{\text{hyp}} \qquad\qquad \text{secant (sec)} = \frac{\text{hyp}}{\text{adj}}$$

$$\text{tangent (tan)} = \frac{\text{opp}}{\text{adj}} \qquad\qquad \text{cotangent cot)} = \frac{\text{adj}}{\text{opp}}$$

These ratios express the relationship between the sides of a right triangle. The decimal equivalents of these ratios are the numbers that appear in trigonometry charts.

Example

The sin of 30° = 0.5 or 1/2. That means that the ratio of the length of the side opposite (opp) to the length of the hypotenuse (hyp) is 1 to 2. If the tan of an angle is 0.75 or 3/4, the length of the side opp to the length of the side adj is 3 to 4. In every case, the trig function can be written as a ratio.

Both **co**functions and inverse functions are stated within the six functions. The sine and **co**sine are **co**functions. That is, the sine of one angle is equal to the **co**sine of its **co**mplement. Recall from Unit 14 that complementary angles add to 90°. Sin 50° = cos 40°. The tangent and **co**tangent are also **co**functions. Tan 60° = cot 30°. Similarly, the secant and **co**secant are **co**functions. Sec 10° = csc 80°.

The pairing of the inverse functions is different. Sin is defined as opp/hyp. The inverse of this ratio is hyp/opp, or csc. Thus, sin and csc are considered inverse functions. Cos and sec are inverse functions because their definitions are inverses of each other. Similarly, tan and cot are inverse functions.

Cofunctions and inverse functions were more important before calculators gained popularity. They were used to determine functions after the cofunction or inverse function were known. With the ease of determining functions with calculators today, their importance has diminished.

CONCEPT APPLICATIONS

1. With respect to angle A, label the sides opp and adj and the hyp in each of the following.

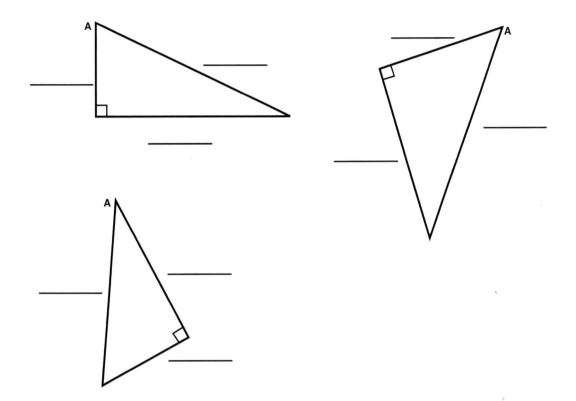

2. State the six trigonometry function abbreviations. Use the left column of blanks.

3. State the definitions of each of the trig functions, in ratio form.

4. State the inverse function for each of the trig functions.

Functions	Definitions	Inverse Functions
_____	_____	_____
_____	_____	_____
_____	_____	_____
_____	_____	_____
_____	_____	_____
_____	_____	_____

5. State the cofunction for each of the following.

Function   Cofunction

sin 25°   _____

csc 18°30′   _____

tan 41°   _____

6. State the ratio of each of the trigonometric functions for the right triangle below. Then use a calculator to find the ratio in decimal form.

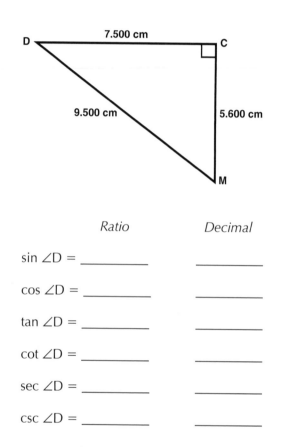

Ratio   Decimal

sin ∠D = _____   _____

cos ∠D = _____   _____

tan ∠D = _____   _____

cot ∠D = _____   _____

sec ∠D = _____   _____

csc ∠D = _____   _____

If you have experience with trigonometry charts, you will be able to determine ∠D by looking through them.

TRIG CHARTS
AND
CALCULATORS

INTRODUCTION

For thousands of years, trigonometry charts have been used to solve right triangles. The recent advent of electronics has provided an alternative: the calculator. The calculator is more accurate because it carries functions to more decimal places. It can be faster than manual interpolation and extrapolation. And the sometimes-confusing column headings are eliminated, decreasing potential errors. However, charts are still valuable as a reference and calculators are only as accurate as the user's skills allow. This unit presents both the table and calculator methods for determining the function of a given angle, and for determining an angle, given its function.

OBJECTIVES

After completing this unit, you will be able to:

- Determine an angle's six trigonometric functions using both a chart and a calculator.
- Determine an angle given its trigonometric function using both a chart and a calculator.

Charts are designed in several ways. Perhaps the most common charts use the same set of numbers for angles between 45° and 90° as they do for angles between 0° and 45°. (See the Appendix.) This approach necessitates a set of column headings for the angles between 0° and 45° and a set of column footings for the angles between 45° and 90°. The number of minutes (') is read *down* on one side of the chart and *up* on the other side. It can be confusing for beginners to locate the correct place from which to read the figures. Also, these charts typically don't include seconds ("), limiting their accuracy or requiring manual interpolation and extrapolation.

CHARTS OF KNOWN ANGLES

Use a trig chart to determine the sine of 22°18'. Find the page for 22°, move down the minute column to 18', and read across to the sine column. The sine of 22°18' is 0.37946. On the same page, determine the cosine of 67°42′. Notice that the function is the same as the sine of 22°18′. The numbering system and arrows on charts vary. Practice using the chart now to gain experience.

PRACTICE

Determine the following values to the greatest degree of accuracy possible by using a chart.

1. tan 40°12′ _____

2. sec 55°55′ _____

3. cot 0°8′ _____

4. cos 81°30′ _____

The correct answers are: 1) 0.84507   2) 1.78445   3) 429.718   4) 0.14781

CHARTS OF KNOWN FUNCTIONS

Finding an angle, given its function, is done in reverse order. First look in the appropriate column and find the given function. Then look at the top (0°–45°) or bottom (45°–90°) of the page to find the number of whole degrees. Finally, read across to determine the number of minutes. Remember to use the correct column for determining the minutes!

To determine the angle whose cosecant is 1.63834, check in the cosecant column to find 1.63834. (Notice that the 1 in the function may be missing. It may be only written every 5′ and is understood for each of the interim minute entries.) The number of degrees is 37. Also, the number of minutes is 37 not 23. (Follow the arrows if necessary.) Therefore, the angle whose cosecant is 1.63834 is 37°37′. 1.63834 is the function of another angle on this page. It is the secant of 52°23′. Pay attention to the arrows on each side of the chart to help avoid confusing the two.

PRACTICE

Determine the angles whose functions are:

1. tan = 0.77661 _____

2. sin = 0.10395 _____

3. sec = 1.43696 _____

4. csc = 26.8636 _____

The correct answers are: 1) 37°50′   2) 5°58′   3) 45°54′   4) 2°8′

Practice using the charts until you have gained confidence. They can verify your work as you learn to use the calculator.

USING THE CALCULATOR TO FIND FUNCTIONS FOR KNOWN ANGLES

Most calculators require that the angle be given in decimal form before a trigonometric function can be found. Converting angles to decimal form is done in different ways with different manufacturers and models. Refer to your notes in Unit 14 for converting between the degree-minute-second form and decimal form. Once the angle is converted to decimal form, press the trigonometric function key. (*Note:* some calculators require that the trigonometric function key be pressed before the angle is entered and converted.) The calculator will display as many decimals as it can.

Many calculators only have three trigonometric function keys. This is done because the sin and csc are reciprocal functions as mentioned in Unit 20. That is, the csc is the reciprocal of the sin and can be determined by finding the sin of the given angle, and pressing the reciprocal key on the calculator. This key is typically displayed as $\boxed{1/x}$ or $\boxed{x^{-1}}$. Cos and sec are reciprocal functions, as are tan and cot. The reciprocal key is used to find any of the reciprocal functions.

Example

Find the cos of 12°13'14".

Enter the angle. Convert it to decimal form. Press the $\boxed{\cos}$ key. The function is 0.97734.

Example

Find the sec of 12°13'14".

Enter the angle. Convert it to decimal form. Press the $\boxed{\cos}$ key. Press the $\boxed{1/x}$ key. The function is 1.02319.

PRACTICE

Determine the following. Carry each to five decimal places.

1. tan 40°12'16" _____

2. sin 55°55'55" _____

3. cot 0°8'30" _____

4. cos 23°30'44" _____

The correct answers are: 1) 0.84520   2) 0.82837   3) 404.43997   4) 0.91697

USING CALCULATORS TO FIND ANGLES FOR KNOWN FUNCTIONS

If the function is known and the angle needs to be determined, most calculators require that the function is entered first. Then press the $\boxed{2^{nd}}$ key and the trigonometric function key. Express the angle in either decimal form, or in degree-minute-second form. If the known function is a reciprocal function, the $\boxed{1/x}$ key needs to be used first to make it match one of the three trigonometric functions on the calculator.

Example

Find the angle whose tan = 0.12345.

Enter 0.12345. Press $\boxed{2^{nd}}\boxed{\tan}$. You now have the angle in decimal form (7.03756°). Convert it if necessary to degree-minute-second form (7°2'15").

Example

Find the angle whose cot = 0.12345

Enter 0.12345. Press the $\boxed{1/x}$ to convert this function to a tan function. Press the $\boxed{2^{nd}}\boxed{\tan}$ keys. You now have the angle in decimal form (82.96244°). Convert it if necessary (82°57'45").

PRACTICE

Determine the following angles, given these functions. Round to the nearest whole second.

1. tan = 0.77668 _____   2. sin = 0.10595 _____

3. sec = 1.43606 _____   4. csc = 26.2336 _____

The correct answers are: 1. 37°50′8″   2. 6°4′55″   3. 45°51′54″   4. 2°11′5″

CONCEPT APPLICATIONS

Work to the nearest minute when using trig charts and to the nearest second when using a calculator. Use the number of decimal places given for functions in the charts, and round functions to five decimal places when using a calculator. Follow instructions as to whether you should use the charts or a calculator. Proficiency in both is important.

Find the function of each. Use a chart only.

1. sin 64° = _____   2. sin 86°6′ = _____

3. cos 41°22′ = _____   4. tan 26°14′ = _____

5. cos 52°58′ = _____   6. tan 72°7′ = _____

Find the angle whose function is given. Use the charts only.

7. sin = 0.42262 _____   8. tan = 0.38386 _____

9. cos = 0.73135 _____   10. tan = 2.05030 _____

11. sin = 0.77715 _____   12. csc = 1.38860 _____

Find the function of each. Use a calculator.

13. sin 1°15′23″ = _____   14. cos 69°23′14″ = _____

15. tan 5°1′2″ = _____   16. csc 89°18′38″ = _____

17. sec 7°33′59″ = _____   18. cot 45°55′18″ = _____

Find the angle whose function is given. Use a calculator.

19. sec = 1.3301 _____

20. tan = 0.716 _____

21. sin = 0.11349 _____

22. cos = 0.94749 _____

23. tan = 0.50331 _____

24. cot = 1.0006 _____

I WONDER . . .

How is it possible that the tangent function in exercise 10 above is greater than one? Can any trig function be greater than one? Consult the charts. What do you find? Think back to the definitions of each trig function. Which functions can be greater than one and which cannot?

INTRODUCTION

The most common application of trigonometry in the metalworking trades is the solution of right triangles. Trigonometry is the tool used to determine angles and the length of sides in right triangles. The basics learned in the previous unit are applied throughout right triangle solutions.

OBJECTIVES

After completing this unit, you will be able to:

- Determine the length of a side of a right triangle, given one angle and the length of one side.
- Determine the measure of an angle given the length of any two sides.

The first step in solving a right triangle is labeling the sides of the triangle as opposite (opp), adjacent (adj), and hypotenuse (hyp). The angle of reference for the labeling process is the given angle. If there is no given angle, use the angle being solved for as the reference angle.

When the principles of algebra are applied to the six trigonometric ratios, the ratios can be rearranged and "solved" for various sides of the triangles.

For example, $\sin = \dfrac{\text{opp}}{\text{hyp}}$.

Applying algebra, we can rearrange this formula to read opp = hyp × sin and hyp = opp ÷ sin. The other five trigonometric ratios can also be rearranged to create useful formulas. This chart summarizes the rearrangements.

Ratio	Rearranged Formulas
$\sin = \dfrac{opp}{hyp}$	opp = hyp × sin hyp = opp ÷ sin
$\cos = \dfrac{adj}{hyp}$	adj = hyp × cos hyp = adj ÷ cos
$\tan = \dfrac{opp}{adj}$	opp = adj × tan adj = opp ÷ tan
$\csc = \dfrac{hyp}{opp}$	hyp = opp × csc opp = hyp ÷ csc
$\sec = \dfrac{hyp}{adj}$	hyp = adj × sec adj = hyp ÷ sec
$\cot = \dfrac{adj}{opp}$	adj = opp × cot opp = adj ÷ cot

These formulas can be found in references such as trig charts, handbooks, and reference manuals. They are used to solve right triangles. During calculations, numbers should be rounded to five decimal places until the final answer is reached, which can be rounded to three decimal places.

Example 1

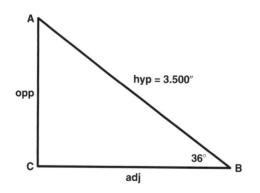

Angle B is the reference angle in the right triangle above. Each side is labeled according to ∠B.

AC = opp = hyp × sin (from the chart above). Here, hyp = 3.500 inches, sin 36° = 0.58779.

The length of AC = 3.5 × 0.58779
AC = 2.057 inches

BC = adj = hyp × cos (from the chart). Here, hyp = 3.500 inches, cos 36° = 0.80902.

The length of BC = 3.5 × 0.80902
BC = 2.832 inches

∠A = 90 − ∠B = 54°.

Now all three sides and angles are known and the triangle is completely solved. Use the Pythagorean theorem to check your work. Is $2.057^2 + 2.832^2 = 3.5^2$? The variance is due to rounding to only three decimal places. The result will be more accurate if five decimal places are used. But the Pythagorean theorem will ALWAYS work with any right triangle and is recommended as a means of checking your work.

Example 2

Solve for ∠A.

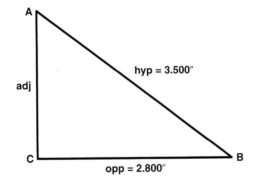

In this example, a reference angle needs to be identified. When solving for ∠A, use ∠A as the reference angle. The sides in the triangle above are labeled accordingly.

The given sides are the side opposite and the hypotenuse. These two sides define both the sin and csc. (See the previous chart.) Most calculators have a sin key, so divide the opposite by the hypotenuse to find the sin of ∠A. 2.8 ÷ 3.5 = 0.8. The angle whose sin = 0.8 is 53.13010° (rounded to five decimal places) = 53°7′48″. And we now know the measure of ∠A.

There are two ways to determine ∠B. One is to apply the principle that all triangles have 180°. To use this principle, subtract 90° and 53°7′48″ from 180°. ∠B = 36°52′12″.

The other method is to set ∠B as the reference angle, relabel the triangle, and use trigonometry. Now BC becomes the side adjacent and the hypotenuse remains as the hypotenuse. The trigonometric functions defined by the two known sides, adjacent and hypotenuse, are cosine (cos) and secant (sec). Again, since most calculators have a cos key, divide the adjacent by the hypotenuse. 2.8 ÷ 3.5 = 0.8. The angle whose cos = 0.8 is 36.86990° (rounded to five decimal places) = 36°52′12″. Since angles A and B are complementary, check to be sure their sum = 90°.

There are also two ways to determine AC. One method is to use the Pythagorean theorem. The second method is to use trigonometry. Since both angles are known, the user may choose either angle as the reference angle. Since the triangle is already labeled for ∠A, we will use ∠A. Both the side opp and the hyp are known. We are solving for the side adj. Again, it is the user's choice as to whether the opp or hyp is used. We will use the hyp for this example. Referring to the previous chart, we know the length of the side adj = hyp × cos OR hyp ÷ sec. With most calculators, it is easier to use cos.

$$AC = adj = hyp × cos$$
$$= 3.5 × 0.6$$
$$= 2.100 \text{ inches}$$

Check this answer using the Pythagorean theorem.

CONCEPT APPLICATIONS

It takes patience and persistence to master the solution of right triangles using trigonometry. Solve several of these at a time, and return to them regularly. You may want to use both the charts and a calculator as you work, and the Pythagorean theorem to check your work.

Determine the following dimensions. Always label the triangles first. Round each final answer to three decimal places or the nearest whole second.

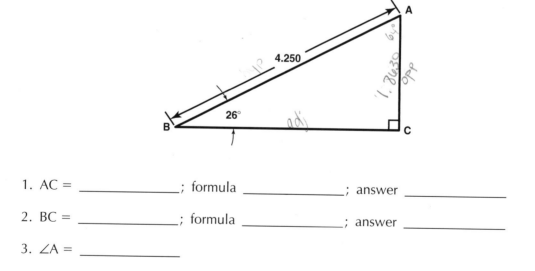

1. AC = _____ ; formula _____ ; answer _____

2. BC = _____ ; formula _____ ; answer _____

3. ∠A = _____

Refer to the drawing below for Problems 4, 5 and 6.

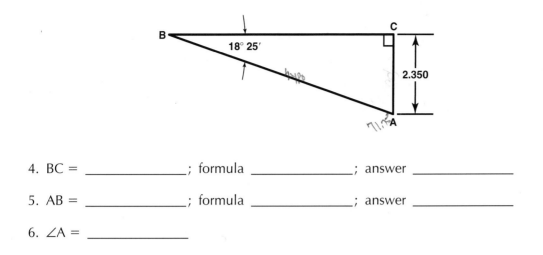

4. BC = _____ ; formula _____ ; answer _____

5. AB = _____ ; formula _____ ; answer _____

6. ∠A = _____

Refer to the drawing below for Problems 7, 8 and 9.

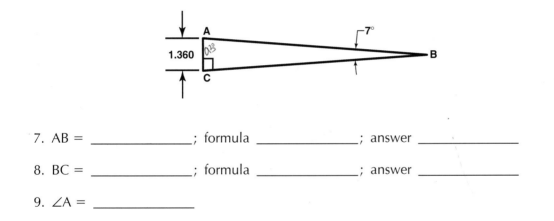

7. AB = _____ ; formula _____ ; answer _____

8. BC = _____ ; formula _____ ; answer _____

9. ∠A = _____

Refer to the drawing below for Problems 10, 11 and 12.

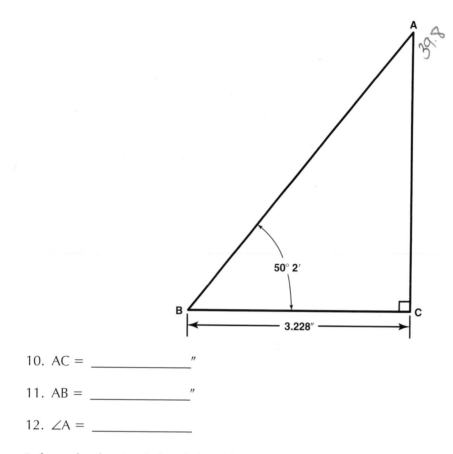

10. AC = _____ "

11. AB = _____ "

12. ∠A = _____

Refer to the drawing below for Problems 13, 14 and 15.

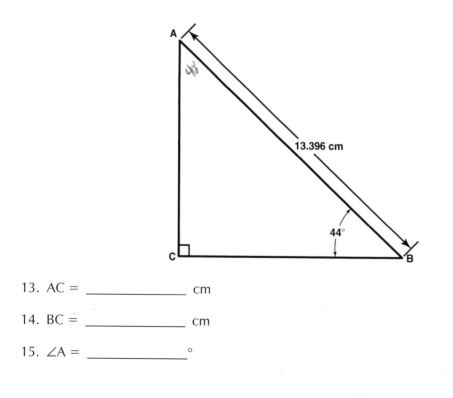

13. AC = _____ cm

14. BC = _____ cm

15. ∠A = _____ °

Refer to the drawing below for Problems 16-20.

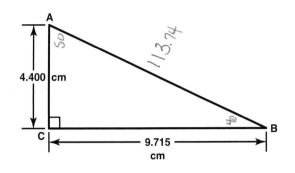

16. What trigonometric function is used to find ∠A? _____

17. ∠A = _____

18. What trigonometric function is used to find ∠B? _____

19. ∠B = _____ °

20. AB = _____ cm. (Did you use trig or the Pythagorean theorem?)

21. The banking for each of the turns on the Indy 500 track is uniform at 12°9'. The track is 600 feet wide midway through each turn. How much higher is the outside of the turn than the inside? _____

Draw a right triangle depicting the situation. Label the sides of the triangle with reference to the given angle and solve it.

UNIT
23

SINE BARS AND SINE PLATES

INTRODUCTION

One of the many practical applications for trigonometry is measurement. The *sine bar* is an instrument used to measure and lay out angles where a close degree of accuracy is desired. It can also be used to set milling machine heads and to test the angle of setting work. Often a sine bar is used to hold a piece of work at a precise angle during machining or inspection. *Sine plates* are magnetic, but used in the same way for grinding operations. As their names imply, they are associated with the sine function.

OBJECTIVES

After completing this unit, you will be able to:

- Determine the height of the gage blocks necessary to tilt a sine bar.
- Determine the angle at which the sine bar is tilted from the horizontal.

The sine function is the length of the side opposite divided by the hypotenuse. The hypotenuse in this case is the length of the sine bar, and the side opposite is the height of the gage block stack used to tilt the sine bar at the proper angle. Remember to carry all numbers to five decimal places until the problem is completed.

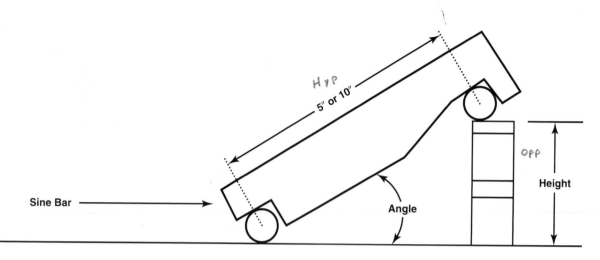

Example 1 — Determining the Height of Gage Blocks

Determine the height of the gage blocks required to tilt a 5-inch sine bar at an angle of 22°30′.

In the drawing above, a right triangle can be drawn with the length of the sine bar representing the hypotenuse and the height of the gage blocks representing the side opposite. Label the side opposite (opp), hypotenuse (hyp) and the 22°30′ angle in the drawing above. To determine the height of the required blocks, find the length of the side opposite. Opp = hyp × sin. Or opp = 5 × 0.38268 = 1.913 inches, rounding to three decimal places. This is the required total height of the gage blocks.

Example 2 — Determining the Angle of Elevation of Gage Blocks

Determine the angle of elevation of a 10-inch sine bar tilted on 1.250-inch gage blocks. Refer to the drawing above for the right triangle. The angle of elevation can be determined by using the sine function. Sin = opp ÷ hyp. Or sin = 1.25 ÷ 10 = 0.125. Use a chart or calculator to find the angle whose sin = 0.125. This angle is 7°10′51, rounding to the nearest whole second.

CONCEPT APPLICATIONS

Round each final answer to three decimal places or the nearest whole second.

1. The height of the gage blocks elevating a 10 inch sine bar is 5.807 inches. What angle is indicated? Sketch a drawing here. _____

2. If a 10-inch sine bar is used to mark an angle of 10°15′, what will the height of the blocks be? Sketch a drawing here. _____

3. What is the measure of ∠A in the drawing below? _____ °

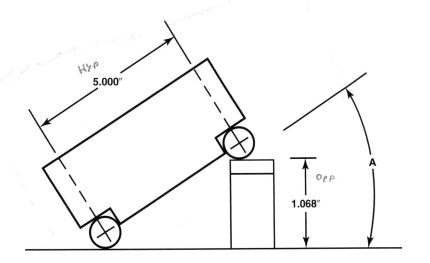

4. What is the measure of ∠A in the drawing below? _____ °

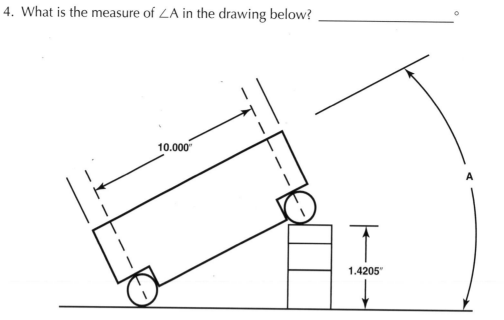

What is the height of gage blocks elevating a 5-inch sine bar used to measure the following angles? Sketch a drawing for each of the problems below.

5. 20°30′ _____ inches

6. 37°20′ _____ inches

7. 72°10′ _____ inches

8. 41°55′18″ _____ inches

9. At what angle is a 5-inch sine bar resting on elevated 4.1041 inch gage blocks? Sketch a drawing here. _____

10. Why are sine bars called "sine bars", rather than "cosine bars" or "tangent bars"? _____

UNIT
24

TAPERS AND WEDGES

INTRODUCTION

One of the many practical uses for trigonometry is calculating the angles and lengths of tapers and wedges. Because many manufactured parts are tapered, it is important for the metalworker to know how to calculate angles, lengths, and tapers.

OBJECTIVES

After completing this unit, you will be able to:

- Calculate the angle of tapers and wedges.
- Calculate the length of tapers and wedges.
- Calculate the large diameter and small diameter of tapers.
- Determine the taper per foot, given the included angle.
- Determine the included angle, given the taper per foot.

Before a taper or wedge problem can be solved, a right triangle must be drawn in the taper or wedge. The right triangle must have two known dimensions, and at least one of these must be a length. The tapers and wedges covered in this unit will be symmetrical. For purposes of accuracy, remember to carry all numbers to five decimal places until the problem is completed.

WEDGES

Example 1 — Determining the Length of Wedges

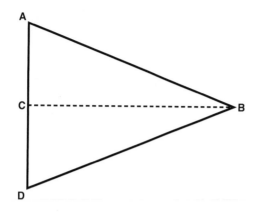

AD = 4.000 inches, ∠ABD = 40°

Determine the length of the wedge.

△ABD is an isosceles triangle. BC is the perpendicular bisector. Therefore, △ABC is a right triangle, AC = 2.000 inches and ∠ABC = 20°. The length of the wedge is line segment BC which must be determined. In right △ABC, referring to ∠B, BC is the side adj and AC is the side opp.

AC = adj = opp ÷ tan
     = 2 ÷ 0.36397
     = 5.495 inches, rounding to three decimal places

Example 2 — Determining the Diameter of Wedges

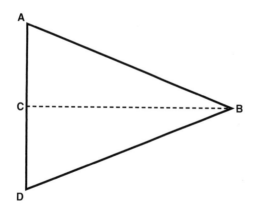

BC = 3.000 inches; ∠ABD = 40°

Determine the diameter, AD, of the wedge.

Once again we have an isosceles triangle and its perpendicular bisector, forming two right triangles. Diameter AD is not a side of either right triangle. But, if we find AC or CD and multiply by 2, the result gives us the whole diameter, AD. If we choose to work with right △ABC, ∠B = 20° and BC = 3.000 inches. Referring to ∠B, BC is the side adjacent and AC is the side opposite.

AC = opp = adj × tan
     = 3 × tan 20°
     = 1.092 inches, rounding to 3 decimal places

Example 3—Determining the Included Angle of Wedges

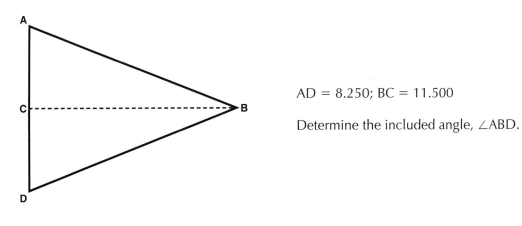

AD = 8.250; BC = 11.500

Determine the included angle, ∠ABD.

△ABD is an isosceles triangle and its perpendicular bisector BC forms two right triangles. AC = CD = 4.125 inches. The tangent of an angle is the ratio of its side opposite to its side adjacent. In this case, that would be 4.125 ÷ 11.5 = 0.35870 to five decimal places. Using the charts or a calculator, we need to find the angle whose tan = 0.35870. This angle is 19.73269°. The included angle is 2 × 19.73269 which is 39°27′55″, rounding to the nearest whole second.

TAPERS

Tapers have two blunt ends. One end is smaller than the other. (See your instructor for a model of a piece of tapered steel so you can better understand what this piece looks like.) Taper problems are similar to wedge problems.

Example 1—Determining the Length of Tapers

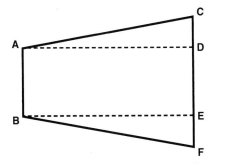

AB = 1.8 cm, CF = 3.4 cm, ∠CAB = 100°.

Determine the length AD.

∠DAB is a right angle. Therefore in right △ACD, ∠A = 100° − 90° = 10°. (The included angle is 10 × 2 = 20°.) We can use subtraction to determine the length of CD. CD = (3.4 − 1.8) ÷ 2 = 0.8 cm. Referring to ∠A, AD is the side adjacent and CD is the side opposite.

AD = adj = opp ÷ tan
    = 0.8 ÷ 0.17633
    = 4.537 inches, rounding to three decimal places

Example 2—Determining the Diameter of Tapers

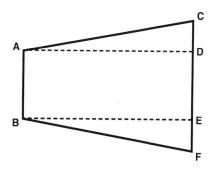

CF = 3.4 cm, AD = 4.657 cm, ∠CAB = 100°.

Determine small diameter AB.

A strategy for finding AB is to realize that AB = DE and DE = CF − (CD + EF). Since CD = EF (symmetric), we can find either one and apply it to our strategy. ∠DAB is a right angle. Therefore in right △ACD, ∠A = 100° − 90° = 10°. (The included angle is 10 × 2 = 20°.) Referring to ∠A in right △ACD, AD is the side adj and CD is the side opp. The side opp = side adj × tan.

CD = opp = 4.657 × 0.17633
$\qquad$ = 0.82115, therefore
$\quad$ AB = 3.4 − (2 × 0.82115)
$\qquad$ = 1.757 cm, rounding to three decimal places

A strategy for finding CF if AB is known is to again realize that AB = DE. Therefore, CF = CD + DE + EF.

Example 3—Determining the Included Angle of Tapers

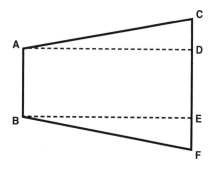

AB = 1.8 cm, CF = 3.4 cm, and AD = 4.7 cm.

Determine the included angle (∠CAD + ∠EBF).

In order to determine an angle, we need to know the lengths of two sides of the right triangle. In right △ACD, we know AD and we can use arithmetic to determine CD. CD = (CF − DE) ÷ 2 OR CD = (3.4 − 1.8) ÷ 2 = 0.8 cm. The tangent of ∠A = opp ÷ adj. Or tan ∠A = 0.8 ÷ 4.7 = 0.17021. Use the charts or a calculator to determine that ∠A = 9.65989°. The included angle = 2 × ∠A = 19°19′11″, rounding to the nearest whole second.

TAPER PER FOOT

To determine the taper per foot (tpf), refer to the taper below. This symmetric taper can be divided into a rectangle and two right triangles. The length is given and either the included angle is given and the tpf must be determined, or the included angle is to be determined and the tpf is given.

Example 1—Determining TPF

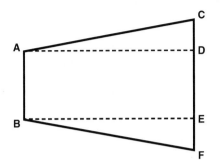

The included angle is 12°.

The taper length = 12 inches = 1 foot.

Determine the tpf.

Half of the included angle is in each of the right triangles. Therefore, in right △ACD, ∠A = 6°. AD = 12 inches (one foot). Tpf is defined to be the change in diameters over each 1 foot of length = CD + EF. (There is no change between AB and DE.) Referring to ∠A, CD is the side opposite and AD is the side adjacent.

opp = adj × tan
    = 12 × 0.10510
    = 1.26125

total tpf = 2 × 1.26125
        = 2.523 inches, rounding to three decimal places

This information is also available in charts. While it is important to know how to determine tpf, use the charts to double-check your work.

Example 2—Determining Included Angle of TPF

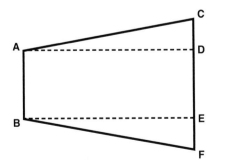

CD = 1.250 inches and AD = 12 inches = 1 foot.

Determine the included angle.

The included angle = 2 × ∠CAD. In right △ACD, both the side opp and side adj are known. The tangent of ∠A = 1.25 ÷ 12 = 0.10417. Using a chart or calculator, we can determine that ∠A = 5.94686°. The included angle is twice this or 11°53′37″, rounding to the nearest whole second. This information is also available in charts. While it's important to know how to determine the included angle, use the charts to double-check your work.

CONCEPT APPLICATIONS

Round final answers to three decimal places or the nearest whole second.

In the wedge below, AD = 2 inches and BC = 6 inches.

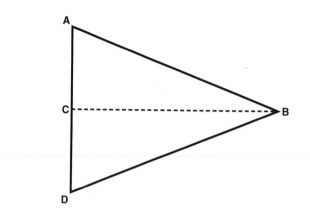

1. ∠ABC = _____

2. The included angle = _____

3. AB = _____

In the taper below, AB = 0.750 inches, AD = 6 inches, and CF ≐ 1.500 inches.

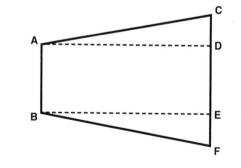

4. ∠CAD = _____

5. The included angle = _____

In the taper below, AB = 2.54 cm, AD = 10.16 cm, and the included angle is 20°.

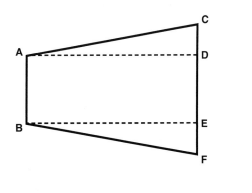

6. What is the large diameter of this taper? _____ cm

In the same taper, if the large diameter = 2 inches, the length = 6 inches, and the included angle = 10°, determine the following.

7. The small diameter = _____ inches

In the taper below, AB = 1 inch, CF = 2 inches, and the included angle = 18°.

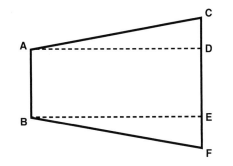

8. The length, BE = _____

Sketch a 12″ taper here. Check your work with a chart.

9. Tpf = 3.150 inches. The included angle = _____ °

Sketch another 12″ taper. Check your work with a chart.

10. The included angle = 20°8′. The tpf = _____

11. Is it possible to solve problem 10 using the sin function? _____

12. Why does it or doesn't it work? _____

25

CENTER-TO-CENTER DISTANCES

INTRODUCTION

Toolmakers are often required to bore holes around the circumference of a circle. Calculating the center-to-center distance between both equally and unequally spaced holes is a means of checking the accuracy of their locations. Charts have been developed and are useful when the holes match the chart descriptions exactly. A chart is included in the appendix. Calculating center-to-center distances in other situations is another practical application of trigonometry.

OBJECTIVES

After completing this unit, you will be able to:

- Calculate the center-to-center distance between any two adjacent holes.
- Calculate the center-to-center distance between any two holes.
- Calculate the diameter of the circle given the center-to-center distance.

Before a center-to-center distance problem can be solved, a right triangle must be drawn inside the circle. The right triangle always includes the center of the circle. The right triangle must have two known measurements, and at least one of these must be a length. In most cases, the diameter of the circle will be known, as well as the number of bored holes. Remember to carry all numbers to five decimal places until the problem is completed.

Example 1—Determining the Distance Between Two Adjacent Holes

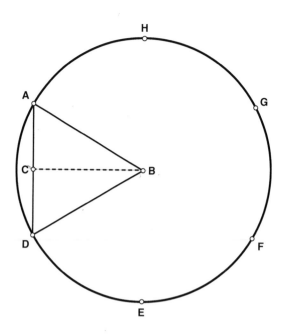

Given: 5-inch bolt circle with six equally spaced holes

In general: the isosceles triangle ABD must be drawn to the center of the bolt circle as in the drawing above. The isosceles triangle is then bisected by BC and two right triangles are formed. The radius of the circle AB becomes the hypotenuse of the right triangle. Angle B of the isosceles triangle is equal to 360° ÷ the number of bored holes. When the isosceles triangle is bisected, the (central) angle is 1/2 the original.

In the case above, the hypotenuse of right △ABC is 5 ÷ 2 = 2.5-inch and the angle is one half of 360 ÷ 6 = 30°.

Once these dimensions are known, the triangle can be solved.

AC = opp = hyp × sin
　　　　 = 2.5 × 0.5
　　　　 = 1.25 inches

The solution to the right triangle is only 1/2 of the center-to-center distance. Therefore, AD, the distance between centers of two adjacent holes = 2.500 inches.

[Be sure to double the side opposite (opp) to determine the complete distance!]

Use the chart in the Appendix to check your work.

Example 2—Determining the Measurement Over Pins

Pins may be inserted and used to check the accuracy of the hole locations. In this case, a micrometer is placed over the pins to measure the distance. After the center-to-center distance is determined using the method outlined above, the radius of each pin must be added to determine the measurement over pins.

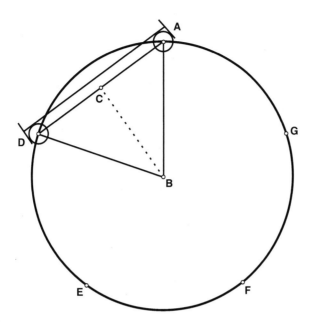

Given: Five equally spaced 1/8-inch holes about a 3-inch bolt circle

AB is the radius = 1.5 inches. Central ∠B = 360° ÷ 5 = 72°. In right △ ABC, ∠B = 36°

AC = opp = hyp × sin
        = 1.5 × 0.58779
        = 0.88168

AD = 2 × AC
    = 2 × 0.88168
    = 1.76336 inches

The distance over pins = 1.76336 + radius of pin + radius of pin = 1.888 inches, rounding to three decimal places.

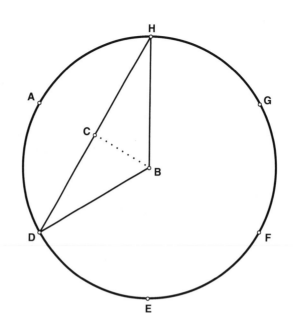

Given: 5-inch bolt circle with six equally spaced holes

HB is the radius = 2.5 inches. Each of the six central angles = 360° ÷ 6 = 60°. In isosceles △BDH, ∠B = 2 × 60 = 120°. In right △BCH, ∠B = 60° and CH is the side opposite (opp).

CH = opp = hyp × sin
$$= 2.5 \times 0.86603$$
$$= 2.16508$$

DH = 2 × CH
$$= 4.33016 \text{ inches}$$

The center-to-center distance between holes is 4.330 inches, rounding to three decimal places.

Example 4—Determining the Diameter Given the Center-to-Center Distance

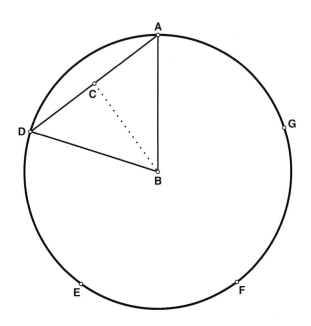

If the center-to-center distance is known, the diameter of the circle can be determined by sketching triangles as in the above examples and determining the hypotenuse in the right triangle. The hypotenuse is the radius of the circle.

Given: AD = 7.62 cm, five equally spaced holes.

Determine the diameter of circle B.

In right $\triangle$ ABC, AC = 7.62 ÷ 2 = 3.81 and $\angle$B = 36°. The hypotenuse, AB is the radius of circle B.

AB = hyp = opp ÷ sin
$\quad\quad\quad$ = 3.81 ÷ 0.58779
$\quad\quad\quad$ = 6.48196, the radius

$\quad$ dia = 2 $\times$ AB
$\quad\quad\quad$ = 12.96392 cm

The diameter = 12.964 cm, rounding to three decimal places.

CONCEPT APPLICATIONS

Round the *final* answer to three decimal places in each of the following. Use the chart to double-check your work.

1. Sketch an 8-inch bolt circle with six equally spaced holes. Determine the distance between centers of two adjacent holes. _____

2. Refer to Exercise 1 and determine the distance between centers of the first and third holes. Redraw the sketch here. _____

3. Insert 1/4-inch pins in the holes in Exercise 2. What is the measurement over the pins?
_____

In each drawing, nine equally spaced holes are drilled on a 6-inch-diameter bolt circle. Determine the following. Three drawings are provided for your use.

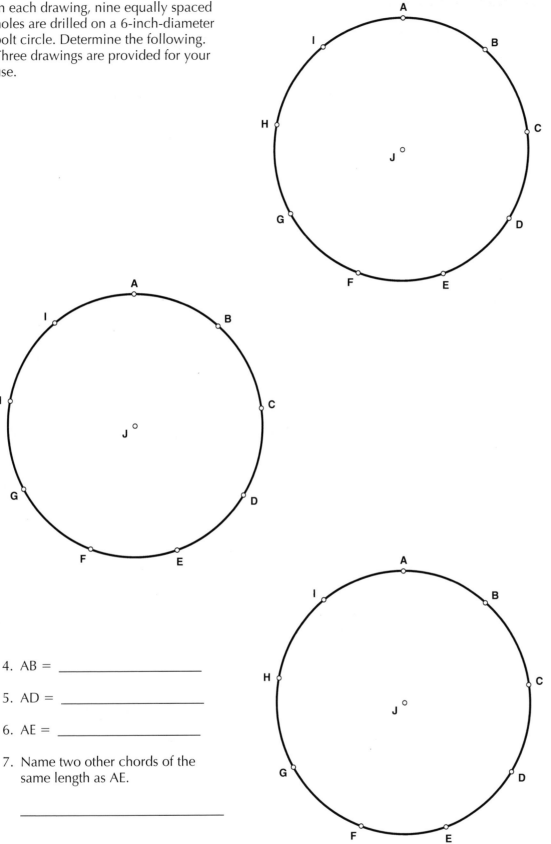

4. AB = _____

5. AD = _____

6. AE = _____

7. Name two other chords of the same length as AE.

_____

_____

AC = 3.000″ in the sketch below.

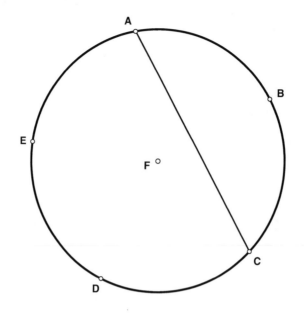

8. Determine the diameter of circle F. _____

9. Which trigonometric function is used in each of these triangles? _____

10. Why? _____

11. Is it possible to use another trigonometric function?
    _____

12. Why or why not? _____

INTRODUCTION

Dovetails are used in situations where accuracy is most important. An example is a mill table where the accuracy of the dovetails allows the table to move without binding. A common way to measure dovetails accurately is to use a micrometer and "mike" over a pair of plugs placed inside or outside the dovetail. This is used with both internal and external dovetail slides. "Miking over plugs" or "miking over rolls" is a common procedure used to check the accuracy of workpieces, including tapers and wedges.

OBJECTIVES

After completing this unit, you will be able to:

- Calculate the overall measurement "over plugs" on the outside of a dovetail.
- Calculate the distance "between plugs" inside the dovetail.
- Calculate the height of a dovetail.
- Calculate the dimension across the top of the slide of a dovetail.
- Calculate the dimension across the bottom of the slide of a dovetail.

The dovetails in this unit are symmetrical. Remember to carry all numbers to five decimal places until the problem is completed.

Example 1—Determining the Measurement Over Plugs

Refer to the drawing and the enlargement below.

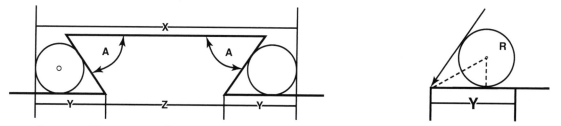

Strategy: X represents the measurement over plugs, which is measured with a micrometer ("mike"). This is made up of distance Y + distance Z + distance Y. Distance Z will be given and distance Y must be calculated.

Given: Angle A = 50°. Plug diameter = 1cm; Z = 3.307 cm.
In a symmetrical dovetail, the angle in the enlargement to the right is also 50° because they are alternate interior angles. Distance Y can be calculated by drawing a right triangle inside the plug. (Refer to the enlarged drawing to the right above.) In the right triangle (a radius and tangent form a right angle), we know the angle is 50° ÷ 2 = 25°. (An extended radius bisects the angle formed by two tangent lines.) And the side opposite is the radius = 0.5 cm. Distance Y is the side adj of the right triangle + the radius of the plug.

adj = opp ÷ tan
   = 0.5 ÷ 0.46631
   = 1.07225
 Y = adj + radius
   = 1.07225 + radius
   = 1.57225

Distance X = Y + Z + Y. Or X = 1.57225 + 3.307 + 1.57225 = 6.452 cm, rounding to three decimal places. In checking the accuracy of this dovetail, the measurement over the plugs must be 6.452 cm.

Example 2—Determining the Measurement Between Plugs

Refer to the drawings below.

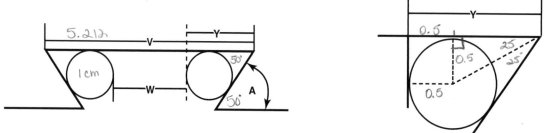

Strategy: W represents the distance between plugs. It can be calculated with this equation: Distance W = distance V − distance Y − distance Y. (Refer to the enlargement to the right for Y.)

Given: Angle A = 50°, plug diameter = 1 cm, V = 5.212 cm.
The angle in the enlargement to the right is also 50° because they are alternate interior angles. Distance Y can be calculated by drawing a right triangle inside the plug. (Refer to the enlargement to the right.) In the right triangle, we know the angle is 50° ÷ 2 = 25°. And the side opposite is the radius = 0.5 cm. Distance Y is the side adjacent of the right triangle + the radius of the plug.

208

adj = opp ÷ tan
        = 0.5 ÷ 0.46631
        = 1.07225
    Y = adj + radius
        = 1.07225 + 0.5
        = 1.57225

Distance W = 5.212 − 1.57225 − 1.57225 = 2.067 cm, rounding to three decimal places. In checking the accuracy of this dovetail, the measurement between the plugs must be 2.067 cm.

Example 3—Determining the Height of the Dovetail

The right triangle's placement for calculating the height of a dovetail is not related to the plug as it was in the first two examples. The triangle reaches both the top and the bottom slides of the dovetail. *This is the second location of the right triangle for dovetail problems.*

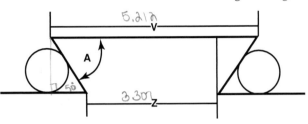

The right triangle is drawn by constructing the vertical line. It extends from the top to the bottom slide. The angle of the triangle corresponding to ∠A = 50°. The side adjacent is equal to (distance V − distance Z) ÷ 2. Distance V = 5.212 cm and distance Z = 3.307 cm. In this example, the side adjacent = 0.9525.

opp = adj × tan
        = 0.9525 × 1.19175
        = 1.13515

The height of the dovetail is 1.135 cm, rounding to three decimal places.

Example 4—Determining the Dimension Across the Top of the Dovetail

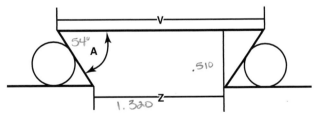

The right triangle again is constructed with the vertical line. The height of the dovetail, ∠A and distance Z are known. Strategy: Distance V = side adjacent + Z + side adjacent. Z = 1.320 inch, ∠A = 54° and the height of the dovetail = 0.510 inch.

adj = opp ÷ tan
        = 0.510 ÷ 1.37638
        = 0.37054

Distance V = 0.37054 + 1.320 + 0.37054 = 2.061 inches, rounding to three decimal places.

Example 5—Determining the Dimension Across the Bottom of the Dovetail

The right triangle again is constructed with the vertical line. The height of the dovetail, ∠A and distance V are known. Strategy: Distance Z = V − side adjacent − side adjacent. V = 2.052 inches, ∠A = 54° and the height of the dovetail = 0.510 inches.

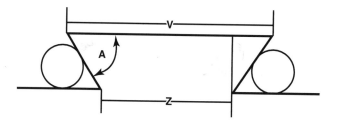

adj = opp ÷ tan
    = 0.510 ÷ 1.37638
    = 0.37054

Distance Z = 2.054 − 0.37054 − 0.37054 = 1.313 inches; rounding to three decimal places.

CONCEPT APPLICATIONS

In each of the following problems, consider which of the two locations of the right triangle is appropriate and then solve. Round your *final* answer to three decimal places.

Refer to the drawing below for Problems 1 and 2.

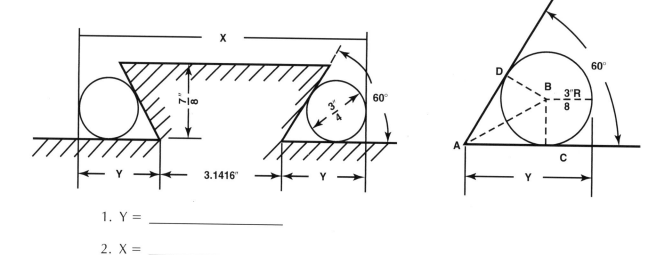

1. Y = _____

2. X = _____

Refer to the drawing below for Problems 3 and 4.

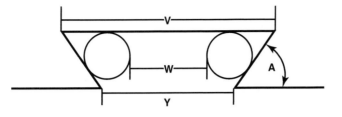

$\angle A = 54°$, V = 4.250"

3. Determine W, using 1/2 inch plugs. _____

4. The height of the dovetail is 1.645". Determine Y. _____

Refer to the drawing below for Problems 5 and 6.

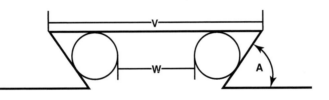

$\angle A = 54°$.

5. The distance across the bottom of the dovetail = 2.313 inch and the height of the dovetail

= 5/8 inch. Determine V (the distance across the top of the dovetail). _____

6. Determine W, using 3/8 inch plugs and the distance V from Problem 5. _____

7. In the drawing below, Z = 2.149 inches, diameter of the plugs = 0.750 inches and ∠A = 60°. Determine X, the measurement over plugs. _____

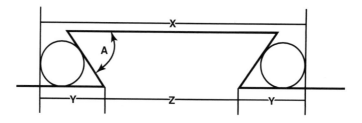

8. In the drawing below, V = 4.000 inches, Z = 2.149 inches, and ∠A = 60°. Determine the height of the dovetail. _____

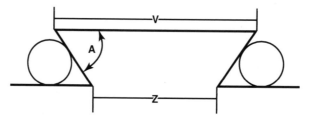

9. In the drawing above, sketch a line indicating the measurement over the plugs. Indicate that this measurement = 3.219 cm, ∠A = 54°, and the plug diameter = 0.5 cm. Determine Z. _____

10. In the drawing below, the distance across the top of the dovetail is 3,000 inches, the angle of the dovetail is 45°, and the distance across the bottom of the dovetail is 4.250 inches. Determine the height of the dovetail. _____

UNIT
27

OTHER BASIC PROBLEMS

INTRODUCTION

This unit presents a variety of problems employing the basics of trigonometry. In each case, one or more right triangles need to be sketched and then solved. Refer to previous chapters to help you place the triangles.

Remember to carry all numbers to five decimal places until the problem is completed. Round final answers to three decimal places or to the nearest whole second.

PROBLEMS

1. Given a 10-inch sine bar in the drawing below, determine the height of the gage block

   stack used to establish an angle of 32°32′32″. _____

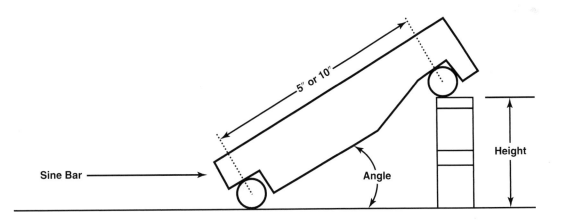

2. The location of the 0.605-diameter hole and the 0.255-diameter reamed hole is checked by inserting pins of the same size in the respective holes and then measuring them with a micrometer. What should the micrometer reading Y be if the holes are properly located?

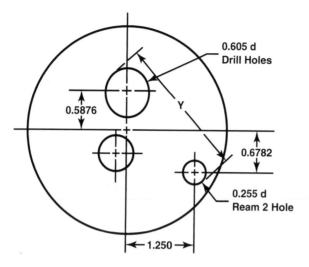

Distance Y = _____

Hint: First determine the center-to-center distance of the hypotenuse.

3. To determine the location of the 0.355-diameter hole, it is necessary to determine its distances from the vertical and horizontal centerlines. Determine these dimensions.

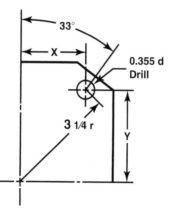

Horizontal distance X = _____

Vertical distance Y = _____

Hint: 3 1/4 r is the hypotenuse.

4. Distance Y = _____

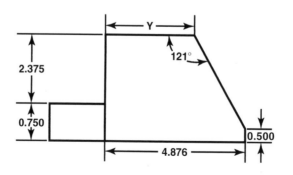

5. Angle Y = _____

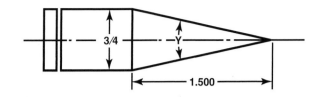

6. Distance Y = _____

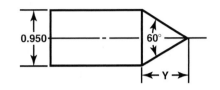

7. Find the small diameter of the tapered part of the shaft in the drawing below.

Small distance Y = _____

8. Find the included angle X of the tapered part of the shaft in the drawing below.

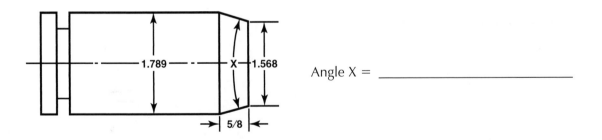

Angle X = _____

9. A shaft tapers 3/4 inch per foot. What is the included angle of the taper? Sketch a drawing here. Included angle = _____

10. Find the taper per foot of an included angle of 8°27″. Sketch a drawing here.

Taper per foot = _____

11. What will the measurement X be if the five sides of this symmetrical figure are each 2 inches in length?

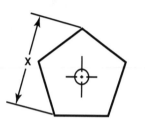

Measurement X = _____

12. Find the distance X on this symmetrical template.

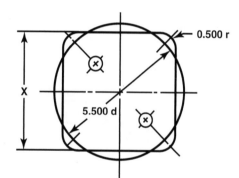

Distance X = _____

13. When you are laying out a piece to be machined it is often necessary to determine the angular displacement of various holes from the vertical and horizontal centerlines that have already been established. Determine the angle X.

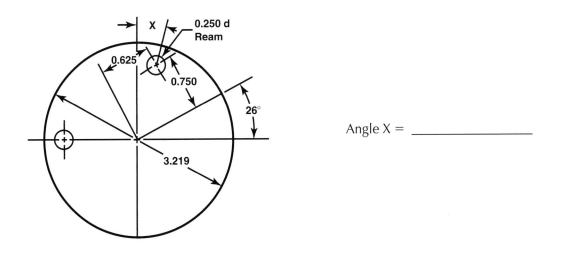

Angle X = _____

14. In order to machine the 5/8 inch radius hole as shown, it is necessary to compute the angle from the vertical centerline to the center of the 5/8 inch radius hole. What is the measure of that angle? Hint: The 5/8″- radius hole extends beyond the centerline.

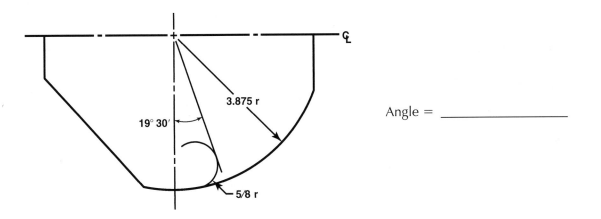

Angle = _____

15. What would be the size of the largest octagon (across flat) that could be milled from a piece of smooth stock 2 inches in diameter?

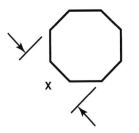

Size = _____

16. The diameter of the circle locating these eight equally spaced drill holes is 8 inches. Find the distances AH, AG, and AF that are needed to check the location of the drill holes.

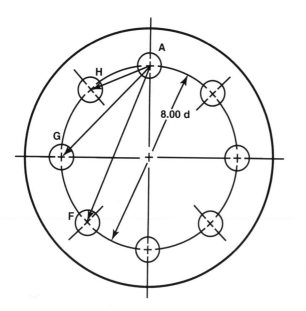

Distance AH = _____

Distance AG = _____

Distance AF = _____

Hint: The radius becomes one of the equal sides of an isosceles triangle.

17. The six holes in the template below are each 1/8 inches in diameter. Pins of the same size are placed in the holes A, B, and C. Find the measurements of GH and JK that are taken over the pins.

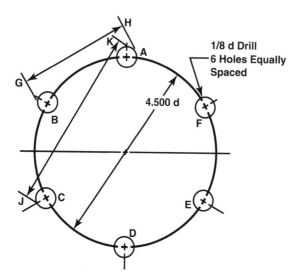

Distance GH = _____

Distance JK = _____

18. Find distance X on the punch that allows 0.010 cutting clearance between punch and die.

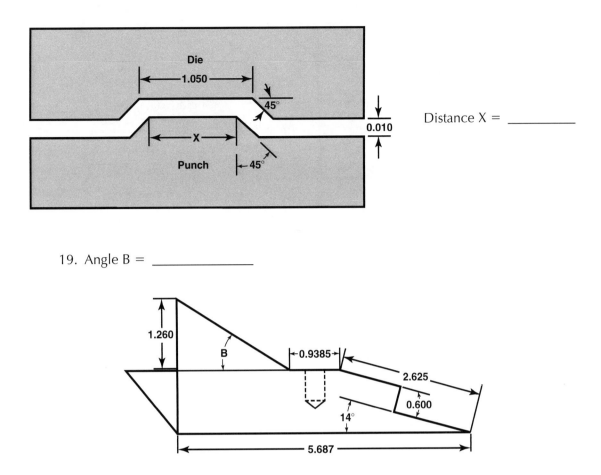

Distance X = _____

19. Angle B = _____

20. To check the location of the 5/8-inch-diameter angular hole, the distance X must be calculated. Note that a 5/8-inch-diameter pin is used in the hole.

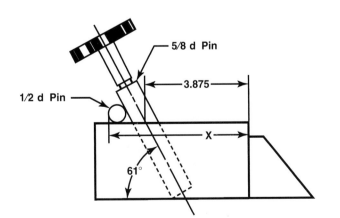

Distance X = _____ inches

21. If two disks 1 1/2 inches and 1 7/8 inch in diameter, respectively, are in contact with each other, what is the included angle between the straight edges?

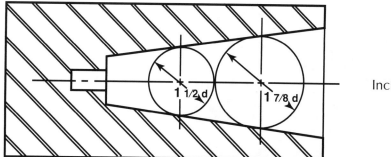

Included angle = _____

22. Two disks, 7/8 inch and other 2 1/4 inches in diameter, are used to measure a tape. The distance between the centers of the disks is 3 7/8 inches. What is the rate of taper per foot?

Taper per foot = _____

23. Find the distance X through which the cutter would have to move to mill the periphery of the pad ZZ.

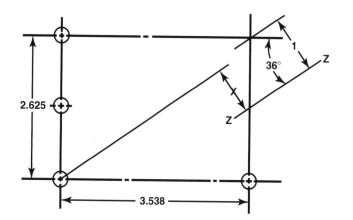

Distance X = _____

24. Find the depth X of the 1 5/16-inch-diameter hole.

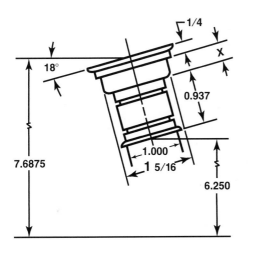

Depth X = _____

25. Find Angle X = _____

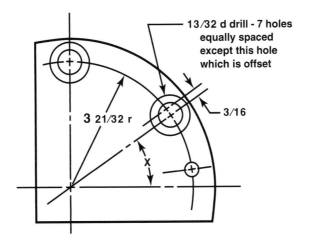

13/32 d drill - 7 holes
equally spaced
except this hole
which is offset

3 21/32 r

3/16

26. The 1 3/8-inch-diameter must be milled and made to end perfectly with the 0.875-inch diameter. To do this, it is necessary to calculate the angle X through which the milling cutter must revolve. What is the measure of angle X?

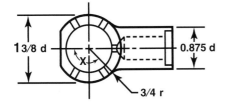

Angle X = _____

27. Angle B = _____

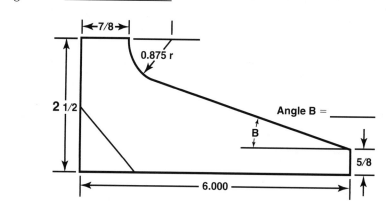

28. Dimension C = _____

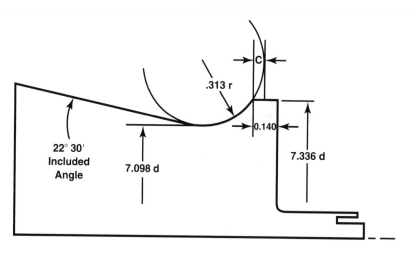

Hint: Sketch the mirror image of the top half below.

Two parallel lines 0.0608 inch apart are to be connected by two radii as shown by the sketch. If the locating distance to the meeting point of the two curves is 1.250 inches, find the locating distances X and Y to the center of the two respective radii.

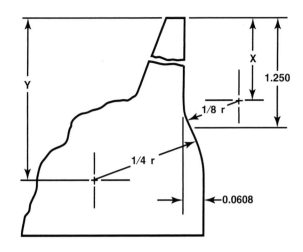

29. Distance X = _____

30. Distance Y = _____

UNIT
28

COMPOUND ANGLES

INTRODUCTION

Compound angles are used in solid geometry and three-dimensional trigonometry. The angles are considered "compound" because they are located in more than one plane. Typical applications of compound angles are the machining of fixture parts, die sections, and cutting tools. This unit presents some of the foundational work on which compound angle situations can be solved. Its intent is to help the metalworker learn the trigonometry principles used to determine missing dimensions and angles and apply them to actual workpieces. Visualization of these principles, understanding them, and applying them to actual work situations are vital to correct machining. Only single-rotation and single-title principles are considered in this unit.

OBJECTIVES

After completing this unit, you will be able to:

- Calculate the lengths of diagonals within a rectangular solid.
- Calculate the angles formed by the diagonal within a rectangular solid.
- Calculate the angle of rotation for boring compound angular holes.
- Calculate the angle of tilt for boring compound angular holes.
- Calculate the angle of rotation for machining compound angular surfaces.
- Calculate the angle of tilt for machining compound angular surfaces.

CALCULATING THE LENGTH OF A DIAGONAL WITHIN A RECTANGULAR SOLID

Refer to the drawing of a rectangular solid below to help visualize the diagonal. It is labeled as the "axis of hole," and is the hypotenuse of a right triangle. The diagonal, the height of the rectangular solid, and the diagonal of the base of the solid form this right triangle.

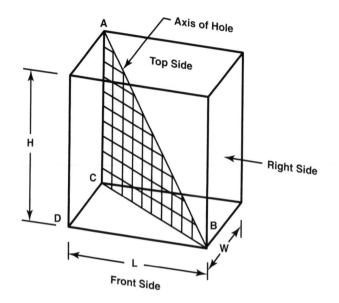

The drawing below represents the views from the top, front, and right side. It may help you visualize the situation if you make a copy of this page, cut out the model, and fold it on the solid lines to form a model.

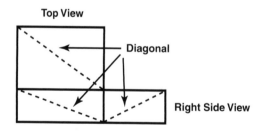

Because the diagonal is drawn on each surface as a two-dimensional line segment, its actual length is not represented. It can be calculated by applying the Pythagorean theorem to two separate right triangles. First, determine the length of the diagonal of the bottom surface. Then consider the right triangle formed by this diagonal, the height of the solid and the diagonal labeled "axis of hole." This triangle is represented by the grid lines you see in the drawings above and and on the next page.

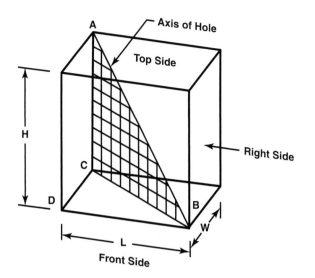

In the drawing above, the height H = 2.500 inches, the length L = 2.250 inches, and the width W = 1.000 inch.

In right triangle BCD,

$$\text{diagonal } BC^2 = CD^2 + BD^2$$
$$= 1^2 + 2.25^2$$
$$= 6.0625$$
$$BC = 2.46221 \text{ inches}$$

In right triangle ABC,

$$\text{diagonal } AB^2 = AC^2 + BC^2$$
$$= 2.5^2 + 2.46221^2$$
$$= 12.3125$$
$$AB = 3.50892 \text{ inches}$$

CALCULATING THE ANGLES FORMED BY A DIAGONAL WITHIN A RECTANGULAR SOLID

Both ∠A and ∠B in right triangle ABC can be calculated using trigonometry if at least two sides are known.

Example

In the drawing below, the height H = 2.500 inches, the length L = 2.250 inches, and the width W = 1.000 inch.

. In right triangle ABC, AB = 3.50892 inches, AC = 2.500 inches, and BC = 2.46221 inches.

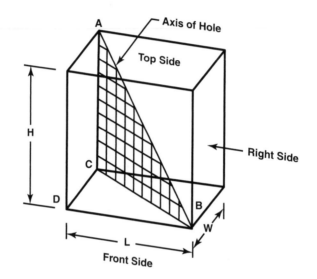

$\sin \angle A = \text{opp} \div \text{hyp}$

$= 2.46221 \div 3.50892$

$= 0.70170$

$\angle A = 44°33'49''$

$\sin \angle B = \text{opp} \div \text{hyp}$

$= 2.5 \div 3.50892$

$= 0.71247$

$\angle B = 45°26'11''$

(rounded for a total of 180°)

CONCEPT APPLICATIONS

Calculate the length of each diagonal AB in the following drawings. Round final answers to three decimal places and round angles to the nearest second.

Refer to the drawing below for Problems 1 and 2.

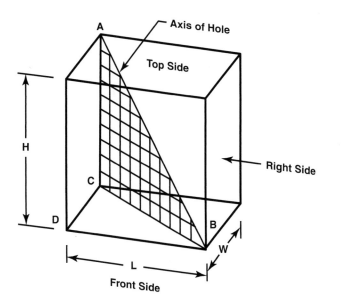

1. H = 2.500 inches

   L = 2.500 inches

   W = 1.250 inches

   BC = _____ inches

   AB = _____ inches

2. H = 6.500 cm

   L = 6.500 cm

   W = 3.000 cm

   BC = _____ cm

   AB = _____ cm

Refer to the drawing below for Problems 3 and 4.

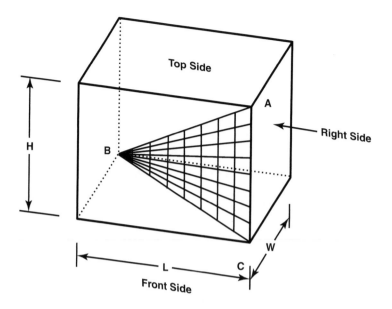

3. H = 2.250 inches

   L = 3.000 inches

   W = 1.500 inches

   BC = _____ inches

   AB = _____ inches

4. H = 5.750 cm

   L = 7.600 cm

   W = 4.000 cm

   BC = _____ cm

   AB = _____ cm

Refer to the drawing below for Problems 5 and 6.

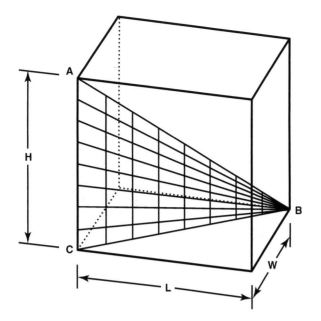

5. H = 2.250 inches

   L = 2.250 inches

   W = 1.125 inches

   BC = _____ inches

   AB = _____ inches

6. H = 5.850 cm

   L = 5.850 cm

   W = 2.700 cm

   BC = _____ cm

   AB = _____ cm

7. Refer to the drawing for Exercise 1. In right triangle ABC, calculate angles A and B.

   ∠A = _____

   ∠B = _____

8. Refer to the drawing for Exercise 3. In right triangle ABC, calculate angles A and B.

   ∠A = _____

   ∠B = _____

9. Refer to the drawing for Exercise 5. In right triangle ABC, calculate angles A and B.

   $\angle A =$ _____

   $\angle B =$ _____

10. Refer to the drawing for Exercise 6. In right triangle ABC, calculate angles A and B.

    $\angle A =$ _____

    $\angle B =$ _____

CALCULATING THE ANGLES OF ROTATION AND TILT FOR BORING COMPOUND ANGULAR HOLES

When drilling or boring compound angular holes, the part is usually placed on a sine plate. The angles at which the part must be rotated ($\angle R$) and tilted ($\angle T$) need to be calculated.

The angle of rotation, $\angle R$, is the angle at which the part must be rotated to place the hole in a plane perpendicular to the face of the sine plate. See the accompanying drawings.

The angle of tilt, $\angle T$, is the angle at which the sine plate must be raised to place the hole in a plane perpendicular to the base of the sine plate. See the accompanying drawings.

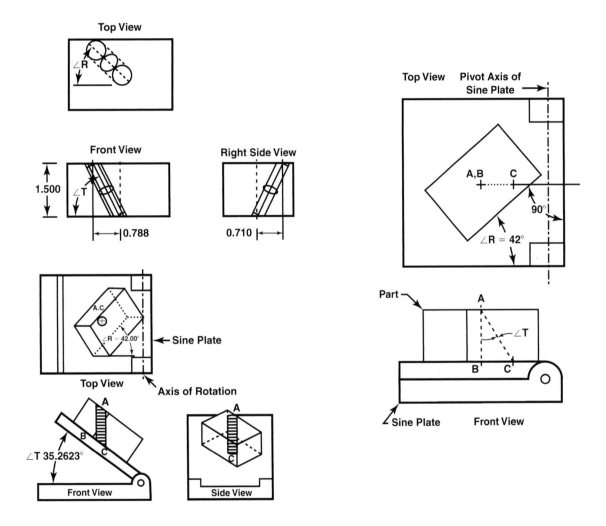

Angles R and T can be determined using the single drawing below. In the drawing below, height = 1.500 inches, length = 0.788 inches, and width = 0.710 inches. In right triangle BCD, ∠R, (the angle of rotation), = ∠CBD.

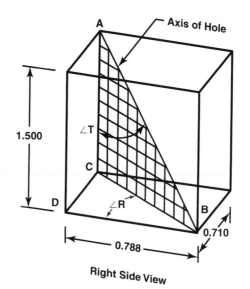

Right Side View

tan ∠R = opp ÷ adj
= 0.710 ÷ 0.788
= 0.90102
∠R = 42°1'10"

NOTE: *Each particular situation needs to be evaluated to ensure that the part is rotated for this angle rather than its complement. When setting the part, take care to visualize the outcome.*

In right triangle ABC, apply the Pythagorean theorem.

$BC^2 = 0.710^2 + 0.788^2$
= 1.12504
BC = 1.06068

tan ∠T = opp ÷ adj
= 1.06068 ÷ 1.5
= 0.70712
∠T = 35°15'54"

The part needs to be placed squarely on the sine plate and then rotated 42°1'10". The sine plate needs to be tilted 35°15'54". The next set of drawings represents this situation, with the angles rounded to 42.000° and 35.2623°.

NOTE: *Throughout the calculations and setup, the visualization and understanding of the particular situation are key. Care and attention need to be given to avoid using the complementary angle or position.*

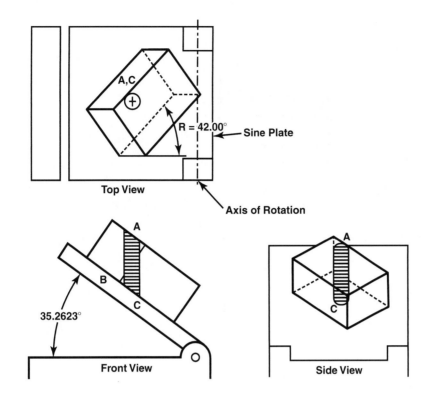

Top View

Axis of Rotation

R = 42.00° — Sine Plate

A,C

35.2623°

Front View

Side View

CONCEPT APPLICATIONS

Refer to the set of drawings below to visualize the scenario, then apply the dimensions H, L, and W to solve for the angle of rotation (∠R) and the angle of tilt (∠T). It may be helpful to refer to page 228 for better visualization.

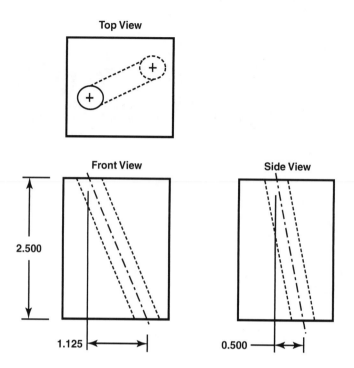

11. H = 2.500 inches

    L = 1.125 inches

    W = 0.500 inches

    ∠R = _____ inches

    ∠T = _____ inches

Top View

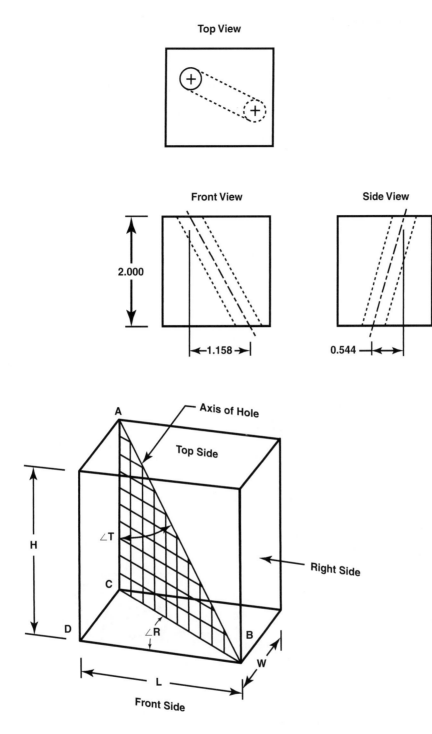

Front View

2.000

←1.158→

Side View

0.544 ←→

A

Axis of Hole

Top Side

∠T

H

C

D

∠R

B

W

L

Front Side

Right Side

12. H = 2.000 inches

L = 1.158 inches

W = 0.544 inches

∠R = _____

∠T = _____

CALCULATING THE ANGLES OF ROTATION AND TILT FOR MACHINING ANGULAR SURFACES

When machining a compound angular surface, the angles at which the part must be rotated (∠R) and tilted (∠T) need to be calculated. *Machining a compound angular surface* refers to removing material in a plane that is neither parallel nor perpendicular to the part. It often means grinding material from three surfaces including the vertex joining those three surfaces.

To aid in visualization, models are included in this section. Make a copy of each, cut on the solid lines, and fold on the dotted lines to create each model. Keep in mind that this unit is limited to single rotation and single-tilt problems.

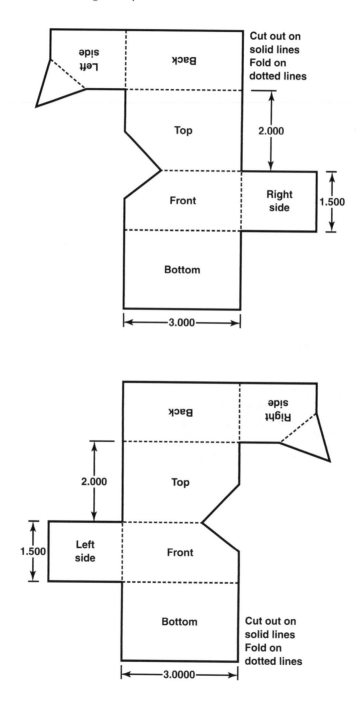

Example

Refer to the drawing below on which machining is required to create surface ABC. Note the two indicated angles: ∠EAC = 36.870° and ∠EBC = 36.870°. The calculations require that DE is projected perpendicular to AB. Also note that no dimensions are given. In this situation, assign a side (common to as many right triangles as possible) to be equal to one unit. We will assign CE = 1 unit.

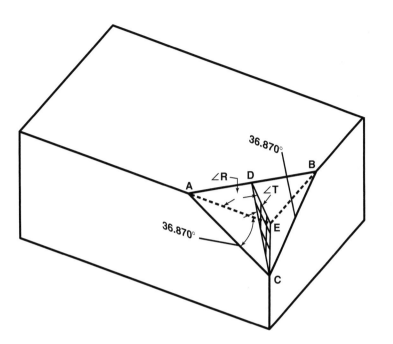

∠R, the angle of rotation, is ∠AED.

∠T, the angle of tilt, is ∠CDE.

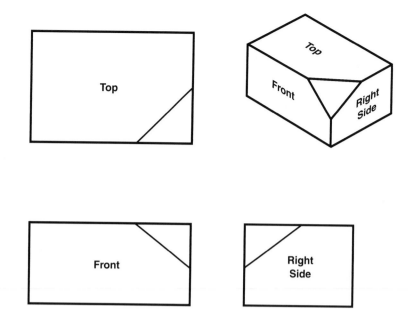

Determine BE

In right triangle BEC, CE = 1, ∠E = 90°, ∠B = 36.870°

BE = adj = opp ÷ tan
 = 1 ÷ 0.75000
 = 1.33333

Determine AE

In right triangle AEC, CE = 1, ∠E = 90°, ∠A = 36.870°

AE = adj = opp ÷ tan
 = 1 ÷ 0.75000
 = 1.33333

Determine ∠A

In right triangle ABE, ∠E = 90°

BE = 1.33333

AE = 1.33333

tan ∠A = opp ÷ adj
 = 1.33333 ÷ 1.33333
 = 1
 ∠A = 45°

Determine ∠R

In right triangle ADE, ∠D = 90°

∠R = 90 − ∠A
    = 45°

Determine DE

In right triangle ADE, ∠A = 45°, AE = 1.33333, ∠D = 90°

DE, opp = hyp × sin
        = 1.33333 × 0.70711
        = 0.94281

Determine ∠T

In right triangle CDE, CE = 1, DE = 0.94281, ∠E = 90°

tan ∠T = opp ÷ adj
        = 1 ÷ 0.94281
        = 1.06066
    ∠T = 46°41′10″

The drawings below depict chamfers in other locations.

Front, left corner

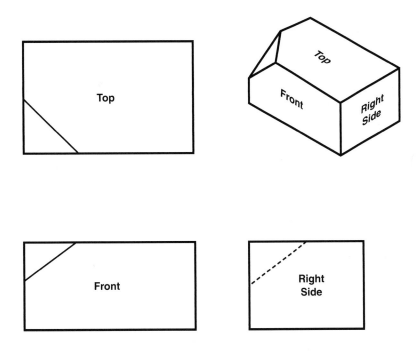

Back, left corner

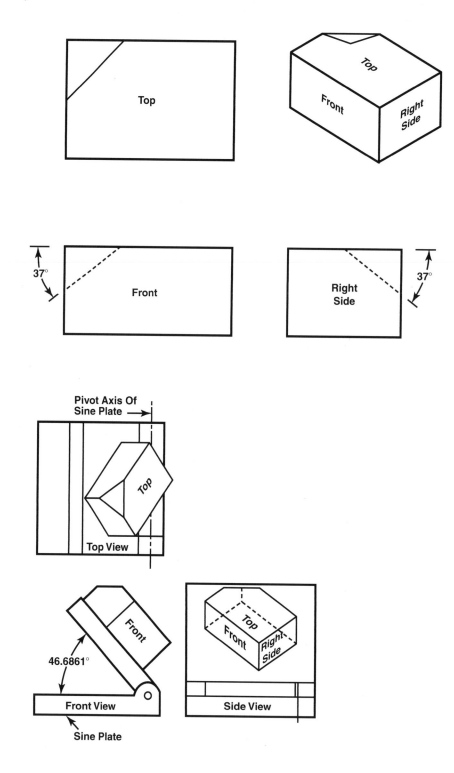

CONCEPT APPLICATIONS

Refer to the set of drawings below to visualize the scenario, then apply the given angles to solve for the angle of rotation (∠R) and the angle of rotation (∠T) from page 239. In each scenario, ∠A is on the front view and ∠B is on the right side view. Assign EC = 1 unit in each case.

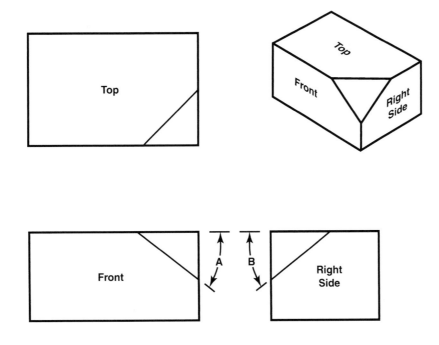

13. ∠EAC = 32°

    ∠EBC = 38°

    ∠R = _____

    ∠T = _____

14. ∠EAC = 30°

    ∠EBC = 40°

    ∠R = _____

    ∠T = _____

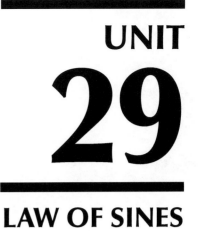

UNIT
29

LAW OF SINES

INTRODUCTION

Not all triangles can be solved as right triangles. In these cases, other laws are applied. This unit presents the law of sines which uses ratios between sides of the nonright (oblique) triangle and the sine of its angles. This law can also be applied to right triangles.

OBJECTIVES

After completing this unit, you will be able to:

• Apply the law of sines to solve oblique triangles for sides and angles.

LAW OF SINES

$$\frac{a}{\sin A} = \frac{b}{\sin B} = \frac{c}{\sin C}$$

One ratio must be known. Either side a and ∠A OR side b and ∠B OR side c and ∠C must be known. It is important to use the sine of the angle, not the number of degrees. Remember to carry all numbers to five decimal places until the problem is completed.

Example 1—Determining a Missing Side

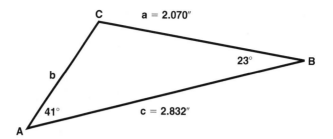

Determine side b.

The law of sines states that

$$\frac{a}{\sin A} = \frac{b}{\sin B} = \frac{c}{\sin C}$$

In this case, $\dfrac{2.070}{\sin 41} = \dfrac{b}{\sin 23}$ OR $\dfrac{2.070}{0.65606} = \dfrac{b}{0.39073}$

After cross-multiplying, we have a new equation: 0.65606 b = 0.80881. Solving for b gives the solution side b = 1.238″, rounding to three decimal places.

Side c wasn't used, however, we could have used side c and ∠C as the ratio since both are known. (∠C = 180 − 41 − 23 = 116°.)

Example 2—Determining a Missing Angle

The law of sines will give the sine of the angle but not the angle itself. As the final step, a chart or calculator must be used to determine the angle

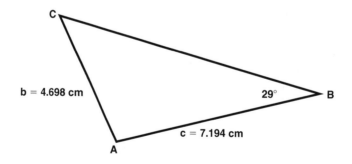

Determine ∠C.

The law of sines states

$$\frac{a}{\sin A} = \frac{b}{\sin B} = \frac{c}{\sin C}$$ In this case, $\dfrac{4.698}{\sin 29} = \dfrac{7.194}{\sin C}$ OR $\dfrac{4.698}{0.48481} = \dfrac{7.194}{\sin C}$

After cross-multiplying, we have a new equation: 4.6898 × sin C = 3.48772. Solving for sin C, we get sin C = 0.74238. Refer to a chart or calculator to determine ∠C = 47°56′6″ to the nearest whole second.

Example 3—Limitations Using the Law of Sines

Using a calculator, determine the sin of 36° and the sin of 144°. How do the sines compare? Using a calculator, find the angle whose sin is 0.587785252. Does the calculator tell you the angle is 36° or 144°? Since both answers would be correct, the programmers of calculators had to make a choice, and their choice was to program calculators to return an acute angle. Hence, calculators always return the acute angle with the same trigonometric function. Try the experiment again with 20° and 160°. Do you find the same results? Predict another pair of angles for which this is true. (It is true for all pairs of supplementary angles?)

This obviously creates a problem when using the law of sines to determine an angle greater than 90°.

Look back at Example 1. $\angle C = 116°$. If we try to apply the law of sines to determine this angle, the calculator would give us 64°.

$$\frac{a}{\sin A} = \frac{b}{\sin B} = \frac{c}{\sin C} \quad \text{In this case,} \quad \frac{2.070}{\sin 41} = \frac{2.832}{\sin C} \quad \text{OR} \quad \frac{2.070}{0.65606} = \frac{2.832}{\sin C}$$

After cross-multiplying, we have a new equation: $2.07 \times \sin C = 1.85796$. Solving for the sin C gives us sin C = 0.89756, and the calculator returns 63.8° (due to rounding). The three angles of the triangle do NOT add to 180°, and all triangles have 180°. The only way to avoid this error is to NEVER use the law of sines to determine the largest angle of a triangle. Remember that the largest angle will be directly across from the longest side of the triangle.

The law of sines has no limitations if the angle is known and is equal to or greater than 90°. The only limitation is determining an angle greater than 90°.

I WONDER . . .

Can the law of sines be used with right triangles?
The answer is "yes." See the next example.

Example 4—Using the Law of Sines With Right Triangles

Experiment using the law of sines with a right triangle.

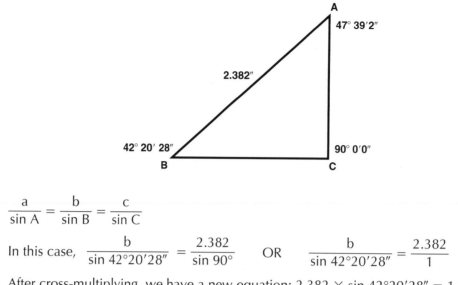

$$\frac{a}{\sin A} = \frac{b}{\sin B} = \frac{c}{\sin C}$$

In this case, $\dfrac{b}{\sin 42°20'28''} = \dfrac{2.382}{\sin 90°}$ OR $\dfrac{b}{\sin 42°20'28''} = \dfrac{2.382}{1}$

After cross-multiplying, we have a new equation: 2.382 × sin 42°20'28'' = 1 × b, which is identical to the equation used to solve this right triangle problem: hyp × sin = opp.

CONCEPT APPLICATIONS

Determine each of the following, rounding final lengths to three decimal places and angles to the nearest whole second.

1. x = _____

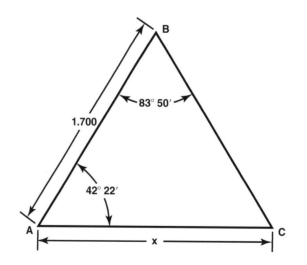

2. x = _____ mm

3. x = _____ cm

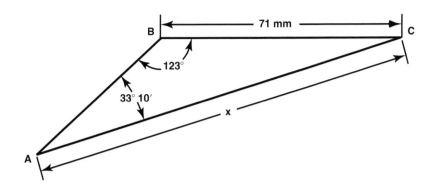

4. ∠x = _____ (Use arithmetic.)

5. x = _____

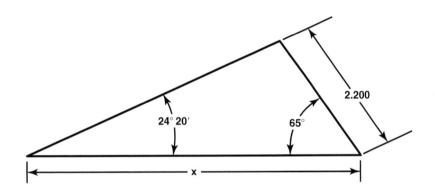

6. x = _____

7. z = _____

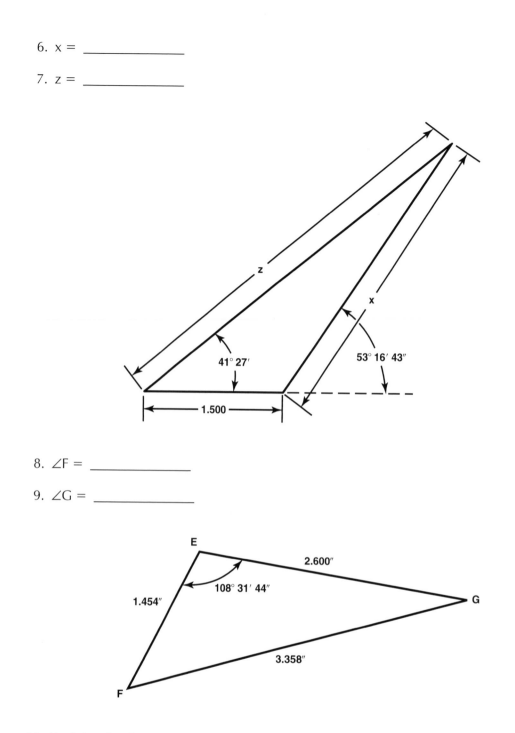

41° 27′

53° 16′ 43″

z

x

1.500

8. ∠F = _____

9. ∠G = _____

E

108° 31′ 44″

2.600″

1.454″

G

3.358″

F

10. Explain what limitations the law of sines would pose in determining ∠E in the drawing above.

UNIT

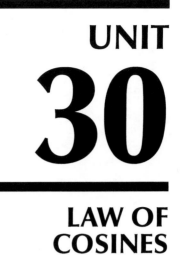

30

LAW OF COSINES

INTRODUCTION

The law of cosines is another special formula used to solve triangles that cannot be solved as right triangles or using the law of sines.

OBJECTIVES

After completing this unit, you will be able to:

• Apply the law of cosines to solve oblique triangles for sides and angles.

There are two parts to the law of cosines. One part is used to determine a missing angle, and the second part is used to determine a missing side. Remember to carry all numbers to five decimal places until the problem is completed. Also, side a is always directly across from ∠A, side b is across from ∠B, and so on.

To determine a missing side, use one of the following formulas. Study the formulas to understand the pattern of sides and angles. These formulas **require two known sides and the third angle.** Keep in mind that the result of these formulas is not the length of a side, but the length of a side squared.

SOLVING FOR SIDES

$a^2 = b^2 + c^2 - 2bc \times \cos A$	Requires sides b and c and ∠A
$b^2 = a^2 + c^2 - 2ac \times \cos B$	Requires sides a and c and ∠B
$c^2 = a^2 + b^2 - 2ab \times \cos C$	Requires sides a and b and ∠C

To determine a missing angle, use one of the following. Study the formulas to understand the pattern of sides and angles. These formulas **require three known sides.** Keep in mind that the result of these formulas is not the angle, but the cos of the angle.

SOLVING FOR ANGLES

$\cos A = \dfrac{b^2 + c^2 - a^2}{2bc}$	Requires all three known sides
$\cos B = \dfrac{a^2 + c^2 - b^2}{2ac}$	Requires all three known sides
$\cos C = \dfrac{a^2 + b^2 - c^2}{2ab}$	Requires all three known sides

GENERAL INFORMATION ON USING CALCULATORS

When using a calculator in any of the formulas above, care must be taken to ensure correct sequencing of input. For example, in the first set of formulas, the equal sign MUST NOT be used until the final step. Inserting an equal sign during the multiplication will result in an error. Take a moment now to manually insert an equal sign at the very end of the formulas. Practice with this to be sure you understand the correct sequence of input.

The second set of formulas is more complicated. Because calculators are programmed to perform division before addition or subtraction, the calculator will automatically divide only the last term of the numerator by the denominator unless the input indicates otherwise. Inserting an equal sign at the end of the numerator can do this. Take a moment now to manually insert an equal sign at the end of the numerators in the three formulas. Attention must also be given to the denominator itself. If entered as $2 \times b \times c$ in the first formula, the calculator will divide the numerator by 2, then multiply the result by b, and then multiply again by c. To avoid this error, insert parentheses around the denominator. Take a moment now to manually insert the parentheses in each of the three formulas. Practice doing this to be sure you understand the correct sequence of input.

Another important consideration in using the law of cosines is the fact that angles between 90° and 180° have negative values for cos. This valuable fact means that the law of cosines does not present a problem in determining angles whose measure is greater than 90°. Experiment with this. Refer to the Appendix for a graphical explanation of trigonometric values.

Example 1—Determining a Missing Side

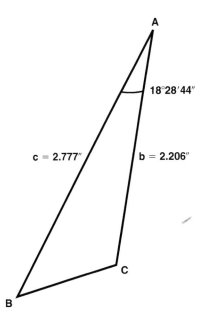

A

18°28′44″

c = 2.777″

b = 2.206″

C

B

Determine side a.

The law of cosines states that $a^2 = b^2 + c^2 - 2bc \times \cos A$. In this case, $a^2 = 2.206^2 + 2.777^2 - 2 \times 2.206 \times 2.777 \times 0.948441 = 0.95775$. Using the square root function, side a = 0.979″, to three decimal places.

If needed, the law of sines can now be used to determine ∠B and arithmetic can then be used to determine ∠C. The law of sines should NOT be used to determine ∠C because it is across from the longest side and may be greater than 90°. Using a = 0.97865 (five decimal places), ∠B = 43°35′55″, ∠C = 117°55′21″.

I WONDER . . .

Can the law of cosines be used to determine both missing angles and the missing side in the previous problem instead of switching to the law of sines?

The answer is "yes," however, many students find the law of sines to be shorter and easier to use.

Example 2—Determining a Missing Angle

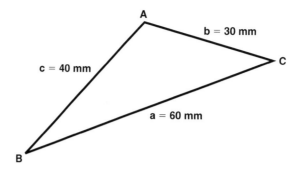

Determine the missing angles.

Strategy: the law of cosines does not present a problem in determining an angle greater than 90°, and the angle that MAY be greater than 90° is ∠A (across from the longest side), so we begin with it. This will eliminate possible errors in using the law of sines later in the problem.

The law of cosines states $\cos A = \dfrac{b^2 + c^2 - a^2}{2bc}$. In this case, $\cos A = \dfrac{30^2 + 40^2 - 60^2}{(2 \times 30 \times 40)} =$

The cos A = −0.45833 which indicates ∠A is greater than 90°. ∠A = 117°16′46″.

If needed, the law of sines can be now used to determine the second angle. Arithmetic can then be used to determine the third angle. ∠B = 26°23′4″, ∠C = 36°20′10″.

I WONDER . . .

Can the law of cosines be used to determine the second and third angles in the previous problem instead of switching to the law of sines?

The answer is "yes," however, many students find the law of sines to be shorter and easier to use.

CONCEPT APPLICATIONS

Determine each of the following, rounding final lengths to three decimal places and angles to the nearest whole second.

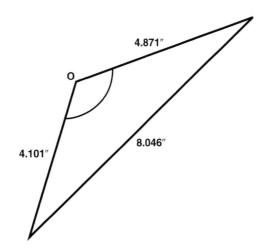

1. ∠O = _____

In the drawing below,

2. side x = _____

3. ∠B = _____

4. Which law or laws can be used to determine side x? _____

5. Which law or laws can then be used to determine ∠B? _____

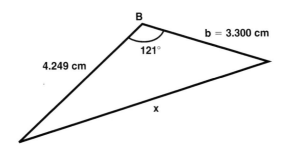

6. ∠O = _____ °

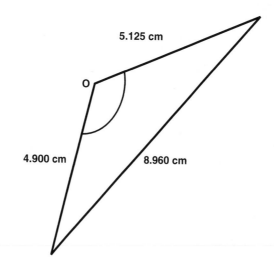

5.125 cm

O

4.900 cm   8.960 cm

In the drawing below,

7. side a = _____

8. ∠B = _____

9. Is there a potential problem using the law of sines to determine ∠B? _____

10. ∠C = _____

- -

NOTE: *This can also be solved with right triangle trigonometry. It would require several steps, but can be a means of verifying your work.*

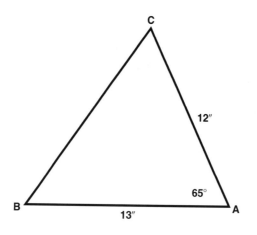

C

12″

65°

B

13″   A

APPENDIX

APPENDIX A

AREA AND VOLUME FORMULAS

Rectangle	Area = Length × Width
Triangle	Area = $\dfrac{\text{Base} \times \text{Height}}{2}$
Circle	Area = $\pi \times \text{radius}^2$
Trapezoid	Area = $\dfrac{\text{Base} + \text{base}}{2} \times \text{Height}$
Parellelogram	Area = Base × Height
Rectangular Solid	Volume = Length × Width × Height
Cylinder	Volume = $\pi \times \text{radius}^2 \times \text{Height}$

APPENDIX B

ANGLES AND LINES

LINES

Parallel lines never intersect
Perpendicular lines intersect at 90° angles (right angles).
Oblique lines intersect at angles other than 90°.
A straight line has 180° on either side.
If 2 or more lines are perpendicular to the same line, they are parallel.
If one of 2 parallel lines is perpendicular to the third line, the other parallel line is also perpendicular to the third line.

PLANES

Parallel planes never intersect.
Perpendicular planes intersect in a straight line and form 90° angles (right angles).
The position of a plane can be established by 1) 3 points or 2) a line and one point 3) two lines.

ANGLES

Angles are named by 3 capital letters, a single capital letter, a single small letter, or a number.
Vertical angles are equal.
Alternate interior angles on parallel lines are equal.
Alternate exterior angles on parallel lines are equal.
Corresponding angles on parallel lines are equal.
If 2 angles have their corresponding sides parallel, the angles are equal.
If 2 angles have their corresponding sides perpendicular, the angles are equal.
There are 60 seconds in one minute and 60 minutes in one degree and 360 degrees in one circle.

CLASSIFICATION OF ANGLES BY MEASURE

Acute angles have measures less than 90°.
Right angles have a measure of exactly 90°.
Obtuse angles have measures between 90° and 180°.
Straight angles have a measure of exactly 180°. (Straight lines have exactly 180° on each side.)
Reflex angles have measures between 180° and 360°.
A **revolution** or **circle** measures exactly 360°.

CLASSIFICATION OF ANGLES BY SUM

Complementary angles are two angles whose *sum* is exactly 90°.
Supplementary angles are two angles whose *sum* is exactly 180°.

APPENDIX C

TRIANGLES

A **RIGHT TRIANGLE** is a triangle containing one 90° right angle.

An **ISOSCELES TRIANGLE** is a triangle with at least one pair of equal sides.
1) Angles opposite the equal sides are equal.
2) The altitude divides the triangle into 2 congruent right triangles.

An **EQUILATERAL TRIANGLE** has 3 equal sides.
1) The 3 angles each have a measure of 60°.
2) The altitudes each divide the triangle into 2 congruent right triangles.

A **SCALENE TRIANGLE** has no equal sides or angles.

Triangles are **SIMILAR TRIANGLES** if corresponding lengths of sides are proportional or if corresponding angles are equal.

If the lengths of sides are proportional, then the corresponding angles are equal.

If the corresponding angles are equal, the sides are proportional.

Two triangles are **CONGRUENT TRIANGLES** if they are identical.

APPENDIX D

FORMULAS FOR FINDING FUNCTIONS OF ANGLES

$$\textbf{Sine} = \frac{\text{Side opposite}}{\text{Hypotenuse}}$$

$$\textbf{Cosine} = \frac{\text{Side adjacent}}{\text{Hypotenuse}}$$

$$\textbf{Tangent} = \frac{\text{Side opposite}}{\text{Side adjacent}}$$

$$\textbf{Cotangent} = \frac{\text{Side adjacent}}{\text{Side opposite}}$$

$$\textbf{Secant} = \frac{\text{Hypotenuse}}{\text{Side adjacent}}$$

$$\textbf{Cosecant} = \frac{\text{Hypotenuse}}{\text{Side opposite}}$$

FORMULAS FOR FINDING THE LENGTH OF SIDES OF RIGHT TRIANGLES WHEN AN ANGLE AND SIDE ARE KNOWN

Length of side opposite
$\begin{cases} \text{Hypotenuse} \times \text{Sine} \\ \text{Hypotenuse} \div \text{Cosecant} \\ \text{Side adjacent} \times \text{Tangent} \\ \text{Side adjacent} \div \text{Cotangent} \end{cases}$

Length of side adjacent
$\begin{cases} \text{Hypotenuse} \times \text{Cosine} \\ \text{Hypotenuse} \div \text{Secant} \\ \text{Side opposite} \times \text{Cotangent} \\ \text{Side opposite} \div \text{Tangent} \end{cases}$

Length of Hypotenuse
$\begin{cases} \text{Side opposite} \times \text{Cosecant} \\ \text{Side opposite} \div \text{Sine} \\ \text{Side adjacent} \times \text{Secant} \\ \text{Side adjacent} \div \text{Cosine} \end{cases}$

APPENDIX E

CENTER-TO-CENTER DISTANCE ON BOLT CIRCLES

Spaces on the Circle	Angle at Center of Circle	Length of Chord*
3	120°0'	0.866025
4	90°0'	0.707106
5	72°0'	0.587785
6	60°0'	0.500000
7	51°26'	0.433883
8	45°0'	0.382683
9	40°0'	0.342020
10	36°0'	0.309017
11	32°44'	0.281732
12	30°0'	0.258819
13	27°41'	0.239315
14	25°43'	0.222520
15	24°0'	0.207911
16	22°30'	0.195090
17	21°11'	0.183749
18	20°0'	0.173648
19	18°57'	0.164594
20	18°0'	0.156434

* Multiply the circle's diameter times this number to determine the length of each center-to-center chord.

APPENDIX F

COMPOUND ANGLES—RECTANGULAR SOLID 1

When $\angle$, $\angle$J and $\angle$K, or when $\angle$D, $\angle$R and $\angle$S form the compound angles, then $\angle$G is the true angle of either compound angle with reference to line e. (See drawing on next page.)

$\angle$K and $\angle$R represents the angles that are to be calculated and are 90° to each other.

The equations in this chart are of use in calculating the positions and dimensions of holes that are drilled, and of objects that are set up to compound angles.

Angles are capitalized and sides are in lower case letters.

Unknown Side or Angle	Equation
dimension a	h × tan D × sin K
dimension b	e × cos D × tan G
dimension c	e × sec D × tan K
tan D	tan J × csc K
tan D	sin J × csc S
sin D	tan R × cot G
dimension e	h × cos G × sec J
dimension f	e × sec J × sec K
tan G	csc D × tan R
sin G	sec D × sin S
cos G	cos K × cos J
dimension h	a × csc K × cot D
tan J	tan R × cos K
sin J	sin D × sin G
cos J	sec K × cos G
tan K	cot D × tan R
sin K	sin S × sec J
cos K	cos G × sec J
tan R	sin D × tan G
sin R	sin J × sec S
cos R	cos G × sec S
tan S	tan K × cos R
sin S	cos D × sin G
cos S	sec R × cos G

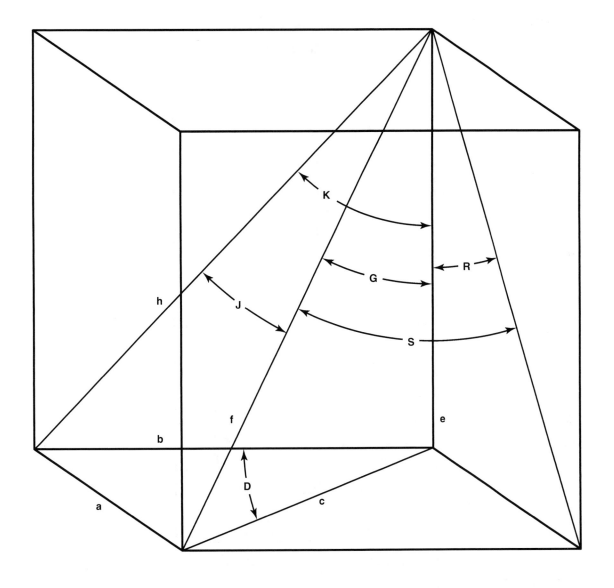

COMPOUND ANGLES—RECTANGULAR SOLID 2

When ∠B, ∠C and ∠E form the compound angles, then ∠A is the true angle of the compound angle with reference to line j. (See drawing on next page.)

When ∠A, ∠B and ∠E form the compound angles, then ∠C is the true angle of the compound angle with reference to line g.

The equations in this chart are of use in calculating the angles between reference lines.

Angles are capitalized and sides are in lower case letters.

Unknown Side or Angle	Equation
tan A	tan E × sin B
sin A	sin E × sin C
cos A	sec B × cos C
sec A	sec C × cos B
tan B	cos E × tan C
sin B	cot E × tan A
cos B	cos C × sec A
sec B	cos A × sec C
tan C	sec E × tan B
sin C	csc E × sin A
cos C	cos B × cos A
sec C	sec A × sec B
d	h × sin E × sin C
tan E	tan A × csc B
sin E	sin A × csc B
cos E	tan B × cot C
sec E	tan C × cot B
f	h × csc E × sin A
g	k × cot C × sec E
h	g × sec A × sec B
h	d × csc C × csc E
j	k × cot A × tan E
j	g × cos A × sec C
k	d × sin B × cot A

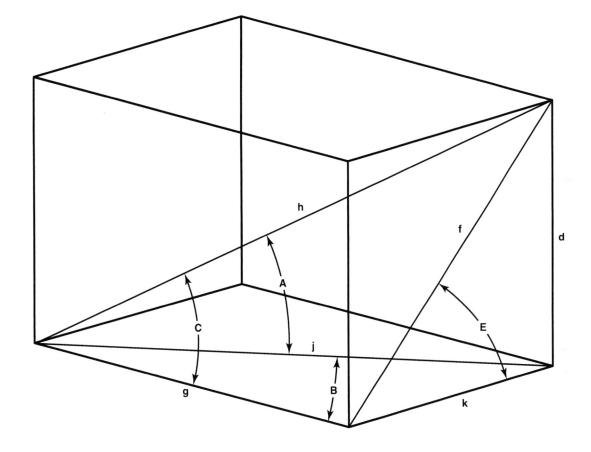

GLOSSARY

ABSOLUTE VALUE — The whole number value of a signed number. The distance a number is located from zero on a number line without regard for its direction from zero. (8)

ACUTE ANGLES — Angles that measure less than 90°. (14)

ALLOWABLE TOLERANCE — The range of acceptable variance in a measurement. (6)

ALTERNATE ANGLES — The pairs of equal angles formed on opposite sides of a line (referred to as the *transversal*), when that line intersects two parallel lines. (14)

ANGLE — Formed by two intersecting lines or by two intersecting rays, their common point and all interior points. (14)

ARC — A curved segment; a segment of a circle. (17)

BASIC DIMENSION — A number used to identify the exact measure or the desired measure between two specific points. (6)

BILATERAL TOLERANCE — The amount that is added to *and* subtracted from a basic dimension to establish maximum and minimum limits. (6)

CANCELLING — The process of dividing common factors to simplify a fraction to lower terms. Also, the process of simplifying a group of fractions in a multiplication operation. (3)

CENTRAL ANGLES — Angles formed between line segments that extend from the vertex of a polygon to the point of intersection of the adjoining sides of the polygon. The angle formed by two radii in a circle. (16, 17)

CHORD — A line segment connecting any two points on a circle. (17)

NOTE:

Numbers in parentheses (   ) following the definition refer to the unit where a further explanation of the subject can be found.

CIRCLE — The set of all points in a plane that are equal distance from a fixed point (called the origin or center). (14, 17)

CIRCUMFERENCE — The distance around a circle. (17)

COMMON FRACTION — A fraction expressed in the form "n/d", where n is the numerator and d is the denominator. (2)

COMPOUND ANGLES — Angles used in solid geometry and three-dimensional trigonometry that are located in more than one plane. (28)

CORRESPONDING ANGLES — The pairs of equal angles formed on the same side of a line (referred to as the *transversal*), when that line intersects two parallel lines. (14)

COSECANT — The ratio between the length of the hypotenuse and the length of the side opposite an angle in a right triangle. (20)

COSINE — The ratio between the length of the side adjacent an angle and the length of the hypotenuse in a right triangle. (20)

COTANGENT — The ratio between the length of the side adjacent an angle and the length of the side opposite the same angle. (20)

CROSS MULTIPLICATION — The process used 1) on fractions to test for equality and 2) to solve equations with fractions. (13)

DECIMAL SYSTEM — A set of numbers taken from the general set of fractions whose denominator is a multiple of 10, such as 10, 100, 1000, etc. (4)

DENOMINATOR — The bottom number in a fraction that represents the total number of equal parts in one whole unit. (2)

DIAMETER — A chord, or measure of a chord, that joins two points on a circle and passes through the origin (center). (17)

DIRECT PROPORTION — A ratio representing a situation where *both* quantities are increasing or *both* quantities are decreasing. (13)

DIVIDEND — The number in a division operation that is divided. (5)

DIVISOR — The number in a division operation by which a dividend is divided. (5)

EQUAL (EQUIVALENT) FRACTIONS — Two or more fractions of equal value. (2)

EQUILATERAL TRIANGLE — A triangle with three equal-length sides. (15)

EXPONENT — The number that indicates how many times a given number is multiplied by itself. (9)

FACTOR — A number that is multiplied by another number. (9)

FRACTION — A number representing a quantity of equal parts taken from a whole unit. (2)

HYPOTENUSE — The longest side of a right triangle, which is also the side opposite the right angle in a right triangle. (9)

IMPROPER FRACTION — A common fraction that has a value greater than one whole unit. (2)

INDIRECT PROPORTION — A ratio representing a situation where one quantity is increasing and the other is decreasing. (13)

INSCRIBED ANGLE — The angle formed by two chords that join at a single point on a circle. (17)

IRREGULAR POLYGON — A polygon with unequal sides. (16)

ISOSCELES TRIANGLE — A triangle with one pair of equal length sides. (15)

LEG — A side of a right triangle that forms the right angle. There are two legs in each right triangle. (9)

LIKE FRACTIONS — Fractions that have the same denominator. (3)

LIKE TERMS — Two or more terms having identical variables and exponents. (12)

LINE — A straight path passing through two established points that continues indefinitely in opposite directions. (14)S

LOWEST TERMS — A fraction with no common factor remaining in the numerator and denominator. Also called *simplest form*. (2)

MAXIMUM CLEARANCE — The largest acceptable space, or gap, between two mating parts. (6)

MAXIMUM DIMENSION — The largest acceptable measure of a dimension. (6)

MAXIMUM INTERFERENCE — The largest acceptable overlap between two mating parts. (6)

MEAN DIMENSION — The dimension that is exactly halfway between the minimum and maximum dimensions. (6)

MEASURE — A number used to indicate length, distance, or comparative size. (6)

MINIMUM CLEARANCE — The smallest acceptable space, or gap, between two mating parts. (6)

MINIMUM DIMENSION — The smallest acceptable measure of a dimension. (6)

MINIMUM INTERFERENCE — The smallest acceptable overlap between two mating parts. (6)

MIXED NUMBER — A number consisting of a whole number and a fraction. (2)

NUMBER LINE — A graphic representation of the set of all real numbers used to relate the value of any number to zero.

NUMERATOR — The top number in a fraction that represents a number of equal parts of one whole unit. (2)

OBLIQUE LINES — Lines that intersect at angles other than 90°. (14)

OBTUSE ANGLE — Angles that measure between 90° and 180°. (14)

OPPOSITE ANGLES — The two pairs of equal angles formed by intersecting lines. (14)

PARALLEL — The property of two or more lines (or planes) extending in the same direction, which never meet or intersect. (14)

PARALLELOGRAM — A quadrilateral with opposite sides of equal length that are parallel to each other. (16)

PERCENT — A method of relating a number of parts of a whole unit as parts per hundred. (7)

PERPENDICULAR — The property of two or more lines (or planes) that meet to form right angles. (14)

PI (π) — The ratio of the circumference of a circle to its diameter. (17)

PLANE — An imaginary flat surface extending infinitely in all directions. (14)

POINT — A specific location or position on a line or in a plane. (14)

POLYGON — A closed figure with three or more sides. (16)

POWER — The number of times that a given factor occurs in a product. (9)

PROPER FRACTION — A common fraction that has a value less than one whole unit. (2)

PROPORTION — A comparison between two ratios. (13)

PYTHAGOREAN THEOREM — The sum of the squares of the two legs of a right triangle is equal to the square of the hypotenuse. Commonly stated as $a^2 + b^2 = c^2$. (9, 18)

QUADRILATERAL — A four-sided polygon. (16)

QUOTIENT — The result of a division operation. (5)

RADIUS — A segment that extends from any point on a circle to the circle's origin. (17)

RATIO — A comparison between two quantities. (13)

RECIPROCAL — The result of switching the numerator and denominator in a common fraction. Also referred to as the *inverse*. (3)

RECTANGLE — A quadrilateral with opposite sides of equal length and four 90° angles. (16)

REGULAR POLYGON — A polygon with equal sides. (16)

RIGHT ANGLE — An angle that measures exactly 90 degrees. (14)

RIGHT TRIANGLE — A triangle that contains one right angle. (9, 15, 22)

ROOT — The number of times that a factor equally divides itself into a number. (9)

ROUNDING — The process of reducing the degree of accuracy to a stated level. (4)

SCALENE TRIANGLE — A triangle with three unequal sides. (15)

SECANT — A line that intersects a circle at exactly two points. In trigonometry, the ratio between the length of the hypotenuse and the length of the side adjacent an angle in a right triangle. (17, 20)

SECTOR — In a circle, the region bounded by two radii and the arc defined by their endpoints. (17)

SEGMENT — The set of any two points on a line and all of the points between them. In a circle, the region bounded by a chord and the arc defined by its endpoints. (17)

SHOP FRACTIONS — The set of proper fractions most commonly used in the shop. (2)

SINE — The ratio between the length of the side opposite an angle and the length of the hypotenuse in a right triangle. (20)

SQUARE — The product of a number multiplied by itself. Also, a quadrilateral with four equal sides and four 90° angles. (16)

SQUARE ROOT — One of the two equal factors of a number. (9)

STEEL SCALE — The basic measuring instrument used to check dimensions expressed as common fractions. (2)

TANGENT — A line that intersects a circle at only one point. In trigonometry, the ratio between the length of the side opposite an angle and the length of the side adjacent to the same angle. (17, 20)

TOLERANCE — The acceptable range of a measurement. (6)

TOTAL TOLERANCE — The range of acceptable variance in a measurement. (6)

TRIANGLE — A three-sided polygon. (15)

TRIGONOMETRY — Triangle measurement based on the relationship between the angles and the ratios of the sides. It means "three" and "measure." (20)

UNILATERAL TOLERANCE — An amount that is *either* added to *or* subtracted from a basic dimension, but not both. (6)

UNIT FRACTION — A common fraction with a numerator of "1". (2)

UNLIKE FRACTIONS — Two or more fractions with different, or *unlike*, denominators. (3)

VERTEX — The point of intersection of two non-parallel lines. (14)

VERTEX ANGLES — Angles formed by adjoining sides of a polygon. (16)

VERTICAL OR OPPOSITE ANGLES — The two pairs of equal angles formed by intersecting lines. (14)

WHOLE NUMBER — An expression of complete units without a fractional portion. (2)

TABLES OF NATURAL TRIGONOMETRIC FUNCTIONS, SQUARES, AND SQUARE ROOTS

TABLES OF NATURAL TRIGONOMETRIC FUNCTIONS

0°→ ↓	sin	csc	tan	cot	sec	cos ←179° ↓	
0	0.00000	∞	0.00000	∞	1.00000	1.00000	60
1	0.00029	3437.75	0.00029	3437.75	1.00000	1.00000	59
2	0.00058	1718.87	0.00058	1718.87	1.00000	1.00000	58
3	0.00087	1145.92	0.00087	1145.92	1.00000	1.00000	57
4	0.00116	859.437	0.00116	859.436	1.00000	1.00000	56
5	0.00145	687.550	0.00145	687.549	1.00000	1.00000	55
6	0.00175	572.958	0.00175	572.957	1.00000	1.00000	54
7	0.00204	491.107	0.00204	491.106	1.00000	1.00000	53
8	0.00233	429.719	0.00233	429.718	1.00000	1.00000	52
9	0.00262	381.972	0.00262	381.971	1.00000	1.00000	51
10	0.00291	343.775	0.00291	343.774	1.00000	1.00000	50
11	0.00320	312.523	0.00320	312.521	1.00001	0.99999	49
12	0.00349	286.479	0.00349	286.478	1.00001	0.99999	48
13	0.00378	264.443	0.00378	264.441	1.00001	0.99999	47
14	0.00407	245.554	0.00407	245.552	1.00001	0.99999	46
15	0.00436	229.184	0.00436	229.182	1.00001	0.99999	45
16	0.00465	214.860	0.00465	214.858	1.00001	0.99999	44
17	0.00495	202.221	0.00495	202.219	1.00001	0.99999	43
18	0.00524	190.987	0.00524	190.984	1.00001	0.99999	42
19	0.00553	180.935	0.00553	180.932	1.00002	0.99998	41
20	0.00582	171.888	0.00582	171.885	1.00002	0.99998	40
21	0.00611	163.703	0.00611	163.700	1.00002	0.99998	39
22	0.00640	156.262	0.00640	156.259	1.00002	0.99998	38
23	0.00669	149.468	0.00669	149.465	1.00002	0.99998	37
24	0.00698	143.241	0.00698	143.237	1.00002	0.99998	36
25	0.00727	137.511	0.00727	137.507	1.00003	0.99997	35
26	0.00756	132.222	0.00756	132.219	1.00003	0.99997	34
27	0.00785	127.325	0.00785	127.321	1.00003	0.99997	33
28	0.00814	122.778	0.00815	122.774	1.00003	0.99997	32
29	0.00844	118.544	0.00844	118.540	1.00004	0.99996	31
30	0.00873	114.593	0.00873	114.589	1.00004	0.99996	30
31	0.00902	110.897	0.00902	110.892	1.00004	0.99996	29
32	0.00931	107.431	0.00931	107.426	1.00004	0.99996	28
33	0.00960	104.176	0.00960	104.171	1.00005	0.99995	27
34	0.00989	101.112	0.00989	101.107	1.00005	0.99995	26
35	0.01018	98.2230	0.01018	98.2179	1.00005	0.99995	25
36	0.01047	95.4947	0.01047	95.4895	1.00005	0.99995	24
37	0.01076	92.9139	0.01076	92.9085	1.00006	0.99994	23
38	0.01105	90.4689	0.01105	90.4633	1.00006	0.99994	22
39	0.01134	88.1492	0.01135	88.1436	1.00006	0.99994	21
40	0.01164	85.9456	0.01164	85.9398	1.00007	0.99993	20
41	0.01193	83.8495	0.01193	83.8435	1.00007	0.99993	19
42	0.01222	81.8531	0.01222	81.8470	1.00007	0.99993	18
43	0.01251	79.9497	0.01251	79.9434	1.00008	0.99992	17
44	0.01280	78.1327	0.01280	78.1263	1.00008	0.99992	16
45	0.01309	76.3966	0.01309	76.3900	1.00009	0.99991	15
46	0.01338	74.7359	0.01338	74.7292	1.00009	0.99991	14
47	0.01367	73.1458	0.01367	73.1390	1.00009	0.99991	13
48	0.01396	71.6221	0.01396	71.6151	1.00010	0.99990	12
49	0.01425	70.1605	0.01425	70.1533	1.00010	0.99990	11
50	0.01454	68.7574	0.01455	68.7501	1.00011	0.99989	10
51	0.01483	67.4093	0.01484	67.4019	1.00011	0.99989	9
52	0.01513	66.1130	0.01513	66.1055	1.00011	0.99989	8
53	0.01542	64.8657	0.01542	64.8580	1.00012	0.99988	7
54	0.01571	63.6646	0.01571	63.6567	1.00012	0.99988	6
55	0.01600	62.5072	0.01600	62.4992	1.00013	0.99987	5
56	0.01629	61.3911	0.01629	61.3829	1.00013	0.99987	4
57	0.01658	60.3141	0.01658	60.3058	1.00014	0.99986	3
58	0.01687	59.2743	0.01687	59.2659	1.00014	0.99986	2
59	0.01716	58.2698	0.01716	58.2612	1.00015	0.99985	1
60	0.01745	57.2987	0.01746	57.2900	1.00015	0.99985	0
90°→ ↑ cos	sec	cot	tan	csc	sin ←89° ↑		

1°→ ↓	sin	csc	tan	cot	sec	cos ←178° ↓	
0	0.01745	57.2987	0.01746	57.2900	1.00015	0.99985	60
1	0.01774	56.3595	0.01775	56.3506	1.00016	0.99984	59
2	0.01803	55.4505	0.01804	55.4415	1.00016	0.99984	58
3	0.01832	54.5705	0.01833	54.5613	1.00017	0.99983	57
4	0.01862	53.7179	0.01862	53.7086	1.00017	0.99983	56
5	0.01891	52.8916	0.01891	52.8821	1.00018	0.99982	55
6	0.01920	52.0903	0.01920	52.0807	1.00018	0.99982	54
7	0.01949	51.3129	0.01949	51.3032	1.00019	0.99981	53
8	0.01978	50.5584	0.01978	50.5485	1.00020	0.99980	52
9	0.02007	49.8258	0.02007	49.8157	1.00020	0.99980	51
10	0.02036	49.1141	0.02036	49.1039	1.00021	0.99979	50
11	0.02065	48.4224	0.02066	48.4121	1.00021	0.99979	49
12	0.02094	47.7500	0.02095	47.7395	1.00022	0.99978	48
13	0.02123	47.0960	0.02124	47.0853	1.00023	0.99977	47
14	0.02152	46.4596	0.02153	46.4489	1.00023	0.99977	46
15	0.02181	45.8403	0.02182	45.8294	1.00024	0.99976	45
16	0.02211	45.2372	0.02211	45.2261	1.00024	0.99976	44
17	0.02240	44.6498	0.02240	44.6386	1.00025	0.99975	43
18	0.02269	44.0775	0.02269	44.0661	1.00026	0.99974	42
19	0.02298	43.5196	0.02298	43.5081	1.00026	0.99974	41
20	0.02327	42.9757	0.02328	42.9641	1.00027	0.99973	40
21	0.02356	42.4452	0.02357	42.4335	1.00028	0.99972	39
22	0.02385	41.9277	0.02386	41.9158	1.00028	0.99972	38
23	0.02414	41.4227	0.02415	41.4106	1.00029	0.99971	37
24	0.02443	40.9296	0.02444	40.9174	1.00030	0.99970	36
25	0.02472	40.4482	0.02473	40.4358	1.00031	0.99969	35
26	0.02501	39.9780	0.02502	39.9655	1.00031	0.99969	34
27	0.02530	39.5185	0.02531	39.5059	1.00032	0.99968	33
28	0.02560	39.0696	0.02560	39.0568	1.00033	0.99967	32
29	0.02589	38.6307	0.02589	38.6177	1.00034	0.99966	31
30	0.02618	38.2016	0.02619	38.1885	1.00034	0.99966	30
31	0.02647	37.7818	0.02648	37.7686	1.00035	0.99965	29
32	0.02676	37.3713	0.02677	37.3579	1.00036	0.99964	28
33	0.02705	36.9695	0.02706	36.9560	1.00037	0.99963	27
34	0.02734	36.5763	0.02735	36.5627	1.00037	0.99963	26
35	0.02763	36.1914	0.02764	36.1776	1.00038	0.99962	25
36	0.02792	35.8145	0.02793	35.8006	1.00039	0.99961	24
37	0.02821	35.4454	0.02822	35.4313	1.00040	0.99960	23
38	0.02850	35.0838	0.02851	35.0695	1.00041	0.99959	22
39	0.02879	34.7295	0.02881	34.7151	1.00041	0.99959	21
40	0.02908	34.3823	0.02910	34.3678	1.00042	0.99958	20
41	0.02938	34.0420	0.02939	34.0273	1.00043	0.99957	19
42	0.02967	33.7083	0.02968	33.6935	1.00044	0.99956	18
43	0.02996	33.3812	0.02997	33.3662	1.00045	0.99955	17
44	0.03025	33.0603	0.03026	33.0452	1.00046	0.99954	16
45	0.03054	32.7455	0.03055	32.7303	1.00047	0.99953	15
46	0.03083	32.4367	0.03084	32.4213	1.00048	0.99952	14
47	0.03112	32.1337	0.03114	32.1181	1.00048	0.99952	13
48	0.03141	31.8362	0.03143	31.8205	1.00049	0.99951	12
49	0.03170	31.5442	0.03172	31.5284	1.00050	0.99950	11
50	0.03199	31.2576	0.03201	31.2416	1.00051	0.99949	10
51	0.03228	30.9761	0.03230	30.9599	1.00052	0.99948	9
52	0.03257	30.6996	0.03259	30.6833	1.00053	0.99947	8
53	0.03286	30.4280	0.03288	30.4116	1.00054	0.99946	7
54	0.03316	30.1612	0.03317	30.1446	1.00055	0.99945	6
55	0.03345	29.8990	0.03346	29.8823	1.00056	0.99944	5
56	0.03374	29.6414	0.03376	29.6245	1.00057	0.99943	4
57	0.03403	29.3881	0.03405	29.3711	1.00058	0.99942	3
58	0.03432	29.1392	0.03434	29.1220	1.00059	0.99941	2
59	0.03461	28.8944	0.03463	28.8771	1.00060	0.99940	1
60	0.03490	28.6537	0.03492	28.6363	1.00061	0.99939	0
91°→ ↑ cos	sec	cot	tan	csc	sin ←88° ↑		

2° →	sin	csc	tan	cot	sec	← 177° cos	
0	0.03490	28.6537	0.03492	28.6363	1.00061	0.99939	60
1	0.03519	28.4170	0.03521	28.3994	1.00062	0.99938	59
2	0.03548	28.1842	0.03550	28.1664	1.00063	0.99937	58
3	0.03577	27.9551	0.03579	27.9372	1.00064	0.99936	57
4	0.03606	27.7298	0.03609	27.7117	1.00065	0.99935	56
5	0.03635	27.5080	0.03638	27.4899	1.00066	0.99934	55
6	0.03664	27.2898	0.03667	27.2715	1.00067	0.99933	54
7	0.03693	27.0750	0.03696	27.0566	1.00068	0.99932	53
8	0.03723	26.8636	0.03725	26.8450	1.00069	0.99931	52
9	0.03752	26.6555	0.03754	26.6367	1.00070	0.99930	51
10	0.03781	26.4505	0.03783	26.4316	1.00072	0.99929	50
11	0.03810	26.2487	0.03812	26.2296	1.00073	0.99927	49
12	0.03839	26.0499	0.03842	26.0307	1.00074	0.99926	48
13	0.03868	25.8542	0.03871	25.8348	1.00075	0.99925	47
14	0.03897	25.6613	0.03900	25.6418	1.00076	0.99924	46
15	0.03926	25.4713	0.03929	25.4517	1.00077	0.99923	45
16	0.03955	25.2841	0.03958	25.2644	1.00078	0.99922	44
17	0.03984	25.0997	0.03987	25.0798	1.00079	0.99921	43
18	0.04013	24.9179	0.04016	24.8978	1.00081	0.99919	42
19	0.04042	24.7387	0.04046	24.7185	1.00082	0.99918	41
20	0.04071	24.5621	0.04075	24.5418	1.00083	0.99917	40
21	0.04100	24.3880	0.04104	24.3675	1.00084	0.99916	39
22	0.04129	24.2164	0.04133	24.1957	1.00085	0.99915	38
23	0.04159	24.0471	0.04162	24.0263	1.00087	0.99913	37
24	0.04188	23.8802	0.04191	23.8593	1.00088	0.99912	36
25	0.04217	23.7156	0.04220	23.6945	1.00089	0.99911	35
26	0.04246	23.5533	0.04250	23.5321	1.00090	0.99910	34
27	0.04275	23.3932	0.04279	23.3718	1.00091	0.99909	33
28	0.04304	23.2352	0.04308	23.2137	1.00093	0.99907	32
29	0.04333	23.0794	0.04337	23.0577	1.00094	0.99906	31
30	0.04362	22.9256	0.04366	22.9038	1.00095	0.99905	30
31	0.04391	22.7739	0.04395	22.7519	1.00097	0.99904	29
32	0.04420	22.6241	0.04424	22.6020	1.00098	0.99902	28
33	0.04449	22.4764	0.04454	22.4541	1.00099	0.99901	27
34	0.04478	22.3305	0.04483	22.3081	1.00100	0.99900	26
35	0.04507	22.1865	0.04512	22.1640	1.00102	0.99898	25
36	0.04536	22.0444	0.04541	22.0217	1.00103	0.99897	24
37	0.04565	21.9041	0.04570	21.8813	1.00104	0.99896	23
38	0.04594	21.7656	0.04599	21.7426	1.00106	0.99894	22
39	0.04623	21.6288	0.04628	21.6056	1.00107	0.99893	21
40	0.04653	21.4937	0.04658	21.4704	1.00108	0.99892	20
41	0.04682	21.3603	0.04687	21.3369	1.00110	0.99890	19
42	0.04711	21.2285	0.04716	21.2049	1.00111	0.99889	18
43	0.04740	21.0984	0.04745	21.0747	1.00113	0.99888	17
44	0.04769	20.9698	0.04774	20.9460	1.00114	0.99886	16
45	0.04798	20.8428	0.04803	20.8188	1.00115	0.99885	15
46	0.04827	20.7174	0.04833	20.6932	1.00117	0.99883	14
47	0.04856	20.5934	0.04862	20.5691	1.00118	0.99882	13
48	0.04885	20.4709	0.04891	20.4465	1.00120	0.99881	12
49	0.04914	20.3499	0.04920	20.3253	1.00121	0.99879	11
50	0.04943	20.2303	0.04949	20.2056	1.00122	0.99878	10
51	0.04972	20.1121	0.04978	20.0872	1.00124	0.99876	9
52	0.05001	19.9952	0.05007	19.9702	1.00125	0.99875	8
53	0.05030	19.8798	0.05037	19.8546	1.00127	0.99873	7
54	0.05059	19.7656	0.05066	19.7403	1.00128	0.99872	6
55	0.05088	19.6528	0.05095	19.6273	1.00130	0.99870	5
56	0.05117	19.5412	0.05124	19.5156	1.00131	0.99869	4
57	0.05146	19.4309	0.05153	19.4051	1.00133	0.99867	3
58	0.05175	19.3218	0.05182	19.2959	1.00134	0.99866	2
59	0.05205	19.2140	0.05212	19.1879	1.00136	0.99864	1
60	0.05234	19.1073	0.05241	19.0811	1.00137	0.99863	0
92° → cos	sec	cot	tan	csc	sin ← 87°		

3° →	sin	csc	tan	cot	sec	← 176° cos	
0	0.05234	19.1073	0.05241	19.0811	1.00137	0.99863	60
1	0.05263	19.0019	0.05270	18.9755	1.00139	0.99861	59
2	0.05292	18.8975	0.05299	18.8711	1.00140	0.99860	58
3	0.05321	18.7944	0.05328	18.7678	1.00142	0.99858	57
4	0.05350	18.6923	0.05357	18.6656	1.00143	0.99857	56
5	0.05379	18.5914	0.05387	18.5645	1.00145	0.99855	55
6	0.05408	18.4915	0.05416	18.4645	1.00147	0.99854	54
7	0.05437	18.3927	0.05445	18.3655	1.00148	0.99852	53
8	0.05466	18.2950	0.05474	18.2677	1.00150	0.99851	52
9	0.05495	18.1983	0.05503	18.1708	1.00151	0.99849	51
10	0.05524	18.1026	0.05533	18.0750	1.00153	0.99847	50
11	0.05553	18.0079	0.05562	17.9802	1.00155	0.99846	49
12	0.05582	17.9142	0.05591	17.8863	1.00156	0.99844	48
13	0.05611	17.8215	0.05620	17.7934	1.00158	0.99842	47
14	0.05640	17.7298	0.05649	17.7015	1.00159	0.99841	46
15	0.05669	17.6389	0.05678	17.6106	1.00161	0.99839	45
16	0.05698	17.5490	0.05708	17.5205	1.00163	0.99838	44
17	0.05727	17.4600	0.05737	17.4314	1.00164	0.99836	43
18	0.05756	17.3720	0.05766	17.3432	1.00166	0.99834	42
19	0.05785	17.2848	0.05795	17.2558	1.00168	0.99833	41
20	0.05814	17.1984	0.05824	17.1693	1.00169	0.99831	40
21	0.05844	17.1130	0.05854	17.0837	1.00171	0.99829	39
22	0.05873	17.0283	0.05883	16.9990	1.00173	0.99827	38
23	0.05902	16.9446	0.05912	16.9150	1.00175	0.99826	37
24	0.05931	16.8616	0.05941	16.8319	1.00176	0.99824	36
25	0.05960	16.7794	0.05970	16.7496	1.00178	0.99822	35
26	0.05989	16.6981	0.05999	16.6681	1.00180	0.99821	34
27	0.06018	16.6175	0.06029	16.5874	1.00182	0.99819	33
28	0.06047	16.5377	0.06058	16.5075	1.00183	0.99817	32
29	0.06076	16.4587	0.06087	16.4283	1.00185	0.99815	31
30	0.06105	16.3804	0.06116	16.3499	1.00187	0.99813	30
31	0.06134	16.3029	0.06145	16.2722	1.00189	0.99812	29
32	0.06163	16.2261	0.06175	16.1952	1.00190	0.99810	28
33	0.06192	16.1500	0.06204	16.1190	1.00192	0.99808	27
34	0.06221	16.0746	0.06233	16.0435	1.00194	0.99806	26
35	0.06250	15.9999	0.06262	15.9687	1.00196	0.99804	25
36	0.06279	15.9260	0.06291	15.8945	1.00198	0.99803	24
37	0.06308	15.8527	0.06321	15.8211	1.00200	0.99801	23
38	0.06337	15.7801	0.06350	15.7483	1.00201	0.99799	22
39	0.06366	15.7081	0.06379	15.6762	1.00203	0.99797	21
40	0.06395	15.6368	0.06408	15.6048	1.00205	0.99795	20
41	0.06424	15.5661	0.06438	15.5340	1.00207	0.99793	19
42	0.06453	15.4961	0.06467	15.4638	1.00209	0.99792	18
43	0.06482	15.4267	0.06496	15.3943	1.00211	0.99790	17
44	0.06511	15.3579	0.06525	15.3254	1.00213	0.99788	16
45	0.06540	15.2898	0.06554	15.2571	1.00215	0.99786	15
46	0.06569	15.2222	0.06584	15.1893	1.00216	0.99784	14
47	0.06598	15.1553	0.06613	15.1222	1.00218	0.99782	13
48	0.06627	15.0889	0.06642	15.0557	1.00220	0.99780	12
49	0.06656	15.0231	0.06671	14.9898	1.00222	0.99778	11
50	0.06685	14.9579	0.06700	14.9244	1.00224	0.99776	10
51	0.06714	14.8932	0.06730	14.8596	1.00226	0.99774	9
52	0.06743	14.8291	0.06759	14.7954	1.00228	0.99772	8
53	0.06773	14.7656	0.06788	14.7317	1.00230	0.99770	7
54	0.06802	14.7026	0.06817	14.6685	1.00232	0.99768	6
55	0.06831	14.6401	0.06847	14.6059	1.00234	0.99766	5
56	0.06860	14.5782	0.06876	14.5438	1.00236	0.99764	4
57	0.06889	14.5168	0.06905	14.4823	1.00238	0.99762	3
58	0.06918	14.4559	0.06934	14.4212	1.00240	0.99760	2
59	0.06947	14.3955	0.06963	14.3607	1.00242	0.99758	1
60	0.06976	14.3356	0.06993	14.3007	1.00244	0.99756	0
93° → cos	sec	cot	tan	csc	sin ← 86°		

4°→ ↓	sin	csc	tan	cot	sec	cos ←175° ↓	
0	0.06976	14.3356	0.06993	14.3007	1.00244	0.99756	60
1	0.07005	14.2762	0.07022	14.2411	1.00246	0.99754	59
2	0.07034	14.2173	0.07051	14.1821	1.00248	0.99752	58
3	0.07063	14.1589	0.07080	14.1235	1.00250	0.99750	57
4	0.07092	14.1010	0.07110	14.0655	1.00252	0.99748	56
5	0.07121	14.0435	0.07139	14.0079	1.00254	0.99746	55
6	0.07150	13.9865	0.07168	13.9507	1.00257	0.99744	54
7	0.07179	13.9300	0.07197	13.8940	1.00259	0.99742	53
8	0.07208	13.8739	0.07227	13.8378	1.00261	0.99740	52
9	0.07237	13.8183	0.07256	13.7821	1.00263	0.99738	51
10	0.07266	13.7631	0.07285	13.7267	1.00265	0.99736	50
11	0.07295	13.7084	0.07314	13.6719	1.00267	0.99734	49
12	0.07324	13.6541	0.07344	13.6174	1.00269	0.99731	48
13	0.07353	13.6002	0.07373	13.5634	1.00271	0.99729	47
14	0.07382	13.5468	0.07402	13.5098	1.00274	0.99727	46
15	0.07411	13.4937	0.07431	13.4566	1.00276	0.99725	45
16	0.07440	13.4411	0.07461	13.4039	1.00278	0.99723	44
17	0.07469	13.3889	0.07490	13.3515	1.00280	0.99721	43
18	0.07498	13.3371	0.07519	13.2996	1.00282	0.99719	42
19	0.07527	13.2857	0.07548	13.2480	1.00284	0.99716	41
20	0.07556	13.2347	0.07578	13.1969	1.00287	0.99714	40
21	0.07585	13.1841	0.07607	13.1461	1.00289	0.99712	39
22	0.07614	13.1339	0.07636	13.0958	1.00291	0.99710	38
23	0.07643	13.0840	0.07665	13.0458	1.00293	0.99708	37
24	0.07672	13.0346	0.07695	12.9962	1.00296	0.99705	36
25	0.07701	12.9855	0.07724	12.9469	1.00298	0.99703	35
26	0.07730	12.9368	0.07753	12.8981	1.00300	0.99701	34
27	0.07759	12.8884	0.07782	12.8496	1.00302	0.99699	33
28	0.07788	12.8404	0.07812	12.8014	1.00305	0.99696	32
29	0.07817	12.7928	0.07841	12.7536	1.00307	0.99694	31
30	0.07846	12.7455	0.07870	12.7062	1.00309	0.99692	30
31	0.07875	12.6986	0.07899	12.6591	1.00312	0.99689	29
32	0.07904	12.6520	0.07929	12.6124	1.00314	0.99687	28
33	0.07933	12.6057	0.07958	12.5660	1.00316	0.99685	27
34	0.07962	12.5598	0.07987	12.5199	1.00318	0.99683	26
35	0.07991	12.5142	0.08017	12.4742	1.00321	0.99680	25
36	0.08020	12.4690	0.08046	12.4288	1.00323	0.99678	24
37	0.08049	12.4241	0.08075	12.3838	1.00326	0.99676	23
38	0.08078	12.3795	0.08104	12.3390	1.00328	0.99673	22
39	0.08107	12.3352	0.08134	12.2946	1.00330	0.99671	21
40	0.08136	12.2913	0.08163	12.2505	1.00333	0.99668	20
41	0.08165	12.2476	0.08192	12.2067	1.00335	0.99666	19
42	0.08194	12.2043	0.08221	12.1632	1.00337	0.99664	18
43	0.08223	12.1612	0.08251	12.1201	1.00340	0.99661	17
44	0.08252	12.1185	0.08280	12.0772	1.00342	0.99659	16
45	0.08281	12.0761	0.08309	12.0346	1.00345	0.99657	15
46	0.08310	12.0340	0.08339	11.9923	1.00347	0.99654	14
47	0.08339	11.9921	0.08368	11.9504	1.00350	0.99652	13
48	0.08368	11.9506	0.08397	11.9087	1.00352	0.99649	12
49	0.08397	11.9093	0.08427	11.8673	1.00354	0.99647	11
50	0.08426	11.8684	0.08456	11.8262	1.00357	0.99644	10
51	0.08455	11.8277	0.08485	11.7853	1.00359	0.99642	9
52	0.08484	11.7873	0.08514	11.7448	1.00362	0.99639	8
53	0.08513	11.7471	0.08544	11.7045	1.00364	0.99637	7
54	0.08542	11.7073	0.08573	11.6645	1.00367	0.99635	6
55	0.08571	11.6677	0.08602	11.6248	1.00369	0.99632	5
56	0.08600	11.6284	0.08632	11.5853	1.00372	0.99630	4
57	0.08629	11.5893	0.08661	11.5461	1.00374	0.99627	3
58	0.08658	11.5505	0.08690	11.5072	1.00377	0.99625	2
59	0.08687	11.5120	0.08720	11.4685	1.00379	0.99622	1
60	0.08716	11.4737	0.08749	11.4301	1.00382	0.99619	0
94°→ cos	sec	cot	tan	csc	sin ←85°		

5°→ ↓	sin	csc	tan	cot	sec	cos ←174° ↓	
0	0.08716	11.4737	0.08749	11.4301	1.00382	0.99619	60
1	0.08745	11.4357	0.08778	11.3919	1.00385	0.99617	59
2	0.08774	11.3979	0.08807	11.3540	1.00387	0.99614	58
3	0.08803	11.3604	0.08837	11.3163	1.00390	0.99612	57
4	0.08831	11.3231	0.08866	11.2789	1.00392	0.99609	56
5	0.08860	11.2861	0.08895	11.2417	1.00395	0.99607	55
6	0.08889	11.2493	0.08925	11.2048	1.00397	0.99604	54
7	0.08918	11.2128	0.08954	11.1681	1.00400	0.99602	53
8	0.08947	11.1765	0.08983	11.1316	1.00403	0.99599	52
9	0.08976	11.1404	0.09013	11.0954	1.00405	0.99596	51
10	0.09005	11.1045	0.09042	11.0594	1.00408	0.99594	50
11	0.09034	11.0689	0.09071	11.0237	1.00411	0.99591	49
12	0.09063	11.0336	0.09101	10.9882	1.00413	0.99588	48
13	0.09092	10.9984	0.09130	10.9529	1.00416	0.99586	47
14	0.09121	10.9635	0.09159	10.9178	1.00419	0.99583	46
15	0.09150	10.9288	0.09189	10.8829	1.00421	0.99580	45
16	0.09179	10.8943	0.09218	10.8483	1.00424	0.99578	44
17	0.09208	10.8600	0.09247	10.8139	1.00427	0.99575	43
18	0.09237	10.8260	0.09277	10.7797	1.00429	0.99572	42
19	0.09266	10.7921	0.09306	10.7457	1.00432	0.99570	41
20	0.09295	10.7585	0.09335	10.7119	1.00435	0.99567	40
21	0.09324	10.7251	0.09365	10.6783	1.00438	0.99564	39
22	0.09353	10.6919	0.09394	10.6450	1.00440	0.99562	38
23	0.09382	10.6589	0.09423	10.6118	1.00443	0.99559	37
24	0.09411	10.6261	0.09453	10.5789	1.00446	0.99556	36
25	0.09440	10.5935	0.09482	10.5462	1.00449	0.99553	35
26	0.09469	10.5611	0.09511	10.5136	1.00451	0.99551	34
27	0.09498	10.5289	0.09541	10.4813	1.00454	0.99548	33
28	0.09527	10.4969	0.09570	10.4491	1.00457	0.99545	32
29	0.09556	10.4650	0.09600	10.4172	1.00460	0.99542	31
30	0.09585	10.4334	0.09629	10.3854	1.00463	0.99540	30
31	0.09614	10.4020	0.09658	10.3538	1.00465	0.99537	29
32	0.09642	10.3708	0.09688	10.3224	1.00468	0.99534	28
33	0.09671	10.3397	0.09717	10.2913	1.00471	0.99531	27
34	0.09700	10.3089	0.09746	10.2602	1.00474	0.99528	26
35	0.09729	10.2782	0.09776	10.2294	1.00477	0.99526	25
36	0.09758	10.2477	0.09805	10.1988	1.00480	0.99523	24
37	0.09787	10.2174	0.09834	10.1683	1.00482	0.99520	23
38	0.09816	10.1873	0.09864	10.1381	1.00485	0.99517	22
39	0.09845	10.1573	0.09893	10.1080	1.00488	0.99514	21
40	0.09874	10.1275	0.09923	10.0780	1.00491	0.99511	20
41	0.09903	10.0979	0.09952	10.0483	1.00494	0.99508	19
42	0.09932	10.0685	0.09981	10.0187	1.00497	0.99506	18
43	0.09961	10.0392	0.10011	9.98931	1.00500	0.99503	17
44	0.09990	10.0101	0.10040	9.96007	1.00503	0.99500	16
45	0.10019	9.98123	0.10069	9.93101	1.00506	0.99497	15
46	0.10048	9.95248	0.10099	9.90211	1.00509	0.99494	14
47	0.10077	9.92389	0.10128	9.87338	1.00512	0.99491	13
48	0.10106	9.89547	0.10158	9.84482	1.00515	0.99488	12
49	0.10135	9.86722	0.10187	9.81641	1.00518	0.99485	11
50	0.10164	9.83912	0.10216	9.78817	1.00521	0.99482	10
51	0.10192	9.81119	0.10246	9.76009	1.00524	0.99479	9
52	0.10221	9.78341	0.10275	9.73217	1.00527	0.99476	8
53	0.10250	9.75579	0.10305	9.70441	1.00530	0.99473	7
54	0.10279	9.72833	0.10334	9.67680	1.00533	0.99470	6
55	0.10308	9.70103	0.10363	9.64935	1.00536	0.99467	5
56	0.10337	9.67387	0.10393	9.62205	1.00539	0.99464	4
57	0.10366	9.64687	0.10422	9.59490	1.00542	0.99461	3
58	0.10395	9.62002	0.10452	9.56791	1.00545	0.99458	2
59	0.10424	9.59332	0.10481	9.54106	1.00548	0.99455	1
60	0.10453	9.56677	0.10510	9.51436	1.00551	0.99452	0
95°→ cos	sec	cot	tan	csc	sin ←84°		

↓	sin	csc	tan	cot	sec	cos	
0	0.10453	9.56677	0.10510	9.51436	1.00551	0.99452	60
1	0.10482	9.54037	0.10540	9.48781	1.00554	0.99449	59
2	0.10511	9.51411	0.10569	9.46141	1.00557	0.99446	58
3	0.10540	9.48800	0.10599	9.43515	1.00560	0.99443	57
4	0.10569	9.46203	0.10628	9.40904	1.00563	0.99440	56
5	0.10597	9.43620	0.10657	9.38307	1.00566	0.99437	55
6	0.10626	9.41052	0.10687	9.35724	1.00569	0.99434	54
7	0.10655	9.38497	0.10716	9.33155	1.00573	0.99431	53
8	0.10684	9.35957	0.10746	9.30599	1.00576	0.99428	52
9	0.10713	9.33430	0.10775	9.28058	1.00579	0.99424	51
10	0.10742	9.30917	0.10805	9.25530	1.00582	0.99421	50
11	0.10771	9.28417	0.10834	9.23016	1.00585	0.99418	49
12	0.10800	9.25931	0.10863	9.20516	1.00588	0.99415	48
13	0.10829	9.23459	0.10893	9.18028	1.00592	0.99412	47
14	0.10858	9.20999	0.10922	9.15554	1.00595	0.99409	46
15	0.10887	9.18553	0.10952	9.13093	1.00598	0.99406	45
16	0.10916	9.16120	0.10981	9.10646	1.00601	0.99402	44
17	0.10945	9.13699	0.11011	9.08211	1.00604	0.99399	43
18	0.10973	9.11292	0.11040	9.05789	1.00608	0.99396	42
19	0.11002	9.08897	0.11070	9.03379	1.00611	0.99393	41
20	0.11031	9.06515	0.11099	9.00983	1.00614	0.99390	40
21	0.11060	9.04146	0.11128	8.98598	1.00617	0.99386	39
22	0.11089	9.01788	0.11158	8.96227	1.00621	0.99383	38
23	0.11118	8.99444	0.11187	8.93867	1.00624	0.99380	37
24	0.11147	8.97111	0.11217	8.91520	1.00627	0.99377	36
25	0.11176	8.94791	0.11246	8.89185	1.00630	0.99374	35
26	0.11205	8.92482	0.11276	8.86862	1.00634	0.99370	34
27	0.11234	8.90186	0.11305	8.84551	1.00637	0.99367	33
28	0.11263	8.87901	0.11335	8.82252	1.00640	0.99364	32
29	0.11291	8.85628	0.11364	8.79964	1.00644	0.99360	31
30	0.11320	8.83367	0.11394	8.77689	1.00647	0.99357	30
31	0.11349	8.81118	0.11423	8.75425	1.00650	0.99354	29
32	0.11378	8.78880	0.11452	8.73172	1.00654	0.99351	28
33	0.11407	8.76653	0.11482	8.70931	1.00657	0.99347	27
34	0.11436	8.74438	0.11511	8.68701	1.00660	0.99344	26
35	0.11465	8.72234	0.11541	8.66482	1.00664	0.99341	25
36	0.11494	8.70041	0.11570	8.64275	1.00667	0.99337	24
37	0.11523	8.67859	0.11600	8.62078	1.00671	0.99334	23
38	0.11552	8.65688	0.11629	8.59893	1.00674	0.99331	22
39	0.11580	8.63528	0.11659	8.57718	1.00677	0.99327	21
40	0.11609	8.61379	0.11688	8.55555	1.00681	0.99324	20
41	0.11638	8.59241	0.11718	8.53402	1.00684	0.99320	19
42	0.11667	8.57113	0.11747	8.51259	1.00688	0.99317	18
43	0.11696	8.54996	0.11777	8.49128	1.00691	0.99314	17
44	0.11725	8.52889	0.11806	8.47007	1.00695	0.99310	16
45	0.11754	8.50793	0.11836	8.44896	1.00698	0.99307	15
46	0.11783	8.48707	0.11865	8.42795	1.00701	0.99303	14
47	0.11812	8.46632	0.11895	8.40705	1.00705	0.99300	13
48	0.11840	8.44566	0.11924	8.38625	1.00708	0.99297	12
49	0.11869	8.42511	0.11954	8.36555	1.00712	0.99293	11
50	0.11898	8.40466	0.11983	8.34496	1.00715	0.99290	10
51	0.11927	8.38431	0.12013	8.32446	1.00719	0.99286	9
52	0.11956	8.36405	0.12042	8.30406	1.00722	0.99283	8
53	0.11985	8.34390	0.12072	8.28376	1.00726	0.99279	7
54	0.12014	8.32384	0.12101	8.26355	1.00730	0.99276	6
55	0.12043	8.30388	0.12131	8.24345	1.00733	0.99272	5
56	0.12071	8.28402	0.12160	8.22344	1.00737	0.99269	4
57	0.12100	8.26425	0.12190	8.20352	1.00740	0.99265	3
58	0.12129	8.24457	0.12219	8.18370	1.00744	0.99262	2
59	0.12158	8.22500	0.12249	8.16398	1.00747	0.99258	1
60	0.12187	8.20551	0.12278	8.14435	1.00751	0.99255	0

↓	sin	csc	tan	cot	sec	cos	
0	0.12187	8.20551	0.12278	8.14435	1.00751	0.99255	60
1	0.12216	8.18612	0.12308	8.12481	1.00755	0.99251	59
2	0.12245	8.16681	0.12338	8.10536	1.00758	0.99248	58
3	0.12274	8.14760	0.12367	8.08600	1.00762	0.99244	57
4	0.12302	8.12849	0.12397	8.06674	1.00765	0.99240	56
5	0.12331	8.10946	0.12426	8.04756	1.00769	0.99237	55
6	0.12360	8.09052	0.12456	8.02848	1.00773	0.99233	54
7	0.12389	8.07167	0.12485	8.00948	1.00776	0.99230	53
8	0.12418	8.05291	0.12515	7.99058	1.00780	0.99226	52
9	0.12447	8.03423	0.12544	7.97176	1.00784	0.99222	51
10	0.12476	8.01565	0.12574	7.95302	1.00787	0.99219	50
11	0.12504	7.99714	0.12603	7.93438	1.00791	0.99215	49
12	0.12533	7.97873	0.12633	7.91582	1.00795	0.99211	48
13	0.12562	7.96040	0.12662	7.89734	1.00799	0.99208	47
14	0.12591	7.94216	0.12692	7.87895	1.00802	0.99204	46
15	0.12620	7.92399	0.12722	7.86064	1.00806	0.99200	45
16	0.12649	7.90592	0.12751	7.84242	1.00810	0.99197	44
17	0.12678	7.88792	0.12781	7.82428	1.00813	0.99193	43
18	0.12706	7.87001	0.12810	7.80622	1.00817	0.99189	42
19	0.12735	7.85218	0.12840	7.78825	1.00821	0.99186	41
20	0.12764	7.83443	0.12869	7.77035	1.00825	0.99182	40
21	0.12793	7.81677	0.12899	7.75254	1.00828	0.99178	39
22	0.12822	7.79918	0.12929	7.73480	1.00832	0.99175	38
23	0.12851	7.78167	0.12958	7.71715	1.00836	0.99171	37
24	0.12880	7.76424	0.12988	7.69957	1.00840	0.99167	36
25	0.12908	7.74689	0.13017	7.68208	1.00844	0.99163	35
26	0.12937	7.72962	0.13047	7.66466	1.00848	0.99160	34
27	0.12966	7.71242	0.13076	7.64732	1.00851	0.99156	33
28	0.12995	7.69530	0.13106	7.63005	1.00855	0.99152	32
29	0.13024	7.67826	0.13136	7.61287	1.00859	0.99148	31
30	0.13053	7.66130	0.13165	7.59575	1.00863	0.99144	30
31	0.13081	7.64441	0.13195	7.57872	1.00867	0.99141	29
32	0.13110	7.62759	0.13224	7.56176	1.00871	0.99137	28
33	0.13139	7.61085	0.13254	7.54487	1.00875	0.99133	27
34	0.13168	7.59418	0.13284	7.52806	1.00878	0.99129	26
35	0.13197	7.57759	0.13313	7.51132	1.00882	0.99125	25
36	0.13226	7.56107	0.13343	7.49465	1.00886	0.99122	24
37	0.13254	7.54462	0.13372	7.47806	1.00890	0.99118	23
38	0.13283	7.52825	0.13402	7.46154	1.00894	0.99114	22
39	0.13312	7.51194	0.13432	7.44509	1.00898	0.99110	21
40	0.13341	7.49571	0.13461	7.42871	1.00902	0.99106	20
41	0.13370	7.47955	0.13491	7.41240	1.00906	0.99102	19
42	0.13399	7.46346	0.13521	7.39616	1.00910	0.99098	18
43	0.13427	7.44743	0.13550	7.37999	1.00914	0.99094	17
44	0.13456	7.43148	0.13580	7.36389	1.00918	0.99091	16
45	0.13485	7.41560	0.13609	7.34786	1.00922	0.99087	15
46	0.13514	7.39978	0.13639	7.33190	1.00926	0.99083	14
47	0.13543	7.38403	0.13669	7.31600	1.00930	0.99079	13
48	0.13572	7.36835	0.13698	7.30018	1.00934	0.99075	12
49	0.13600	7.35274	0.13728	7.28442	1.00938	0.99071	11
50	0.13629	7.33719	0.13758	7.26873	1.00942	0.99067	10
51	0.13658	7.32171	0.13787	7.25310	1.00946	0.99063	9
52	0.13687	7.30630	0.13817	7.23754	1.00950	0.99059	8
53	0.13716	7.29095	0.13846	7.22204	1.00954	0.99055	7
54	0.13744	7.27566	0.13876	7.20661	1.00958	0.99051	6
55	0.13773	7.26044	0.13906	7.19125	1.00962	0.99047	5
56	0.13802	7.24529	0.13935	7.17594	1.00966	0.99043	4
57	0.13831	7.23019	0.13965	7.16071	1.00970	0.99039	3
58	0.13860	7.21517	0.13995	7.14553	1.00975	0.99035	2
59	0.13889	7.20020	0.14024	7.13042	1.00979	0.99031	1
60	0.13917	7.18530	0.14054	7.11537	1.00983	0.99027	0

8°→ ↓	sin	csc	tan	cot	sec	cos ←171° ↓	
0	0.13917	7.18530	0.14054	7.11537	1.00983	0.99027	60
1	0.13946	7.17046	0.14084	7.10038	1.00987	0.99023	59
2	0.13975	7.15568	0.14113	7.08546	1.00991	0.99019	58
3	0.14004	7.14096	0.14143	7.07059	1.00995	0.99015	57
4	0.14033	7.12630	0.14173	7.05579	1.00999	0.99011	56
5	0.14061	7.11171	0.14202	7.04105	1.01004	0.99006	55
6	0.14090	7.09717	0.14232	7.02637	1.01008	0.99002	54
7	0.14119	7.08269	0.14262	7.01174	1.01012	0.98998	53
8	0.14148	7.06828	0.14291	6.99718	1.01016	0.98994	52
9	0.14177	7.05392	0.14321	6.98268	1.01020	0.98990	51
10	0.14205	7.03962	0.14351	6.96823	1.01024	0.98986	50
11	0.14234	7.02538	0.14381	6.95385	1.01029	0.98982	49
12	0.14263	7.01120	0.14410	6.93952	1.01033	0.98978	48
13	0.14292	6.99708	0.14440	6.92525	1.01037	0.98973	47
14	0.14320	6.98301	0.14470	6.91104	1.01041	0.98969	46
15	0.14349	6.96900	0.14499	6.89688	1.01046	0.98965	45
16	0.14378	6.95505	0.14529	6.88278	1.01050	0.98961	44
17	0.14407	6.94115	0.14559	6.86874	1.01054	0.98957	43
18	0.14436	6.92731	0.14588	6.85475	1.01059	0.98953	42
19	0.14464	6.91352	0.14618	6.84082	1.01063	0.98948	41
20	0.14493	6.89979	0.14648	6.82694	1.01067	0.98944	40
21	0.14522	6.88612	0.14678	6.81312	1.01071	0.98940	39
22	0.14551	6.87250	0.14707	6.79936	1.01076	0.98936	38
23	0.14580	6.85893	0.14737	6.78564	1.01080	0.98931	37
24	0.14608	6.84542	0.14767	6.77199	1.01084	0.98927	36
25	0.14637	6.83196	0.14796	6.75838	1.01089	0.98923	35
26	0.14666	6.81856	0.14826	6.74483	1.01093	0.98919	34
27	0.14695	6.80521	0.14856	6.73133	1.01097	0.98914	33
28	0.14723	6.79191	0.14886	6.71789	1.01102	0.98910	32
29	0.14752	6.77866	0.14915	6.70450	1.01106	0.98906	31
30	0.14781	6.76547	0.14945	6.69116	1.01111	0.98902	30
31	0.14810	6.75233	0.14975	6.67787	1.01115	0.98897	29
32	0.14838	6.73924	0.15005	6.66463	1.01119	0.98893	28
33	0.14867	6.72620	0.15034	6.65144	1.01124	0.98889	27
34	0.14896	6.71321	0.15064	6.63831	1.01128	0.98884	26
35	0.14925	6.70027	0.15094	6.62523	1.01133	0.98880	25
36	0.14954	6.68738	0.15124	6.61219	1.01137	0.98876	24
37	0.14982	6.67454	0.15153	6.59921	1.01142	0.98871	23
38	0.15011	6.66176	0.15183	6.58627	1.01146	0.98867	22
39	0.15040	6.64902	0.15213	6.57339	1.01151	0.98863	21
40	0.15069	6.63633	0.15243	6.56055	1.01155	0.98858	20
41	0.15097	6.62369	0.15272	6.54777	1.01160	0.98854	19
42	0.15126	6.61110	0.15302	6.53503	1.01164	0.98849	18
43	0.15155	6.59855	0.15332	6.52234	1.01169	0.98845	17
44	0.15184	6.58606	0.15362	6.50970	1.01173	0.98841	16
45	0.15212	6.57361	0.15391	6.49710	1.01178	0.98836	15
46	0.15241	6.56121	0.15421	6.48456	1.01182	0.98832	14
47	0.15270	6.54886	0.15451	6.47206	1.01187	0.98827	13
48	0.15299	6.53655	0.15481	6.45961	1.01191	0.98823	12
49	0.15327	6.52429	0.15511	6.44720	1.01196	0.98818	11
50	0.15356	6.51208	0.15540	6.43484	1.01200	0.98814	10
51	0.15385	6.49991	0.15570	6.42253	1.01205	0.98809	9
52	0.15414	6.48779	0.15600	6.41026	1.01209	0.98805	8
53	0.15442	6.47572	0.15630	6.39804	1.01214	0.98800	7
54	0.15471	6.46369	0.15660	6.38587	1.01219	0.98796	6
55	0.15500	6.45171	0.15689	6.37374	1.01223	0.98791	5
56	0.15529	6.43977	0.15719	6.36165	1.01228	0.98787	4
57	0.15557	6.42787	0.15749	6.34961	1.01233	0.98782	3
58	0.15586	6.41602	0.15779	6.33761	1.01237	0.98778	2
59	0.15615	6.40422	0.15809	6.32566	1.01242	0.98773	1
60	0.15643	6.39245	0.15838	6.31375	1.01247	0.98769	0

| ↑ 98°→ cos | sec | cot | tan | csc | sin ←81° ↑ | |

9°→ ↓	sin	csc	tan	cot	sec	cos ←170° ↓	
0	0.15643	6.39245	0.15838	6.31375	1.01247	0.98769	60
1	0.15672	6.38073	0.15868	6.30189	1.01251	0.98764	59
2	0.15701	6.36906	0.15898	6.29007	1.01256	0.98760	58
3	0.15730	6.35743	0.15928	6.27829	1.01261	0.98755	57
4	0.15758	6.34584	0.15958	6.26655	1.01265	0.98751	56
5	0.15787	6.33429	0.15988	6.25486	1.01270	0.98746	55
6	0.15816	6.32279	0.16017	6.24321	1.01275	0.98741	54
7	0.15845	6.31133	0.16047	6.23160	1.01279	0.98737	53
8	0.15873	6.29991	0.16077	6.22003	1.01284	0.98732	52
9	0.15902	6.28853	0.16107	6.20851	1.01289	0.98728	51
10	0.15931	6.27719	0.16137	6.19703	1.01294	0.98723	50
11	0.15959	6.26590	0.16167	6.18559	1.01298	0.98718	49
12	0.15988	6.25464	0.16196	6.17419	1.01303	0.98714	48
13	0.16017	6.24343	0.16226	6.16283	1.01308	0.98709	47
14	0.16046	6.23226	0.16256	6.15151	1.01313	0.98704	46
15	0.16074	6.22113	0.16286	6.14023	1.01317	0.98700	45
16	0.16103	6.21004	0.16316	6.12899	1.01322	0.98695	44
17	0.16132	6.19898	0.16346	6.11779	1.01327	0.98690	43
18	0.16160	6.18797	0.16376	6.10664	1.01332	0.98686	42
19	0.16189	6.17700	0.16405	6.09552	1.01337	0.98681	41
20	0.16218	6.16607	0.16435	6.08444	1.01342	0.98676	40
21	0.16246	6.15517	0.16465	6.07340	1.01346	0.98671	39
22	0.16275	6.14432	0.16495	6.06240	1.01351	0.98667	38
23	0.16304	6.13350	0.16525	6.05143	1.01356	0.98662	37
24	0.16333	6.12273	0.16555	6.04051	1.01361	0.98657	36
25	0.16361	6.11199	0.16585	6.02962	1.01366	0.98652	35
26	0.16390	6.10129	0.16615	6.01878	1.01371	0.98648	34
27	0.16419	6.09062	0.16645	6.00797	1.01376	0.98643	33
28	0.16447	6.08000	0.16674	5.99720	1.01381	0.98638	32
29	0.16476	6.06941	0.16704	5.98646	1.01386	0.98633	31
30	0.16505	6.05886	0.16734	5.97576	1.01391	0.98629	30
31	0.16533	6.04834	0.16764	5.96510	1.01395	0.98624	29
32	0.16562	6.03787	0.16794	5.95448	1.01400	0.98619	28
33	0.16591	6.02743	0.16824	5.94390	1.01405	0.98614	27
34	0.16620	6.01702	0.16854	5.93335	1.01410	0.98609	26
35	0.16648	6.00666	0.16884	5.92283	1.01415	0.98604	25
36	0.16677	5.99633	0.16914	5.91236	1.01420	0.98600	24
37	0.16706	5.98603	0.16944	5.90191	1.01425	0.98595	23
38	0.16734	5.97577	0.16974	5.89151	1.01430	0.98590	22
39	0.16763	5.96555	0.17004	5.88114	1.01435	0.98585	21
40	0.16792	5.95536	0.17033	5.87080	1.01440	0.98580	20
41	0.16820	5.94521	0.17063	5.86051	1.01445	0.98575	19
42	0.16849	5.93509	0.17093	5.85024	1.01450	0.98570	18
43	0.16878	5.92501	0.17123	5.84001	1.01455	0.98565	17
44	0.16906	5.91496	0.17153	5.82982	1.01460	0.98561	16
45	0.16935	5.90495	0.17183	5.81966	1.01466	0.98556	15
46	0.16964	5.89497	0.17213	5.80953	1.01471	0.98551	14
47	0.16992	5.88502	0.17243	5.79944	1.01476	0.98546	13
48	0.17021	5.87511	0.17273	5.78938	1.01481	0.98541	12
49	0.17050	5.86524	0.17303	5.77936	1.01486	0.98536	11
50	0.17078	5.85539	0.17333	5.76937	1.01491	0.98531	10
51	0.17107	5.84558	0.17363	5.75941	1.01496	0.98526	9
52	0.17136	5.83581	0.17393	5.74949	1.01501	0.98521	8
53	0.17164	5.82606	0.17423	5.73960	1.01506	0.98516	7
54	0.17193	5.81635	0.17453	5.72974	1.01512	0.98511	6
55	0.17222	5.80667	0.17483	5.71992	1.01517	0.98506	5
56	0.17250	5.79703	0.17513	5.71013	1.01522	0.98501	4
57	0.17279	5.78742	0.17543	5.70037	1.01527	0.98496	3
58	0.17308	5.77783	0.17573	5.69064	1.01532	0.98491	2
59	0.17336	5.76829	0.17603	5.68094	1.01537	0.98486	1
60	0.17365	5.75877	0.17633	5.67128	1.01543	0.98481	0

| ↑ 99°→ cos | sec | cot | tan | csc | sin ←80° ↑ | |

10°→	sin	csc	tan	cot	sec	cos	←169°
0	0.17365	5.75877	0.17633	5.67128	1.01543	0.98481	60
1	0.17393	5.74929	0.17663	5.66165	1.01548	0.98476	59
2	0.17422	5.73983	0.17693	5.65205	1.01553	0.98471	58
3	0.17451	5.73041	0.17723	5.64248	1.01558	0.98466	57
4	0.17479	5.72102	0.17753	5.63295	1.01564	0.98461	56
5	0.17508	5.71166	0.17783	5.62344	1.01569	0.98455	55
6	0.17537	5.70234	0.17813	5.61397	1.01574	0.98450	54
7	0.17565	5.69304	0.17843	5.60452	1.01579	0.98445	53
8	0.17594	5.68377	0.17873	5.59511	1.01585	0.98440	52
9	0.17623	5.67454	0.17903	5.58573	1.01590	0.98435	51
10	0.17651	5.66533	0.17933	5.57638	1.01595	0.98430	50
11	0.17680	5.65616	0.17963	5.56706	1.01601	0.98425	49
12	0.17708	5.64701	0.17993	5.55777	1.01606	0.98420	48
13	0.17737	5.63790	0.18023	5.54851	1.01611	0.98414	47
14	0.17766	5.62881	0.18053	5.53927	1.01616	0.98409	46
15	0.17794	5.61976	0.18083	5.53007	1.01622	0.98404	45
16	0.17823	5.61073	0.18113	5.52090	1.01627	0.98399	44
17	0.17852	5.60174	0.18143	5.51176	1.01633	0.98394	43
18	0.17880	5.59277	0.18173	5.50264	1.01638	0.98389	42
19	0.17909	5.58383	0.18203	5.49356	1.01643	0.98383	41
20	0.17937	5.57493	0.18233	5.48451	1.01649	0.98378	40
21	0.17966	5.56605	0.18263	5.47548	1.01654	0.98373	39
22	0.17995	5.55720	0.18293	5.46648	1.01659	0.98368	38
23	0.18023	5.54837	0.18323	5.45751	1.01665	0.98362	37
24	0.18052	5.53958	0.18353	5.44857	1.01670	0.98357	36
25	0.18081	5.53081	0.18384	5.43966	1.01676	0.98352	35
26	0.18109	5.52208	0.18414	5.43077	1.01681	0.98347	34
27	0.18138	5.51337	0.18444	5.42192	1.01687	0.98341	33
28	0.18166	5.50468	0.18474	5.41309	1.01692	0.98336	32
29	0.18195	5.49603	0.18504	5.40429	1.01698	0.98331	31
30	0.18224	5.48740	0.18534	5.39552	1.01703	0.98325	30
31	0.18252	5.47881	0.18564	5.38677	1.01709	0.98320	29
32	0.18281	5.47023	0.18594	5.37805	1.01714	0.98315	28
33	0.18309	5.46169	0.18624	5.36936	1.01720	0.98310	27
34	0.18338	5.45317	0.18654	5.36070	1.01725	0.98304	26
35	0.18367	5.44468	0.18684	5.35206	1.01731	0.98299	25
36	0.18395	5.43622	0.18714	5.34345	1.01736	0.98294	24
37	0.18424	5.42778	0.18745	5.33487	1.01742	0.98288	23
38	0.18452	5.41937	0.18775	5.32631	1.01747	0.98283	22
39	0.18481	5.41099	0.18805	5.31778	1.01753	0.98277	21
40	0.18509	5.40263	0.18835	5.30928	1.01758	0.98272	20
41	0.18538	5.39430	0.18865	5.30080	1.01764	0.98267	19
42	0.18567	5.38600	0.18895	5.29235	1.01769	0.98261	18
43	0.18595	5.37772	0.18925	5.28393	1.01775	0.98256	17
44	0.18624	5.36947	0.18955	5.27553	1.01781	0.98250	16
45	0.18652	5.36124	0.18986	5.26715	1.01786	0.98245	15
46	0.18681	5.35304	0.19016	5.25880	1.01792	0.98240	14
47	0.18710	5.34486	0.19046	5.25048	1.01798	0.98234	13
48	0.18738	5.33671	0.19076	5.24218	1.01803	0.98229	12
49	0.18767	5.32859	0.19106	5.23391	1.01809	0.98223	11
50	0.18795	5.32049	0.19136	5.22566	1.01815	0.98218	10
51	0.18824	5.31241	0.19166	5.21744	1.01820	0.98212	9
52	0.18852	5.30436	0.19197	5.20925	1.01826	0.98207	8
53	0.18881	5.29634	0.19227	5.20107	1.01832	0.98201	7
54	0.18910	5.28833	0.19257	5.19293	1.01837	0.98196	6
55	0.18938	5.28036	0.19287	5.18480	1.01843	0.98190	5
56	0.18967	5.27241	0.19317	5.17671	1.01849	0.98185	4
57	0.18995	5.26448	0.19347	5.16863	1.01854	0.98179	3
58	0.19024	5.25658	0.19378	5.16058	1.01860	0.98174	2
59	0.19052	5.24870	0.19408	5.15256	1.01866	0.98168	1
60	0.19081	5.24084	0.19438	5.14455	1.01872	0.98163	0
100°→	cos	sec	cot	tan	csc	sin	←79°

11°→	sin	csc	tan	cot	sec	cos	←168°
0	0.19081	5.24084	0.19438	5.14455	1.01872	0.98163	60
1	0.19109	5.23301	0.19468	5.13658	1.01877	0.98157	59
2	0.19138	5.22521	0.19498	5.12862	1.01883	0.98152	58
3	0.19167	5.21742	0.19529	5.12069	1.01889	0.98146	57
4	0.19195	5.20966	0.19559	5.11279	1.01895	0.98140	56
5	0.19224	5.20193	0.19589	5.10490	1.01901	0.98135	55
6	0.19252	5.19421	0.19619	5.09704	1.01906	0.98129	54
7	0.19281	5.18652	0.19649	5.08921	1.01912	0.98124	53
8	0.19309	5.17886	0.19680	5.08139	1.01918	0.98118	52
9	0.19338	5.17121	0.19710	5.07360	1.01924	0.98112	51
10	0.19366	5.16359	0.19740	5.06584	1.01930	0.98107	50
11	0.19395	5.15599	0.19770	5.05809	1.01936	0.98101	49
12	0.19423	5.14842	0.19801	5.05037	1.01941	0.98096	48
13	0.19452	5.14087	0.19831	5.04267	1.01947	0.98090	47
14	0.19481	5.13334	0.19861	5.03499	1.01953	0.98084	46
15	0.19509	5.12583	0.19891	5.02734	1.01959	0.98079	45
16	0.19538	5.11835	0.19921	5.01971	1.01965	0.98073	44
17	0.19566	5.11088	0.19952	5.01210	1.01971	0.98067	43
18	0.19595	5.10344	0.19982	5.00451	1.01977	0.98061	42
19	0.19623	5.09602	0.20012	4.99695	1.01983	0.98056	41
20	0.19652	5.08863	0.20042	4.98940	1.01989	0.98050	40
21	0.19680	5.08125	0.20073	4.98188	1.01995	0.98044	39
22	0.19709	5.07390	0.20103	4.97438	1.02001	0.98039	38
23	0.19737	5.06657	0.20133	4.96690	1.02007	0.98033	37
24	0.19766	5.05926	0.20164	4.95945	1.02013	0.98027	36
25	0.19794	5.05197	0.20194	4.95201	1.02019	0.98021	35
26	0.19823	5.04471	0.20224	4.94460	1.02025	0.98016	34
27	0.19851	5.03746	0.20254	4.93721	1.02031	0.98010	33
28	0.19880	5.03024	0.20285	4.92984	1.02037	0.98004	32
29	0.19908	5.02303	0.20315	4.92249	1.02043	0.97998	31
30	0.19937	5.01585	0.20345	4.91516	1.02049	0.97992	30
31	0.19965	5.00869	0.20376	4.90785	1.02055	0.97987	29
32	0.19994	5.00155	0.20406	4.90056	1.02061	0.97981	28
33	0.20022	4.99443	0.20436	4.89330	1.02067	0.97975	27
34	0.20051	4.98733	0.20466	4.88605	1.02073	0.97969	26
35	0.20079	4.98025	0.20497	4.87882	1.02079	0.97963	25
36	0.20108	4.97320	0.20527	4.87162	1.02085	0.97958	24
37	0.20136	4.96616	0.20557	4.86444	1.02091	0.97952	23
38	0.20165	4.95914	0.20588	4.85727	1.02097	0.97946	22
39	0.20193	4.95215	0.20618	4.85013	1.02103	0.97940	21
40	0.20222	4.94517	0.20648	4.84300	1.02110	0.97934	20
41	0.20250	4.93821	0.20679	4.83590	1.02116	0.97928	19
42	0.20279	4.93128	0.20709	4.82882	1.02122	0.97922	18
43	0.20307	4.92436	0.20739	4.82175	1.02128	0.97916	17
44	0.20336	4.91746	0.20770	4.81471	1.02134	0.97910	16
45	0.20364	4.91058	0.20800	4.80769	1.02140	0.97905	15
46	0.20393	4.90373	0.20830	4.80068	1.02146	0.97899	14
47	0.20421	4.89689	0.20861	4.79370	1.02153	0.97893	13
48	0.20450	4.89007	0.20891	4.78673	1.02159	0.97887	12
49	0.20478	4.88327	0.20921	4.77978	1.02165	0.97881	11
50	0.20507	4.87649	0.20952	4.77286	1.02171	0.97875	10
51	0.20535	4.86973	0.20982	4.76595	1.02178	0.97869	9
52	0.20563	4.86299	0.21013	4.75906	1.02184	0.97863	8
53	0.20592	4.85627	0.21043	4.75219	1.02190	0.97857	7
54	0.20620	4.84956	0.21073	4.74534	1.02196	0.97851	6
55	0.20649	4.84288	0.21104	4.73851	1.02203	0.97845	5
56	0.20677	4.83621	0.21134	4.73170	1.02209	0.97839	4
57	0.20706	4.82956	0.21164	4.72490	1.02215	0.97833	3
58	0.20734	4.82294	0.21195	4.71813	1.02221	0.97827	2
59	0.20763	4.81633	0.21225	4.71137	1.02228	0.97821	1
60	0.20791	4.80973	0.21256	4.70463	1.02234	0.97815	0
101°→	cos	sec	cot	tan	csc	sin	←78°

12°→	sin	csc	tan	cot	sec	cos ←167°	
0	0.20791	4.80973	0.21256	4.70463	1.02234	0.97815	60
1	0.20820	4.80316	0.21286	4.69791	1.02240	0.97809	59
2	0.20848	4.79661	0.21316	4.69121	1.02247	0.97803	58
3	0.20877	4.79007	0.21347	4.68452	1.02253	0.97797	57
4	0.20905	4.78355	0.21377	4.67786	1.02259	0.97791	56
5	0.20933	4.77705	0.21408	4.67121	1.02266	0.97784	55
6	0.20962	4.77057	0.21438	4.66458	1.02272	0.97778	54
7	0.20990	4.76411	0.21469	4.65797	1.02279	0.97772	53
8	0.21019	4.75766	0.21499	4.65138	1.02285	0.97766	52
9	0.21047	4.75123	0.21529	4.64480	1.02291	0.97760	51
10	0.21076	4.74482	0.21560	4.63825	1.02298	0.97754	50
11	0.21104	4.73843	0.21590	4.63171	1.02304	0.97748	49
12	0.21132	4.73205	0.21621	4.62518	1.02311	0.97742	48
13	0.21161	4.72569	0.21651	4.61868	1.02317	0.97735	47
14	0.21189	4.71935	0.21682	4.61219	1.02323	0.97729	46
15	0.21218	4.71303	0.21712	4.60572	1.02330	0.97723	45
16	0.21246	4.70673	0.21743	4.59927	1.02336	0.97717	44
17	0.21275	4.70044	0.21773	4.59283	1.02343	0.97711	43
18	0.21303	4.69417	0.21804	4.58641	1.02349	0.97705	42
19	0.21331	4.68791	0.21834	4.58001	1.02356	0.97698	41
20	0.21360	4.68167	0.21864	4.57363	1.02362	0.97692	40
21	0.21388	4.67545	0.21895	4.56726	1.02369	0.97686	39
22	0.21417	4.66925	0.21925	4.56091	1.02375	0.97680	38
23	0.21445	4.66307	0.21956	4.55458	1.02382	0.97673	37
24	0.21474	4.65690	0.21986	4.54826	1.02388	0.97667	36
25	0.21502	4.65074	0.22017	4.54196	1.02395	0.97661	35
26	0.21530	4.64461	0.22047	4.53568	1.02402	0.97655	34
27	0.21559	4.63849	0.22078	4.52941	1.02408	0.97648	33
28	0.21587	4.63238	0.22108	4.52316	1.02415	0.97642	32
29	0.21616	4.62630	0.22139	4.51693	1.02421	0.97636	31
30	0.21644	4.62023	0.22169	4.51071	1.02428	0.97630	30
31	0.21672	4.61417	0.22200	4.50451	1.02435	0.97623	29
32	0.21701	4.60813	0.22231	4.49832	1.02441	0.97617	28
33	0.21729	4.60211	0.22261	4.49215	1.02448	0.97611	27
34	0.21758	4.59611	0.22292	4.48600	1.02454	0.97604	26
35	0.21786	4.59012	0.22322	4.47986	1.02461	0.97598	25
36	0.21814	4.58414	0.22353	4.47374	1.02468	0.97592	24
37	0.21843	4.57819	0.22383	4.46764	1.02474	0.97585	23
38	0.21871	4.57224	0.22414	4.46155	1.02481	0.97579	22
39	0.21899	4.56632	0.22444	4.45548	1.02488	0.97573	21
40	0.21928	4.56041	0.22475	4.44942	1.02494	0.97566	20
41	0.21956	4.55451	0.22505	4.44338	1.02501	0.97560	19
42	0.21985	4.54863	0.22536	4.43735	1.02508	0.97553	18
43	0.22013	4.54277	0.22567	4.43134	1.02515	0.97547	17
44	0.22041	4.53692	0.22597	4.42534	1.02521	0.97541	16
45	0.22070	4.53109	0.22628	4.41936	1.02528	0.97534	15
46	0.22098	4.52527	0.22658	4.41340	1.02535	0.97528	14
47	0.22126	4.51947	0.22689	4.40745	1.02542	0.97521	13
48	0.22155	4.51368	0.22719	4.40152	1.02548	0.97515	12
49	0.22183	4.50791	0.22750	4.39560	1.02555	0.97508	11
50	0.22212	4.50216	0.22781	4.38969	1.02562	0.97502	10
51	0.22240	4.49642	0.22811	4.38381	1.02569	0.97496	9
52	0.22268	4.49069	0.22842	4.37793	1.02576	0.97489	8
53	0.22297	4.48498	0.22872	4.37207	1.02582	0.97483	7
54	0.22325	4.47928	0.22903	4.36623	1.02589	0.97476	6
55	0.22353	4.47360	0.22934	4.36040	1.02596	0.97470	5
56	0.22382	4.46793	0.22964	4.35459	1.02603	0.97463	4
57	0.22410	4.46228	0.22995	4.34879	1.02610	0.97457	3
58	0.22438	4.45664	0.23026	4.34300	1.02617	0.97450	2
59	0.22467	4.45102	0.23056	4.33723	1.02624	0.97444	1
60	0.22495	4.44541	0.23087	4.33148	1.02630	0.97437	0

102°→ cos	sec	cot	tan	csc	sin ←77°	

13°→	sin	csc	tan	cot	sec	cos ←166°	
0	0.22495	4.44541	0.23087	4.33148	1.02630	0.97437	60
1	0.22523	4.43982	0.23117	4.32573	1.02637	0.97430	59
2	0.22552	4.43424	0.23148	4.32001	1.02644	0.97424	58
3	0.22580	4.42867	0.23179	4.31430	1.02651	0.97417	57
4	0.22608	4.42312	0.23209	4.30860	1.02658	0.97411	56
5	0.22637	4.41759	0.23240	4.30291	1.02665	0.97404	55
6	0.22665	4.41206	0.23271	4.29724	1.02672	0.97398	54
7	0.22693	4.40656	0.23301	4.29159	1.02679	0.97391	53
8	0.22722	4.40106	0.23332	4.28595	1.02686	0.97384	52
9	0.22750	4.39558	0.23363	4.28032	1.02693	0.97378	51
10	0.22778	4.39012	0.23393	4.27471	1.02700	0.97371	50
11	0.22807	4.38466	0.23424	4.26911	1.02707	0.97365	49
12	0.22835	4.37923	0.23455	4.26352	1.02714	0.97358	48
13	0.22863	4.37380	0.23485	4.25795	1.02721	0.97351	47
14	0.22892	4.36839	0.23516	4.25239	1.02728	0.97345	46
15	0.22920	4.36299	0.23547	4.24685	1.02735	0.97338	45
16	0.22948	4.35761	0.23578	4.24132	1.02742	0.97331	44
17	0.22977	4.35224	0.23608	4.23580	1.02749	0.97325	43
18	0.23005	4.34689	0.23639	4.23030	1.02756	0.97318	42
19	0.23033	4.34154	0.23670	4.22481	1.02763	0.97311	41
20	0.23062	4.33622	0.23700	4.21933	1.02770	0.97304	40
21	0.23090	4.33090	0.23731	4.21387	1.02777	0.97298	39
22	0.23118	4.32560	0.23762	4.20842	1.02784	0.97291	38
23	0.23146	4.32031	0.23793	4.20298	1.02791	0.97284	37
24	0.23175	4.31503	0.23823	4.19756	1.02799	0.97278	36
25	0.23203	4.30977	0.23854	4.19215	1.02806	0.97271	35
26	0.23231	4.30452	0.23885	4.18675	1.02813	0.97264	34
27	0.23260	4.29929	0.23916	4.18137	1.02820	0.97257	33
28	0.23288	4.29406	0.23946	4.17600	1.02827	0.97251	32
29	0.23316	4.28885	0.23977	4.17064	1.02834	0.97244	31
30	0.23345	4.28366	0.24008	4.16530	1.02842	0.97237	30
31	0.23373	4.27847	0.24039	4.15997	1.02849	0.97230	29
32	0.23401	4.27330	0.24069	4.15465	1.02856	0.97223	28
33	0.23429	4.26814	0.24100	4.14934	1.02863	0.97217	27
34	0.23458	4.26300	0.24131	4.14405	1.02870	0.97210	26
35	0.23486	4.25787	0.24162	4.13877	1.02878	0.97203	25
36	0.23514	4.25275	0.24193	4.13350	1.02885	0.97196	24
37	0.23542	4.24764	0.24223	4.12825	1.02892	0.97189	23
38	0.23571	4.24255	0.24254	4.12301	1.02899	0.97182	22
39	0.23599	4.23746	0.24285	4.11778	1.02907	0.97176	21
40	0.23627	4.23239	0.24316	4.11256	1.02914	0.97169	20
41	0.23656	4.22734	0.24347	4.10736	1.02921	0.97162	19
42	0.23684	4.22229	0.24377	4.10216	1.02928	0.97155	18
43	0.23712	4.21726	0.24408	4.09699	1.02936	0.97148	17
44	0.23740	4.21224	0.24439	4.09182	1.02943	0.97141	16
45	0.23769	4.20723	0.24470	4.08666	1.02950	0.97134	15
46	0.23797	4.20224	0.24501	4.08152	1.02958	0.97127	14
47	0.23825	4.19725	0.24532	4.07639	1.02965	0.97120	13
48	0.23853	4.19228	0.24562	4.07127	1.02972	0.97113	12
49	0.23882	4.18733	0.24593	4.06616	1.02980	0.97106	11
50	0.23910	4.18238	0.24624	4.06107	1.02987	0.97100	10
51	0.23938	4.17744	0.24655	4.05599	1.02994	0.97093	9
52	0.23966	4.17252	0.24686	4.05092	1.03002	0.97086	8
53	0.23995	4.16761	0.24717	4.04586	1.03009	0.97079	7
54	0.24023	4.16271	0.24747	4.04081	1.03017	0.97072	6
55	0.24051	4.15782	0.24778	4.03578	1.03024	0.97065	5
56	0.24079	4.15295	0.24809	4.03076	1.03032	0.97058	4
57	0.24108	4.14809	0.24840	4.02574	1.03039	0.97051	3
58	0.24136	4.14323	0.24871	4.02074	1.03046	0.97044	2
59	0.24164	4.13839	0.24902	4.01576	1.03054	0.97037	1
60	0.24192	4.13357	0.24933	4.01078	1.03061	0.97030	0

103°→ cos	sec	cot	tan	csc	sin ←76°	

14°→ ↓	sin	csc	tan	cot	sec	cos 165° ↓	
0	0.24192	4.13357	0.24933	4.01078	1.03061	0.97030	60
1	0.24220	4.12875	0.24964	4.00582	1.03069	0.97023	59
2	0.24249	4.12394	0.24995	4.00086	1.03076	0.97015	58
3	0.24277	4.11915	0.25026	3.99592	1.03084	0.97008	57
4	0.24305	4.11437	0.25056	3.99099	1.03091	0.97001	56
5	0.24333	4.10960	0.25087	3.98607	1.03099	0.96994	55
6	0.24362	4.10484	0.25118	3.98117	1.03106	0.96987	54
7	0.24390	4.10009	0.25149	3.97627	1.03114	0.96980	53
8	0.24418	4.09535	0.25180	3.97139	1.03121	0.96973	52
9	0.24446	4.09063	0.25211	3.96651	1.03129	0.96966	51
10	0.24474	4.08591	0.25242	3.96165	1.03137	0.96959	50
11	0.24503	4.08121	0.25273	3.95680	1.03144	0.96952	49
12	0.24531	4.07652	0.25304	3.95196	1.03152	0.96945	48
13	0.24559	4.07184	0.25335	3.94713	1.03159	0.96937	47
14	0.24587	4.06717	0.25366	3.94232	1.03167	0.96930	46
15	0.24615	4.06251	0.25397	3.93751	1.03175	0.96923	45
16	0.24644	4.05786	0.25428	3.93271	1.03182	0.96916	44
17	0.24672	4.05322	0.25459	3.92793	1.03190	0.96909	43
18	0.24700	4.04860	0.25490	3.92316	1.03197	0.96902	42
19	0.24728	4.04398	0.25521	3.91839	1.03205	0.96894	41
20	0.24756	4.03938	0.25552	3.91364	1.03213	0.96887	40
21	0.24784	4.03479	0.25583	3.90890	1.03220	0.96880	39
22	0.24813	4.03020	0.25614	3.90417	1.03228	0.96873	38
23	0.24841	4.02563	0.25645	3.89945	1.03236	0.96866	37
24	0.24869	4.02107	0.25676	3.89474	1.03244	0.96858	36
25	0.24897	4.01652	0.25707	3.89004	1.03251	0.96851	35
26	0.24925	4.01198	0.25738	3.88536	1.03259	0.96844	34
27	0.24954	4.00745	0.25769	3.88068	1.03267	0.96837	33
28	0.24982	4.00293	0.25800	3.87601	1.03275	0.96829	32
29	0.25010	3.99843	0.25831	3.87136	1.03282	0.96822	31
30	0.25038	3.99393	0.25862	3.86671	1.03290	0.96815	30
31	0.25066	3.98944	0.25893	3.86208	1.03298	0.96807	29
32	0.25094	3.98497	0.25924	3.85745	1.03306	0.96800	28
33	0.25122	3.98050	0.25955	3.85284	1.03313	0.96793	27
34	0.25151	3.97604	0.25986	3.84824	1.03321	0.96786	26
35	0.25179	3.97160	0.26017	3.84364	1.03329	0.96778	25
36	0.25207	3.96716	0.26048	3.83906	1.03337	0.96771	24
37	0.25235	3.96274	0.26079	3.83449	1.03345	0.96764	23
38	0.25263	3.95832	0.26110	3.82992	1.03353	0.96756	22
39	0.25291	3.95392	0.26141	3.82537	1.03360	0.96749	21
40	0.25320	3.94952	0.26172	3.82083	1.03368	0.96742	20
41	0.25348	3.94514	0.26203	3.81630	1.03376	0.96734	19
42	0.25376	3.94076	0.26235	3.81177	1.03384	0.96727	18
43	0.25404	3.93640	0.26266	3.80726	1.03392	0.96719	17
44	0.25432	3.93204	0.26297	3.80276	1.03400	0.96712	16
45	0.25460	3.92770	0.26328	3.79827	1.03408	0.96705	15
46	0.25488	3.92337	0.26359	3.79378	1.03416	0.96697	14
47	0.25516	3.91904	0.26390	3.78931	1.03424	0.96690	13
48	0.25545	3.91473	0.26421	3.78485	1.03432	0.96682	12
49	0.25573	3.91042	0.26452	3.78040	1.03439	0.96675	11
50	0.25601	3.90613	0.26483	3.77595	1.03447	0.96667	10
51	0.25629	3.90184	0.26515	3.77152	1.03455	0.96660	9
52	0.25657	3.89756	0.26546	3.76709	1.03463	0.96653	8
53	0.25685	3.89330	0.26577	3.76268	1.03471	0.96645	7
54	0.25713	3.88904	0.26608	3.75828	1.03479	0.96638	6
55	0.25741	3.88479	0.26639	3.75388	1.03487	0.96630	5
56	0.25769	3.88056	0.26670	3.74950	1.03495	0.96623	4
57	0.25798	3.87633	0.26701	3.74512	1.03503	0.96615	3
58	0.25826	3.87211	0.26733	3.74075	1.03511	0.96608	2
59	0.25854	3.86790	0.26764	3.73640	1.03520	0.96600	1
60	0.25882	3.86370	0.26795	3.73205	1.03528	0.96593	0
↑ 104°→ cos		sec	cot	tan	csc	sin ↑ ←75°	

15°→ ↓	sin	csc	tan	cot	sec	cos 164° ↓	
0	0.25882	3.86370	0.26795	3.73205	1.03528	0.96593	60
1	0.25910	3.85951	0.26826	3.72771	1.03536	0.96585	59
2	0.25938	3.85533	0.26857	3.72338	1.03544	0.96578	58
3	0.25966	3.85116	0.26888	3.71907	1.03552	0.96570	57
4	0.25994	3.84700	0.26920	3.71476	1.03560	0.96562	56
5	0.26022	3.84285	0.26951	3.71046	1.03568	0.96555	55
6	0.26050	3.83871	0.26982	3.70616	1.03576	0.96547	54
7	0.26079	3.83457	0.27013	3.70188	1.03584	0.96540	53
8	0.26107	3.83045	0.27044	3.69761	1.03592	0.96532	52
9	0.26135	3.82633	0.27076	3.69335	1.03601	0.96524	51
10	0.26163	3.82223	0.27107	3.68909	1.03609	0.96517	50
11	0.26191	3.81813	0.27138	3.68485	1.03617	0.96509	49
12	0.26219	3.81404	0.27169	3.68061	1.03625	0.96502	48
13	0.26247	3.80996	0.27201	3.67638	1.03633	0.96494	47
14	0.26275	3.80589	0.27232	3.67217	1.03642	0.96486	46
15	0.26303	3.80183	0.27263	3.66796	1.03650	0.96479	45
16	0.26331	3.79778	0.27294	3.66376	1.03658	0.96471	44
17	0.26359	3.79374	0.27326	3.65957	1.03666	0.96463	43
18	0.26387	3.78970	0.27357	3.65538	1.03674	0.96456	42
19	0.26415	3.78568	0.27388	3.65121	1.03683	0.96448	41
20	0.26443	3.78166	0.27419	3.64705	1.03691	0.96440	40
21	0.26471	3.77765	0.27451	3.64289	1.03699	0.96433	39
22	0.26500	3.77365	0.27482	3.63874	1.03708	0.96425	38
23	0.26528	3.76966	0.27513	3.63461	1.03716	0.96417	37
24	0.26556	3.76568	0.27545	3.63048	1.03724	0.96410	36
25	0.26584	3.76171	0.27576	3.62636	1.03732	0.96402	35
26	0.26612	3.75775	0.27607	3.62224	1.03741	0.96394	34
27	0.26640	3.75379	0.27638	3.61814	1.03749	0.96386	33
28	0.26668	3.74984	0.27670	3.61405	1.03757	0.96379	32
29	0.26696	3.74591	0.27701	3.60996	1.03766	0.96371	31
30	0.26724	3.74198	0.27732	3.60588	1.03774	0.96363	30
31	0.26752	3.73806	0.27764	3.60181	1.03783	0.96355	29
32	0.26780	3.73414	0.27795	3.59775	1.03791	0.96347	28
33	0.26808	3.73024	0.27826	3.59370	1.03799	0.96340	27
34	0.26836	3.72635	0.27858	3.58966	1.03808	0.96332	26
35	0.26864	3.72246	0.27889	3.58562	1.03816	0.96324	25
36	0.26892	3.71858	0.27921	3.58160	1.03825	0.96316	24
37	0.26920	3.71471	0.27952	3.57758	1.03833	0.96308	23
38	0.26948	3.71085	0.27983	3.57357	1.03842	0.96301	22
39	0.26976	3.70700	0.28015	3.56957	1.03850	0.96293	21
40	0.27004	3.70315	0.28046	3.56557	1.03858	0.96285	20
41	0.27032	3.69931	0.28077	3.56159	1.03867	0.96277	19
42	0.27060	3.69549	0.28109	3.55761	1.03875	0.96269	18
43	0.27088	3.69167	0.28140	3.55364	1.03884	0.96261	17
44	0.27116	3.68785	0.28172	3.54968	1.03892	0.96253	16
45	0.27144	3.68405	0.28203	3.54573	1.03901	0.96246	15
46	0.27172	3.68025	0.28234	3.54179	1.03909	0.96238	14
47	0.27200	3.67647	0.28266	3.53785	1.03918	0.96230	13
48	0.27228	3.67269	0.28297	3.53393	1.03927	0.96222	12
49	0.27256	3.66892	0.28329	3.53001	1.03935	0.96214	11
50	0.27284	3.66515	0.28360	3.52609	1.03944	0.96206	10
51	0.27312	3.66140	0.28391	3.52219	1.03952	0.96198	9
52	0.27340	3.65765	0.28423	3.51829	1.03961	0.96190	8
53	0.27368	3.65391	0.28454	3.51441	1.03969	0.96182	7
54	0.27396	3.65018	0.28486	3.51053	1.03978	0.96174	6
55	0.27424	3.64645	0.28517	3.50666	1.03987	0.96166	5
56	0.27452	3.64274	0.28549	3.50279	1.03995	0.96158	4
57	0.27480	3.63903	0.28580	3.49894	1.04004	0.96150	3
58	0.27508	3.63533	0.28612	3.49509	1.04013	0.96142	2
59	0.27536	3.63164	0.28643	3.49125	1.04021	0.96134	1
60	0.27564	3.62796	0.28675	3.48741	1.04030	0.96126	0
↑ 105°→ cos		sec	cot	tan	csc	sin ↑ ←74°	

284

16°→ ↓	sin	csc	tan	cot	sec	cos ←163° ↓	
0	0.27564	3.62796	0.28675	3.48741	1.04030	0.96126	60
1	0.27592	3.62428	0.28706	3.48359	1.04039	0.96118	59
2	0.27620	3.62061	0.28738	3.47977	1.04047	0.96110	58
3	0.27648	3.61695	0.28769	3.47596	1.04056	0.96102	57
4	0.27676	3.61330	0.28801	3.47216	1.04065	0.96094	56
5	0.27704	3.60965	0.28832	3.46837	1.04073	0.96086	55
6	0.27731	3.60601	0.28864	3.46458	1.04082	0.96078	54
7	0.27759	3.60238	0.28895	3.46080	1.04091	0.96070	53
8	0.27787	3.59876	0.28927	3.45703	1.04100	0.96062	52
9	0.27815	3.59514	0.28958	3.45327	1.04108	0.96054	51
10	0.27843	3.59154	0.28990	3.44951	1.04117	0.96046	50
11	0.27871	3.58794	0.29021	3.44576	1.04126	0.96037	49
12	0.27899	3.58434	0.29053	3.44202	1.04135	0.96029	48
13	0.27927	3.58076	0.29084	3.43829	1.04144	0.96021	47
14	0.27955	3.57718	0.29116	3.43456	1.04152	0.96013	46
15	0.27983	3.57361	0.29147	3.43084	1.04161	0.96005	45
16	0.28011	3.57005	0.29179	3.42713	1.04170	0.95997	44
17	0.28039	3.56649	0.29210	3.42343	1.04179	0.95989	43
18	0.28067	3.56294	0.29242	3.41973	1.04188	0.95981	42
19	0.28095	3.55940	0.29274	3.41604	1.04197	0.95972	41
20	0.28123	3.55587	0.29305	3.41236	1.04206	0.95964	40
21	0.28150	3.55234	0.29337	3.40869	1.04214	0.95956	39
22	0.28178	3.54883	0.29368	3.40502	1.04223	0.95948	38
23	0.28206	3.54531	0.29400	3.40136	1.04232	0.95940	37
24	0.28234	3.54181	0.29432	3.39771	1.04241	0.95931	36
25	0.28262	3.53831	0.29463	3.39406	1.04250	0.95923	35
26	0.28290	3.53482	0.29495	3.39042	1.04259	0.95915	34
27	0.28318	3.53134	0.29526	3.38679	1.04268	0.95907	33
28	0.28346	3.52787	0.29558	3.38317	1.04277	0.95898	32
29	0.28374	3.52440	0.29590	3.37955	1.04286	0.95890	31
30	0.28402	3.52094	0.29621	3.37594	1.04295	0.95882	30
31	0.28429	3.51748	0.29653	3.37234	1.04304	0.95874	29
32	0.28457	3.51404	0.29685	3.36875	1.04313	0.95865	28
33	0.28485	3.51060	0.29716	3.36516	1.04322	0.95857	27
34	0.28513	3.50716	0.29748	3.36158	1.04331	0.95849	26
35	0.28541	3.50374	0.29780	3.35800	1.04340	0.95841	25
36	0.28569	3.50032	0.29811	3.35443	1.04349	0.95832	24
37	0.28597	3.49691	0.29843	3.35087	1.04358	0.95824	23
38	0.28625	3.49350	0.29875	3.34732	1.04367	0.95816	22
39	0.28652	3.49010	0.29906	3.34377	1.04376	0.95807	21
40	0.28680	3.48671	0.29938	3.34023	1.04385	0.95799	20
41	0.28708	3.48333	0.29970	3.33670	1.04394	0.95791	19
42	0.28736	3.47995	0.30001	3.33317	1.04403	0.95782	18
43	0.28764	3.47658	0.30033	3.32965	1.04413	0.95774	17
44	0.28792	3.47321	0.30065	3.32614	1.04422	0.95766	16
45	0.28820	3.46986	0.30097	3.32264	1.04431	0.95757	15
46	0.28847	3.46651	0.30128	3.31914	1.04440	0.95749	14
47	0.28875	3.46316	0.30160	3.31565	1.04449	0.95740	13
48	0.28903	3.45983	0.30192	3.31216	1.04458	0.95732	12
49	0.28931	3.45650	0.30224	3.30868	1.04468	0.95724	11
50	0.28959	3.45317	0.30255	3.30521	1.04477	0.95715	10
51	0.28987	3.44986	0.30287	3.30174	1.04486	0.95707	9
52	0.29015	3.44655	0.30319	3.29829	1.04495	0.95698	8
53	0.29042	3.44324	0.30351	3.29483	1.04504	0.95690	7
54	0.29070	3.43995	0.30382	3.29139	1.04514	0.95681	6
55	0.29098	3.43666	0.30414	3.28795	1.04523	0.95673	5
56	0.29126	3.43337	0.30446	3.28452	1.04532	0.95664	4
57	0.29154	3.43010	0.30478	3.28109	1.04541	0.95656	3
58	0.29182	3.42683	0.30509	3.27767	1.04551	0.95647	2
59	0.29209	3.42356	0.30541	3.27426	1.04560	0.95639	1
60	0.29237	3.42030	0.30573	3.27085	1.04569	0.95630	0

↑ 106°cos →	sec	cot	tan	csc	sin ← 73° ↑	

17°→ ↓	sin	csc	tan	cot	sec	cos ←162° ↓	
0	0.29237	3.42030	0.30573	3.27085	1.04569	0.95630	60
1	0.29265	3.41705	0.30605	3.26745	1.04578	0.95622	59
2	0.29293	3.41381	0.30637	3.26406	1.04588	0.95613	58
3	0.29321	3.41057	0.30669	3.26067	1.04597	0.95605	57
4	0.29348	3.40734	0.30700	3.25729	1.04606	0.95596	56
5	0.29376	3.40411	0.30732	3.25392	1.04616	0.95588	55
6	0.29404	3.40089	0.30764	3.25055	1.04625	0.95579	54
7	0.29432	3.39768	0.30796	3.24719	1.04635	0.95571	53
8	0.29460	3.39448	0.30828	3.24383	1.04644	0.95562	52
9	0.29487	3.39128	0.30860	3.24049	1.04653	0.95554	51
10	0.29515	3.38808	0.30891	3.23714	1.04663	0.95545	50
11	0.29543	3.38489	0.30923	3.23381	1.04672	0.95536	49
12	0.29571	3.38171	0.30955	3.23048	1.04682	0.95528	48
13	0.29599	3.37854	0.30987	3.22715	1.04691	0.95519	47
14	0.29626	3.37537	0.31019	3.22384	1.04700	0.95511	46
15	0.29654	3.37221	0.31051	3.22053	1.04710	0.95502	45
16	0.29682	3.36905	0.31083	3.21722	1.04719	0.95493	44
17	0.29710	3.36590	0.31115	3.21392	1.04729	0.95485	43
18	0.29737	3.36276	0.31147	3.21063	1.04738	0.95476	42
19	0.29765	3.35962	0.31178	3.20734	1.04748	0.95467	41
20	0.29793	3.35649	0.31210	3.20406	1.04757	0.95459	40
21	0.29821	3.35336	0.31242	3.20079	1.04767	0.95450	39
22	0.29849	3.35025	0.31274	3.19752	1.04776	0.95441	38
23	0.29876	3.34713	0.31306	3.19426	1.04786	0.95433	37
24	0.29904	3.34403	0.31338	3.19100	1.04795	0.95424	36
25	0.29932	3.34092	0.31370	3.18775	1.04805	0.95415	35
26	0.29960	3.33783	0.31402	3.18451	1.04815	0.95407	34
27	0.29987	3.33474	0.31434	3.18127	1.04824	0.95398	33
28	0.30015	3.33166	0.31466	3.17804	1.04834	0.95389	32
29	0.30043	3.32858	0.31498	3.17481	1.04843	0.95380	31
30	0.30071	3.32551	0.31530	3.17159	1.04853	0.95372	30
31	0.30098	3.32244	0.31562	3.16838	1.04863	0.95363	29
32	0.30126	3.31939	0.31594	3.16517	1.04872	0.95354	28
33	0.30154	3.31633	0.31626	3.16197	1.04882	0.95345	27
34	0.30182	3.31328	0.31658	3.15877	1.04891	0.95337	26
35	0.30209	3.31024	0.31690	3.15558	1.04901	0.95328	25
36	0.30237	3.30721	0.31722	3.15240	1.04911	0.95319	24
37	0.30265	3.30418	0.31754	3.14922	1.04920	0.95310	23
38	0.30292	3.30115	0.31786	3.14605	1.04930	0.95301	22
39	0.30320	3.29814	0.31818	3.14288	1.04940	0.95293	21
40	0.30348	3.29512	0.31850	3.13972	1.04950	0.95284	20
41	0.30376	3.29212	0.31882	3.13656	1.04959	0.95275	19
42	0.30403	3.28912	0.31914	3.13341	1.04969	0.95266	18
43	0.30431	3.28612	0.31946	3.13027	1.04979	0.95257	17
44	0.30459	3.28313	0.31978	3.12713	1.04989	0.95248	16
45	0.30486	3.28015	0.32010	3.12400	1.04998	0.95240	15
46	0.30514	3.27717	0.32042	3.12087	1.05008	0.95231	14
47	0.30542	3.27420	0.32074	3.11775	1.05018	0.95222	13
48	0.30570	3.27123	0.32106	3.11464	1.05028	0.95213	12
49	0.30597	3.26827	0.32139	3.11153	1.05038	0.95204	11
50	0.30625	3.26531	0.32171	3.10842	1.05047	0.95195	10
51	0.30653	3.26237	0.32203	3.10532	1.05057	0.95186	9
52	0.30680	3.25942	0.32235	3.10223	1.05067	0.95177	8
53	0.30708	3.25648	0.32267	3.09914	1.05077	0.95168	7
54	0.30736	3.25355	0.32299	3.09606	1.05087	0.95159	6
55	0.30763	3.25062	0.32331	3.09298	1.05097	0.95150	5
56	0.30791	3.24770	0.32363	3.08991	1.05107	0.95142	4
57	0.30819	3.24478	0.32396	3.08685	1.05116	0.95133	3
58	0.30846	3.24187	0.32428	3.08379	1.05126	0.95124	2
59	0.30874	3.23897	0.32460	3.08073	1.05136	0.95115	1
60	0.30902	3.23607	0.32492	3.07768	1.05146	0.95106	0

↑ 107°cos →	sec	cot	tan	csc	sin ← 72° ↑	

18°→ ↓	sin	csc	tan	cot	sec	cos ←161° ↓	
0	0.30902	3.23607	0.32492	3.07768	1.05146	0.95106	60
1	0.30929	3.23317	0.32524	3.07464	1.05156	0.95097	59
2	0.30957	3.23028	0.32556	3.07160	1.05166	0.95088	58
3	0.30985	3.22740	0.32588	3.06857	1.05176	0.95079	57
4	0.31012	3.22452	0.32621	3.06554	1.05186	0.95070	56
5	0.31040	3.22165	0.32653	3.06252	1.05196	0.95061	55
6	0.31068	3.21878	0.32685	3.05950	1.05206	0.95052	54
7	0.31095	3.21592	0.32717	3.05649	1.05216	0.95043	53
8	0.31123	3.21306	0.32749	3.05349	1.05226	0.95033	52
9	0.31151	3.21021	0.32782	3.05049	1.05236	0.95024	51
10	0.31178	3.20737	0.32814	3.04749	1.05246	0.95015	50
11	0.31206	3.20453	0.32846	3.04450	1.05256	0.95006	49
12	0.31233	3.20169	0.32878	3.04152	1.05266	0.94997	48
13	0.31261	3.19886	0.32911	3.03854	1.05276	0.94988	47
14	0.31289	3.19604	0.32943	3.03556	1.05286	0.94979	46
15	0.31316	3.19322	0.32975	3.03260	1.05297	0.94970	45
16	0.31344	3.19040	0.33007	3.02963	1.05307	0.94961	44
17	0.31372	3.18759	0.33040	3.02667	1.05317	0.94952	43
18	0.31399	3.18479	0.33072	3.02372	1.05327	0.94943	42
19	0.31427	3.18199	0.33104	3.02077	1.05337	0.94933	41
20	0.31454	3.17920	0.33136	3.01783	1.05347	0.94924	40
21	0.31482	3.17641	0.33169	3.01489	1.05357	0.94915	39
22	0.31510	3.17363	0.33201	3.01196	1.05367	0.94906	38
23	0.31537	3.17085	0.33233	3.00903	1.05378	0.94897	37
24	0.31565	3.16808	0.33266	3.00611	1.05388	0.94888	36
25	0.31593	3.16531	0.33298	3.00319	1.05398	0.94878	35
26	0.31620	3.16255	0.33330	3.00028	1.05408	0.94869	34
27	0.31648	3.15979	0.33363	2.99738	1.05418	0.94860	33
28	0.31675	3.15704	0.33395	2.99447	1.05429	0.94851	32
29	0.31703	3.15429	0.33427	2.99158	1.05439	0.94842	31
30	0.31730	3.15155	0.33460	2.98868	1.05449	0.94832	30
31	0.31758	3.14881	0.33492	2.98580	1.05459	0.94823	29
32	0.31786	3.14608	0.33524	2.98292	1.05470	0.94814	28
33	0.31813	3.14335	0.33557	2.98004	1.05480	0.94805	27
34	0.31841	3.14063	0.33589	2.97717	1.05490	0.94795	26
35	0.31868	3.13791	0.33621	2.97430	1.05501	0.94786	25
36	0.31896	3.13520	0.33654	2.97144	1.05511	0.94777	24
37	0.31923	3.13249	0.33686	2.96858	1.05521	0.94768	23
38	0.31951	3.12979	0.33718	2.96573	1.05532	0.94758	22
39	0.31979	3.12709	0.33751	2.96288	1.05542	0.94749	21
40	0.32006	3.12440	0.33783	2.96004	1.05552	0.94740	20
41	0.32034	3.12171	0.33816	2.95721	1.05563	0.94730	19
42	0.32061	3.11903	0.33848	2.95437	1.05573	0.94721	18
43	0.32089	3.11635	0.33881	2.95155	1.05584	0.94712	17
44	0.32116	3.11367	0.33913	2.94872	1.05594	0.94702	16
45	0.32144	3.11101	0.33945	2.94591	1.05604	0.94693	15
46	0.32171	3.10834	0.33978	2.94309	1.05615	0.94684	14
47	0.32199	3.10568	0.34010	2.94028	1.05625	0.94674	13
48	0.32227	3.10303	0.34043	2.93748	1.05636	0.94665	12
49	0.32254	3.10038	0.34075	2.93468	1.05646	0.94656	11
50	0.32282	3.09774	0.34108	2.93189	1.05657	0.94646	10
51	0.32309	3.09510	0.34140	2.92910	1.05667	0.94637	9
52	0.32337	3.09246	0.34173	2.92632	1.05678	0.94627	8
53	0.32364	3.08983	0.34205	2.92354	1.05688	0.94618	7
54	0.32392	3.08721	0.34238	2.92076	1.05699	0.94609	6
55	0.32419	3.08459	0.34270	2.91799	1.05709	0.94599	5
56	0.32447	3.08197	0.34303	2.91523	1.05720	0.94590	4
57	0.32474	3.07936	0.34335	2.91246	1.05730	0.94580	3
58	0.32502	3.07675	0.34368	2.90971	1.05741	0.94571	2
59	0.32529	3.07415	0.34400	2.90696	1.05751	0.94561	1
60	0.32557	3.07155	0.34433	2.90421	1.05762	0.94552	0

108°→ ↑ cos	sec	cot	tan	csc	sin ←71° ↑	

19°→ ↓	sin	csc	tan	cot	sec	cos ←160° ↓	
0	0.32557	3.07155	0.34433	2.90421	1.05762	0.94552	60
1	0.32584	3.06896	0.34465	2.90147	1.05773	0.94542	59
2	0.32612	3.06637	0.34498	2.89873	1.05783	0.94533	58
3	0.32639	3.06379	0.34530	2.89600	1.05794	0.94523	57
4	0.32667	3.06121	0.34563	2.89327	1.05805	0.94514	56
5	0.32694	3.05864	0.34596	2.89055	1.05815	0.94504	55
6	0.32722	3.05607	0.34628	2.88783	1.05826	0.94495	54
7	0.32749	3.05350	0.34661	2.88511	1.05836	0.94485	53
8	0.32777	3.05094	0.34693	2.88240	1.05847	0.94476	52
9	0.32804	3.04839	0.34726	2.87970	1.05858	0.94466	51
10	0.32832	3.04584	0.34758	2.87700	1.05869	0.94457	50
11	0.32859	3.04329	0.34791	2.87430	1.05879	0.94447	49
12	0.32887	3.04075	0.34824	2.87161	1.05890	0.94438	48
13	0.32914	3.03821	0.34856	2.86892	1.05901	0.94428	47
14	0.32942	3.03568	0.34889	2.86624	1.05911	0.94418	46
15	0.32969	3.03315	0.34922	2.86356	1.05922	0.94409	45
16	0.32997	3.03062	0.34954	2.86089	1.05933	0.94399	44
17	0.33024	3.02810	0.34987	2.85822	1.05944	0.94390	43
18	0.33051	3.02559	0.35020	2.85555	1.05955	0.94380	42
19	0.33079	3.02308	0.35052	2.85289	1.05965	0.94370	41
20	0.33106	3.02057	0.35085	2.85023	1.05976	0.94361	40
21	0.33134	3.01807	0.35118	2.84758	1.05987	0.94351	39
22	0.33161	3.01557	0.35150	2.84494	1.05998	0.94342	38
23	0.33189	3.01308	0.35183	2.84229	1.06009	0.94332	37
24	0.33216	3.01059	0.35216	2.83965	1.06020	0.94322	36
25	0.33244	3.00810	0.35248	2.83702	1.06030	0.94313	35
26	0.33271	3.00562	0.35281	2.83439	1.06041	0.94303	34
27	0.33298	3.00315	0.35314	2.83176	1.06052	0.94293	33
28	0.33326	3.00067	0.35346	2.82914	1.06063	0.94284	32
29	0.33353	2.99821	0.35379	2.82653	1.06074	0.94274	31
30	0.33381	2.99574	0.35412	2.82391	1.06085	0.94264	30
31	0.33408	2.99329	0.35445	2.82130	1.06096	0.94254	29
32	0.33436	2.99083	0.35477	2.81870	1.06107	0.94245	28
33	0.33463	2.98838	0.35510	2.81610	1.06118	0.94235	27
34	0.33490	2.98594	0.35543	2.81350	1.06129	0.94225	26
35	0.33518	2.98349	0.35576	2.81091	1.06140	0.94215	25
36	0.33545	2.98106	0.35608	2.80833	1.06151	0.94206	24
37	0.33573	2.97862	0.35641	2.80574	1.06162	0.94196	23
38	0.33600	2.97619	0.35674	2.80316	1.06173	0.94186	22
39	0.33627	2.97377	0.35707	2.80059	1.06184	0.94176	21
40	0.33655	2.97135	0.35740	2.79802	1.06195	0.94167	20
41	0.33682	2.96893	0.35772	2.79545	1.06206	0.94157	19
42	0.33710	2.96652	0.35805	2.79289	1.06217	0.94147	18
43	0.33737	2.96411	0.35838	2.79033	1.06228	0.94137	17
44	0.33764	2.96171	0.35871	2.78778	1.06239	0.94127	16
45	0.33792	2.95931	0.35904	2.78523	1.06250	0.94118	15
46	0.33819	2.95691	0.35937	2.78269	1.06261	0.94108	14
47	0.33846	2.95452	0.35969	2.78014	1.06272	0.94098	13
48	0.33874	2.95213	0.36002	2.77761	1.06283	0.94088	12
49	0.33901	2.94975	0.36035	2.77507	1.06295	0.94078	11
50	0.33929	2.94737	0.36068	2.77254	1.06306	0.94068	10
51	0.33956	2.94500	0.36101	2.77002	1.06317	0.94058	9
52	0.33983	2.94263	0.36134	2.76750	1.06328	0.94049	8
53	0.34011	2.94026	0.36167	2.76498	1.06339	0.94039	7
54	0.34038	2.93790	0.36199	2.76247	1.06350	0.94029	6
55	0.34065	2.93554	0.36232	2.75996	1.06362	0.94019	5
56	0.34093	2.93318	0.36265	2.75746	1.06373	0.94009	4
57	0.34120	2.93083	0.36298	2.75496	1.06384	0.93999	3
58	0.34147	2.92849	0.36331	2.75246	1.06395	0.93989	2
59	0.34175	2.92614	0.36364	2.74997	1.06407	0.93979	1
60	0.34202	2.92380	0.36397	2.74748	1.06418	0.93969	0

109°→ ↑ cos	sec	cot	tan	csc	sin ←70° ↑	

20°→ ↓	sin	csc	tan	cot	sec	cos→159° ↓	
0	0.34202	2.92380	0.36397	2.74748	1.06418	0.93969	60
1	0.34229	2.92147	0.36430	2.74499	1.06429	0.93959	59
2	0.34257	2.91914	0.36463	2.74251	1.06440	0.93949	58
3	0.34284	2.91681	0.36496	2.74004	1.06452	0.93939	57
4	0.34311	2.91449	0.36529	2.73756	1.06463	0.93929	56
5	0.34339	2.91217	0.36562	2.73509	1.06474	0.93919	55
6	0.34366	2.90986	0.36595	2.73263	1.06486	0.93909	54
7	0.34393	2.90754	0.36628	2.73017	1.06497	0.93899	53
8	0.34421	2.90524	0.36661	2.72771	1.06508	0.93889	52
9	0.34448	2.90293	0.36694	2.72526	1.06520	0.93879	51
10	0.34475	2.90063	0.36727	2.72281	1.06531	0.93869	50
11	0.34503	2.89834	0.36760	2.72036	1.06542	0.93859	49
12	0.34530	2.89605	0.36793	2.71792	1.06554	0.93849	48
13	0.34557	2.89376	0.36826	2.71548	1.06565	0.93839	47
14	0.34584	2.89148	0.36859	2.71305	1.06577	0.93829	46
15	0.34612	2.88920	0.36892	2.71062	1.06588	0.93819	45
16	0.34639	2.88692	0.36925	2.70819	1.06600	0.93809	44
17	0.34666	2.88465	0.36958	2.70577	1.06611	0.93799	43
18	0.34694	2.88238	0.36991	2.70335	1.06622	0.93789	42
19	0.34721	2.88011	0.37024	2.70094	1.06634	0.93779	41
20	0.34748	2.87785	0.37057	2.69853	1.06645	0.93769	40
21	0.34775	2.87560	0.37090	2.69612	1.06657	0.93759	39
22	0.34803	2.87334	0.37123	2.69371	1.06668	0.93748	38
23	0.34830	2.87109	0.37157	2.69131	1.06680	0.93738	37
24	0.34857	2.86885	0.37190	2.68892	1.06691	0.93728	36
25	0.34884	2.86661	0.37223	2.68653	1.06703	0.93718	35
26	0.34912	2.86437	0.37256	2.68414	1.06715	0.93708	34
27	0.34939	2.86213	0.37289	2.68175	1.06726	0.93698	33
28	0.34966	2.85990	0.37322	2.67937	1.06738	0.93688	32
29	0.34993	2.85767	0.37355	2.67700	1.06749	0.93677	31
30	0.35021	2.85545	0.37388	2.67462	1.06761	0.93667	30
31	0.35048	2.85323	0.37422	2.67225	1.06773	0.93657	29
32	0.35075	2.85102	0.37455	2.66989	1.06784	0.93647	28
33	0.35102	2.84880	0.37488	2.66752	1.06796	0.93637	27
34	0.35130	2.84659	0.37521	2.66516	1.06807	0.93626	26
35	0.35157	2.84439	0.37554	2.66281	1.06819	0.93616	25
36	0.35184	2.84219	0.37588	2.66046	1.06831	0.93606	24
37	0.35211	2.83999	0.37621	2.65811	1.06842	0.93596	23
38	0.35239	2.83780	0.37654	2.65576	1.06854	0.93585	22
39	0.35266	2.83561	0.37687	2.65342	1.06866	0.93575	21
40	0.35293	2.83342	0.37720	2.65109	1.06878	0.93565	20
41	0.35320	2.83124	0.37754	2.64875	1.06889	0.93555	19
42	0.35347	2.82906	0.37787	2.64642	1.06901	0.93544	18
43	0.35375	2.82688	0.37820	2.64410	1.06913	0.93534	17
44	0.35402	2.82471	0.37853	2.64177	1.06925	0.93524	16
45	0.35429	2.82254	0.37887	2.63945	1.06936	0.93514	15
46	0.35456	2.82037	0.37920	2.63714	1.06948	0.93503	14
47	0.35484	2.81821	0.37953	2.63483	1.06960	0.93493	13
48	0.35511	2.81605	0.37986	2.63252	1.06972	0.93483	12
49	0.35538	2.81390	0.38020	2.63021	1.06984	0.93472	11
50	0.35565	2.81175	0.38053	2.62791	1.06995	0.93462	10
51	0.35592	2.80960	0.38086	2.62561	1.07007	0.93452	9
52	0.35619	2.80746	0.38120	2.62332	1.07019	0.93441	8
53	0.35647	2.80531	0.38153	2.62103	1.07031	0.93431	7
54	0.35674	2.80318	0.38186	2.61874	1.07043	0.93420	6
55	0.35701	2.80104	0.38220	2.61646	1.07055	0.93410	5
56	0.35728	2.79891	0.38253	2.61418	1.07067	0.93400	4
57	0.35755	2.79679	0.38286	2.61190	1.07079	0.93389	3
58	0.35782	2.79466	0.38320	2.60963	1.07091	0.93379	2
59	0.35810	2.79254	0.38353	2.60736	1.07103	0.93368	1
60	0.35837	2.79043	0.38386	2.60509	1.07114	0.93358	0
↑ 110°cos →	sec	cot	tan	csc	sin←69° ↑		

21°→ ↓	sin	csc	tan	cot	sec	cos→158° ↓	
0	0.35837	2.79043	0.38386	2.60509	1.07114	0.93358	60
1	0.35864	2.78832	0.38420	2.60283	1.07126	0.93348	59
2	0.35891	2.78621	0.38453	2.60057	1.07138	0.93337	58
3	0.35918	2.78410	0.38487	2.59831	1.07150	0.93327	57
4	0.35945	2.78200	0.38520	2.59606	1.07162	0.93316	56
5	0.35973	2.77990	0.38553	2.59381	1.07174	0.93306	55
6	0.36000	2.77780	0.38587	2.59156	1.07186	0.93295	54
7	0.36027	2.77571	0.38620	2.58932	1.07199	0.93285	53
8	0.36054	2.77362	0.38654	2.58708	1.07211	0.93274	52
9	0.36081	2.77154	0.38687	2.58484	1.07223	0.93264	51
10	0.36108	2.76945	0.38721	2.58261	1.07235	0.93253	50
11	0.36135	2.76737	0.38754	2.58038	1.07247	0.93243	49
12	0.36162	2.76530	0.38787	2.57815	1.07259	0.93232	48
13	0.36190	2.76323	0.38821	2.57593	1.07271	0.93222	47
14	0.36217	2.76116	0.38854	2.57371	1.07283	0.93211	46
15	0.36244	2.75909	0.38888	2.57150	1.07295	0.93201	45
16	0.36271	2.75703	0.38921	2.56928	1.07307	0.93190	44
17	0.36298	2.75497	0.38955	2.56707	1.07320	0.93180	43
18	0.36325	2.75292	0.38988	2.56487	1.07332	0.93169	42
19	0.36352	2.75086	0.39022	2.56266	1.07344	0.93159	41
20	0.36379	2.74881	0.39055	2.56046	1.07356	0.93148	40
21	0.36406	2.74677	0.39089	2.55827	1.07368	0.93137	39
22	0.36434	2.74473	0.39122	2.55608	1.07380	0.93127	38
23	0.36461	2.74269	0.39156	2.55389	1.07393	0.93116	37
24	0.36488	2.74065	0.39190	2.55170	1.07405	0.93106	36
25	0.36515	2.73862	0.39223	2.54952	1.07417	0.93095	35
26	0.36542	2.73659	0.39257	2.54734	1.07429	0.93084	34
27	0.36569	2.73456	0.39290	2.54516	1.07442	0.93074	33
28	0.36596	2.73254	0.39324	2.54299	1.07454	0.93063	32
29	0.36623	2.73052	0.39357	2.54082	1.07466	0.93052	31
30	0.36650	2.72850	0.39391	2.53865	1.07479	0.93042	30
31	0.36677	2.72649	0.39425	2.53648	1.07491	0.93031	29
32	0.36704	2.72448	0.39458	2.53432	1.07503	0.93020	28
33	0.36731	2.72247	0.39492	2.53217	1.07516	0.93010	27
34	0.36758	2.72047	0.39526	2.53001	1.07528	0.92999	26
35	0.36785	2.71847	0.39559	2.52786	1.07540	0.92988	25
36	0.36812	2.71647	0.39593	2.52571	1.07553	0.92978	24
37	0.36839	2.71448	0.39626	2.52357	1.07565	0.92967	23
38	0.36867	2.71249	0.39660	2.52142	1.07578	0.92956	22
39	0.36894	2.71050	0.39694	2.51929	1.07590	0.92945	21
40	0.36921	2.70851	0.39727	2.51715	1.07602	0.92935	20
41	0.36948	2.70653	0.39761	2.51502	1.07615	0.92924	19
42	0.36975	2.70455	0.39795	2.51289	1.07627	0.92913	18
43	0.37002	2.70258	0.39829	2.51076	1.07640	0.92902	17
44	0.37029	2.70061	0.39862	2.50864	1.07652	0.92892	16
45	0.37056	2.69864	0.39896	2.50652	1.07665	0.92881	15
46	0.37083	2.69667	0.39930	2.50440	1.07677	0.92870	14
47	0.37110	2.69471	0.39963	2.50229	1.07690	0.92859	13
48	0.37137	2.69275	0.39997	2.50018	1.07702	0.92849	12
49	0.37164	2.69079	0.40031	2.49807	1.07715	0.92838	11
50	0.37191	2.68884	0.40065	2.49597	1.07727	0.92827	10
51	0.37218	2.68689	0.40098	2.49386	1.07740	0.92816	9
52	0.37245	2.68494	0.40132	2.49177	1.07752	0.92805	8
53	0.37272	2.68299	0.40166	2.48967	1.07765	0.92794	7
54	0.37299	2.68105	0.40200	2.48758	1.07778	0.92784	6
55	0.37326	2.67911	0.40234	2.48549	1.07790	0.92773	5
56	0.37353	2.67718	0.40267	2.48340	1.07803	0.92762	4
57	0.37380	2.67525	0.40301	2.48132	1.07816	0.92751	3
58	0.37407	2.67332	0.40335	2.47924	1.07828	0.92740	2
59	0.37434	2.67139	0.40369	2.47716	1.07841	0.92729	1
60	0.37461	2.66947	0.40403	2.47509	1.07853	0.92718	0
↑ 111°cos →	sec	cot	tan	csc	sin←68° ↑		

	sin	csc	tan	cot	sec	cos	
0	0.37461	2.66947	0.40403	2.47509	1.07853	0.92718	60
1	0.37488	2.66755	0.40436	2.47302	1.07866	0.92707	59
2	0.37515	2.66563	0.40470	2.47095	1.07879	0.92697	58
3	0.37542	2.66371	0.40504	2.46888	1.07892	0.92686	57
4	0.37569	2.66180	0.40538	2.46682	1.07904	0.92675	56
5	0.37595	2.65989	0.40572	2.46476	1.07917	0.92664	55
6	0.37622	2.65799	0.40606	2.46270	1.07930	0.92653	54
7	0.37649	2.65609	0.40640	2.46065	1.07943	0.92642	53
8	0.37676	2.65419	0.40674	2.45860	1.07955	0.92631	52
9	0.37703	2.65229	0.40707	2.45655	1.07968	0.92620	51
10	0.37730	2.65040	0.40741	2.45451	1.07981	0.92609	50
11	0.37757	2.64851	0.40775	2.45246	1.07994	0.92598	49
12	0.37784	2.64662	0.40809	2.45043	1.08006	0.92587	48
13	0.37811	2.64473	0.40843	2.44839	1.08019	0.92576	47
14	0.37838	2.64285	0.40877	2.44636	1.08032	0.92565	46
15	0.37865	2.64097	0.40911	2.44433	1.08045	0.92554	45
16	0.37892	2.63909	0.40945	2.44230	1.08058	0.92543	44
17	0.37919	2.63722	0.40979	2.44027	1.08071	0.92532	43
18	0.37946	2.63535	0.41013	2.43825	1.08084	0.92521	42
19	0.37973	2.63348	0.41047	2.43623	1.08097	0.92510	41
20	0.37999	2.63162	0.41081	2.43422	1.08109	0.92499	40
21	0.38026	2.62976	0.41115	2.43220	1.08122	0.92488	39
22	0.38053	2.62790	0.41149	2.43019	1.08135	0.92477	38
23	0.38080	2.62604	0.41183	2.42819	1.08148	0.92466	37
24	0.38107	2.62419	0.41217	2.42618	1.08161	0.92455	36
25	0.38134	2.62234	0.41251	2.42418	1.08174	0.92444	35
26	0.38161	2.62049	0.41285	2.42218	1.08187	0.92432	34
27	0.38188	2.61864	0.41319	2.42019	1.08200	0.92421	33
28	0.38215	2.61680	0.41353	2.41819	1.08213	0.92410	32
29	0.38241	2.61496	0.41387	2.41620	1.08226	0.92399	31
30	0.38268	2.61313	0.41421	2.41421	1.08239	0.92388	30
31	0.38295	2.61129	0.41455	2.41223	1.08252	0.92377	29
32	0.38322	2.60946	0.41490	2.41025	1.08265	0.92366	28
33	0.38349	2.60763	0.41524	2.40827	1.08278	0.92355	27
34	0.38376	2.60581	0.41558	2.40629	1.08291	0.92343	26
35	0.38403	2.60399	0.41592	2.40432	1.08305	0.92332	25
36	0.38430	2.60217	0.41626	2.40235	1.08318	0.92321	24
37	0.38456	2.60035	0.41660	2.40038	1.08331	0.92310	23
38	0.38483	2.59853	0.41694	2.39841	1.08344	0.92299	22
39	0.38510	2.59672	0.41728	2.39645	1.08357	0.92287	21
40	0.38537	2.59491	0.41763	2.39449	1.08370	0.92276	20
41	0.38564	2.59311	0.41797	2.39253	1.08383	0.92265	19
42	0.38591	2.59130	0.41831	2.39058	1.08397	0.92254	18
43	0.38617	2.58950	0.41865	2.38863	1.08410	0.92243	17
44	0.38644	2.58771	0.41899	2.38668	1.08423	0.92231	16
45	0.38671	2.58591	0.41933	2.38473	1.08436	0.92220	15
46	0.38698	2.58412	0.41968	2.38279	1.08449	0.92209	14
47	0.38725	2.58233	0.42002	2.38084	1.08463	0.92198	13
48	0.38752	2.58054	0.42036	2.37891	1.08476	0.92186	12
49	0.38778	2.57876	0.42070	2.37697	1.08489	0.92175	11
50	0.38805	2.57698	0.42105	2.37504	1.08503	0.92164	10
51	0.38832	2.57520	0.42139	2.37311	1.08516	0.92152	9
52	0.38859	2.57342	0.42173	2.37118	1.08529	0.92141	8
53	0.38886	2.57165	0.42207	2.36925	1.08542	0.92130	7
54	0.38912	2.56988	0.42242	2.36733	1.08556	0.92119	6
55	0.38939	2.56811	0.42276	2.36541	1.08569	0.92107	5
56	0.38966	2.56634	0.42310	2.36349	1.08582	0.92096	4
57	0.38993	2.56458	0.42345	2.36158	1.08596	0.92085	3
58	0.39020	2.56282	0.42379	2.35967	1.08609	0.92073	2
59	0.39046	2.56106	0.42413	2.35776	1.08623	0.92062	1
60	0.39073	2.55930	0.42447	2.35585	1.08636	0.92050	0

	sin	csc	tan	cot	sec	cos	
0	0.39073	2.55930	0.42447	2.35585	1.08636	0.92050	60
1	0.39100	2.55755	0.42482	2.35395	1.08649	0.92039	59
2	0.39127	2.55580	0.42516	2.35205	1.08663	0.92028	58
3	0.39153	2.55405	0.42551	2.35015	1.08676	0.92016	57
4	0.39180	2.55231	0.42585	2.34825	1.08690	0.92005	56
5	0.39207	2.55057	0.42619	2.34636	1.08703	0.91994	55
6	0.39234	2.54883	0.42654	2.34447	1.08717	0.91982	54
7	0.39260	2.54709	0.42688	2.34258	1.08730	0.91971	53
8	0.39287	2.54536	0.42722	2.34069	1.08744	0.91959	52
9	0.39314	2.54363	0.42757	2.33881	1.08757	0.91948	51
10	0.39341	2.54190	0.42791	2.33693	1.08771	0.91936	50
11	0.39367	2.54017	0.42826	2.33505	1.08784	0.91925	49
12	0.39394	2.53845	0.42860	2.33317	1.08798	0.91914	48
13	0.39421	2.53672	0.42894	2.33130	1.08811	0.91902	47
14	0.39448	2.53500	0.42929	2.32943	1.08825	0.91891	46
15	0.39474	2.53329	0.42963	2.32756	1.08839	0.91879	45
16	0.39501	2.53157	0.42998	2.32570	1.08852	0.91868	44
17	0.39528	2.52986	0.43032	2.32383	1.08866	0.91856	43
18	0.39555	2.52815	0.43067	2.32197	1.08880	0.91845	42
19	0.39581	2.52645	0.43101	2.32012	1.08893	0.91833	41
20	0.39608	2.52474	0.43136	2.31826	1.08907	0.91822	40
21	0.39635	2.52304	0.43170	2.31641	1.08920	0.91810	39
22	0.39661	2.52134	0.43205	2.31456	1.08934	0.91799	38
23	0.39688	2.51965	0.43239	2.31271	1.08948	0.91787	37
24	0.39715	2.51795	0.43274	2.31086	1.08962	0.91775	36
25	0.39741	2.51626	0.43308	2.30902	1.08975	0.91764	35
26	0.39768	2.51457	0.43343	2.30718	1.08989	0.91752	34
27	0.39795	2.51289	0.43378	2.30534	1.09003	0.91741	33
28	0.39822	2.51120	0.43412	2.30351	1.09017	0.91729	32
29	0.39848	2.50952	0.43447	2.30167	1.09030	0.91718	31
30	0.39875	2.50784	0.43481	2.29984	1.09044	0.91706	30
31	0.39902	2.50617	0.43516	2.29801	1.09058	0.91694	29
32	0.39928	2.50449	0.43550	2.29619	1.09072	0.91683	28
33	0.39955	2.50282	0.43585	2.29437	1.09086	0.91671	27
34	0.39982	2.50115	0.43620	2.29254	1.09099	0.91660	26
35	0.40008	2.49948	0.43654	2.29073	1.09113	0.91648	25
36	0.40035	2.49782	0.43689	2.28891	1.09127	0.91636	24
37	0.40062	2.49616	0.43724	2.28710	1.09141	0.91625	23
38	0.40088	2.49450	0.43758	2.28528	1.09155	0.91613	22
39	0.40115	2.49284	0.43793	2.28348	1.09169	0.91601	21
40	0.40141	2.49119	0.43828	2.28167	1.09183	0.91590	20
41	0.40168	2.48954	0.43862	2.27987	1.09197	0.91578	19
42	0.40195	2.48789	0.43897	2.27806	1.09211	0.91566	18
43	0.40221	2.48624	0.43932	2.27626	1.09224	0.91555	17
44	0.40248	2.48459	0.43966	2.27447	1.09238	0.91543	16
45	0.40275	2.48295	0.44001	2.27267	1.09252	0.91531	15
46	0.40301	2.48131	0.44036	2.27088	1.09266	0.91519	14
47	0.40328	2.47967	0.44071	2.26909	1.09280	0.91508	13
48	0.40355	2.47804	0.44105	2.26730	1.09294	0.91496	12
49	0.40381	2.47640	0.44140	2.26552	1.09308	0.91484	11
50	0.40408	2.47477	0.44175	2.26374	1.09323	0.91472	10
51	0.40434	2.47314	0.44210	2.26196	1.09337	0.91461	9
52	0.40461	2.47152	0.44244	2.26018	1.09351	0.91449	8
53	0.40488	2.46989	0.44279	2.25840	1.09365	0.91437	7
54	0.40514	2.46827	0.44314	2.25663	1.09379	0.91425	6
55	0.40541	2.46665	0.44349	2.25486	1.09393	0.91414	5
56	0.40567	2.46504	0.44384	2.25309	1.09407	0.91402	4
57	0.40594	2.46342	0.44418	2.25132	1.09421	0.91390	3
58	0.40621	2.46181	0.44453	2.24956	1.09435	0.91378	2
59	0.40647	2.46020	0.44488	2.24780	1.09449	0.91366	1
60	0.40674	2.45859	0.44523	2.24604	1.09464	0.91355	0

24°→ ↓	sin	csc	tan	cot	sec	cos ←155° ↓	
0	0.40674	2.45859	0.44523	2.24604	1.09464	0.91355	60
1	0.40700	2.45699	0.44558	2.24428	1.09478	0.91343	59
2	0.40727	2.45539	0.44593	2.24252	1.09492	0.91331	58
3	0.40753	2.45378	0.44627	2.24077	1.09506	0.91319	57
4	0.40780	2.45219	0.44662	2.23902	1.09520	0.91307	56
5	0.40806	2.45059	0.44697	2.23727	1.09535	0.91295	55
6	0.40833	2.44900	0.44732	2.23553	1.09549	0.91283	54
7	0.40860	2.44741	0.44767	2.23378	1.09563	0.91272	53
8	0.40886	2.44582	0.44802	2.23204	1.09577	0.91260	52
9	0.40913	2.44423	0.44837	2.23030	1.09592	0.91248	51
10	0.40939	2.44264	0.44872	2.22857	1.09606	0.91236	50
11	0.40966	2.44106	0.44907	2.22683	1.09620	0.91224	49
12	0.40992	2.43948	0.44942	2.22510	1.09635	0.91212	48
13	0.41019	2.43790	0.44977	2.22337	1.09649	0.91200	47
14	0.41045	2.43633	0.45012	2.22164	1.09663	0.91188	46
15	0.41072	2.43476	0.45047	2.21992	1.09678	0.91176	45
16	0.41098	2.43318	0.45082	2.21819	1.09692	0.91164	44
17	0.41125	2.43162	0.45117	2.21647	1.09707	0.91152	43
18	0.41151	2.43005	0.45152	2.21475	1.09721	0.91140	42
19	0.41178	2.42848	0.45187	2.21304	1.09735	0.91128	41
20	0.41204	2.42692	0.45222	2.21132	1.09750	0.91116	40
21	0.41231	2.42536	0.45257	2.20961	1.09764	0.91104	39
22	0.41257	2.42380	0.45292	2.20790	1.09779	0.91092	38
23	0.41284	2.42225	0.45327	2.20619	1.09793	0.91080	37
24	0.41310	2.42070	0.45362	2.20449	1.09808	0.91068	36
25	0.41337	2.41914	0.45397	2.20278	1.09822	0.91056	35
26	0.41363	2.41760	0.45432	2.20108	1.09837	0.91044	34
27	0.41390	2.41605	0.45467	2.19938	1.09851	0.91032	33
28	0.41416	2.41450	0.45502	2.19769	1.09866	0.91020	32
29	0.41443	2.41296	0.45538	2.19599	1.09880	0.91008	31
30	0.41469	2.41142	0.45573	2.19430	1.09895	0.90996	30
31	0.41496	2.40988	0.45608	2.19261	1.09909	0.90984	29
32	0.41522	2.40835	0.45643	2.19092	1.09924	0.90972	28
33	0.41549	2.40681	0.45678	2.18923	1.09939	0.90960	27
34	0.41575	2.40528	0.45713	2.18755	1.09953	0.90948	26
35	0.41602	2.40375	0.45748	2.18587	1.09968	0.90936	25
36	0.41628	2.40222	0.45784	2.18419	1.09982	0.90924	24
37	0.41655	2.40070	0.45819	2.18251	1.09997	0.90911	23
38	0.41681	2.39918	0.45854	2.18084	1.10012	0.90899	22
39	0.41707	2.39766	0.45889	2.17916	1.10026	0.90887	21
40	0.41734	2.39614	0.45924	2.17749	1.10041	0.90875	20
41	0.41760	2.39462	0.45960	2.17582	1.10056	0.90863	19
42	0.41787	2.39311	0.45995	2.17416	1.10071	0.90851	18
43	0.41813	2.39159	0.46030	2.17249	1.10085	0.90839	17
44	0.41840	2.39008	0.46065	2.17083	1.10100	0.90826	16
45	0.41866	2.38857	0.46101	2.16917	1.10115	0.90814	15
46	0.41892	2.38707	0.46136	2.16751	1.10130	0.90802	14
47	0.41919	2.38556	0.46171	2.16585	1.10144	0.90790	13
48	0.41945	2.38406	0.46206	2.16420	1.10159	0.90778	12
49	0.41972	2.38256	0.46242	2.16255	1.10174	0.90766	11
50	0.41998	2.38106	0.46277	2.16090	1.10189	0.90753	10
51	0.42024	2.37957	0.46312	2.15925	1.10204	0.90741	9
52	0.42051	2.37808	0.46348	2.15760	1.10218	0.90729	8
53	0.42077	2.37658	0.46383	2.15596	1.10233	0.90717	7
54	0.42104	2.37509	0.46418	2.15432	1.10248	0.90704	6
55	0.42130	2.37361	0.46454	2.15268	1.10263	0.90692	5
56	0.42156	2.37212	0.46489	2.15104	1.10278	0.90680	4
57	0.42183	2.37064	0.46525	2.14940	1.10293	0.90668	3
58	0.42209	2.36916	0.46560	2.14777	1.10308	0.90655	2
59	0.42235	2.36768	0.46595	2.14614	1.10323	0.90643	1
60	0.42262	2.36620	0.46631	2.14451	1.10338	0.90631	0
↑ 114°cos →	sec	cot	tan	csc	sin ←65° ↑		

25°→ ↓	sin	csc	tan	cot	sec	cos ←154° ↓	
0	0.42262	2.36620	0.46631	2.14451	1.10338	0.90631	60
1	0.42288	2.36473	0.46666	2.14288	1.10353	0.90618	59
2	0.42315	2.36325	0.46702	2.14125	1.10368	0.90606	58
3	0.42341	2.36178	0.46737	2.13963	1.10383	0.90594	57
4	0.42367	2.36031	0.46772	2.13801	1.10398	0.90582	56
5	0.42394	2.35885	0.46808	2.13639	1.10413	0.90569	55
6	0.42420	2.35738	0.46843	2.13477	1.10428	0.90557	54
7	0.42446	2.35592	0.46879	2.13316	1.10443	0.90545	53
8	0.42473	2.35446	0.46914	2.13154	1.10458	0.90532	52
9	0.42499	2.35300	0.46950	2.12993	1.10473	0.90520	51
10	0.42525	2.35154	0.46985	2.12832	1.10488	0.90507	50
11	0.42552	2.35009	0.47021	2.12671	1.10503	0.90495	49
12	0.42578	2.34863	0.47056	2.12511	1.10518	0.90483	48
13	0.42604	2.34718	0.47092	2.12350	1.10533	0.90470	47
14	0.42631	2.34573	0.47128	2.12190	1.10549	0.90458	46
15	0.42657	2.34429	0.47163	2.12030	1.10564	0.90446	45
16	0.42683	2.34284	0.47199	2.11871	1.10579	0.90433	44
17	0.42709	2.34140	0.47234	2.11711	1.10594	0.90421	43
18	0.42736	2.33996	0.47270	2.11552	1.10609	0.90408	42
19	0.42762	2.33852	0.47305	2.11392	1.10625	0.90396	41
20	0.42788	2.33708	0.47341	2.11233	1.10640	0.90383	40
21	0.42815	2.33565	0.47377	2.11075	1.10655	0.90371	39
22	0.42841	2.33422	0.47412	2.10916	1.10670	0.90358	38
23	0.42867	2.33278	0.47448	2.10758	1.10686	0.90346	37
24	0.42894	2.33135	0.47483	2.10600	1.10701	0.90334	36
25	0.42920	2.32993	0.47519	2.10442	1.10716	0.90321	35
26	0.42946	2.32850	0.47555	2.10284	1.10731	0.90309	34
27	0.42972	2.32708	0.47590	2.10126	1.10747	0.90296	33
28	0.42999	2.32566	0.47626	2.09969	1.10762	0.90284	32
29	0.43025	2.32424	0.47662	2.09811	1.10777	0.90271	31
30	0.43051	2.32282	0.47698	2.09654	1.10793	0.90259	30
31	0.43077	2.32140	0.47733	2.09498	1.10808	0.90246	29
32	0.43104	2.31999	0.47769	2.09341	1.10824	0.90233	28
33	0.43130	2.31858	0.47805	2.09184	1.10839	0.90221	27
34	0.43156	2.31717	0.47840	2.09028	1.10854	0.90208	26
35	0.43182	2.31576	0.47876	2.08872	1.10870	0.90196	25
36	0.43209	2.31436	0.47912	2.08716	1.10885	0.90183	24
37	0.43235	2.31295	0.47948	2.08560	1.10901	0.90171	23
38	0.43261	2.31155	0.47984	2.08405	1.10916	0.90158	22
39	0.43287	2.31015	0.48019	2.08250	1.10932	0.90146	21
40	0.43313	2.30875	0.48055	2.08094	1.10947	0.90133	20
41	0.43340	2.30735	0.48091	2.07939	1.10963	0.90120	19
42	0.43366	2.30596	0.48127	2.07785	1.10978	0.90108	18
43	0.43392	2.30457	0.48163	2.07630	1.10994	0.90095	17
44	0.43418	2.30318	0.48198	2.07476	1.11009	0.90082	16
45	0.43445	2.30179	0.48234	2.07321	1.11025	0.90070	15
46	0.43471	2.30040	0.48270	2.07167	1.11041	0.90057	14
47	0.43497	2.29901	0.48306	2.07014	1.11056	0.90045	13
48	0.43523	2.29763	0.48342	2.06860	1.11072	0.90032	12
49	0.43549	2.29625	0.48378	2.06706	1.11087	0.90019	11
50	0.43575	2.29487	0.48414	2.06553	1.11103	0.90007	10
51	0.43602	2.29349	0.48450	2.06400	1.11119	0.89994	9
52	0.43628	2.29211	0.48486	2.06247	1.11134	0.89981	8
53	0.43654	2.29074	0.48521	2.06094	1.11150	0.89968	7
54	0.43680	2.28937	0.48557	2.05942	1.11166	0.89956	6
55	0.43706	2.28800	0.48593	2.05790	1.11181	0.89943	5
56	0.43733	2.28663	0.48629	2.05637	1.11197	0.89930	4
57	0.43759	2.28526	0.48665	2.05485	1.11213	0.89918	3
58	0.43785	2.28390	0.48701	2.05333	1.11229	0.89905	2
59	0.43811	2.28253	0.48737	2.05182	1.11244	0.89892	1
60	0.43837	2.28117	0.48773	2.05030	1.11260	0.89879	0
↑ 115°cos →	sec	cot	tan	csc	sin ←64° ↑		

26°→ ↓	sin	csc	tan	cot	sec	cos ←153° ↓	
0	0.43837	2.28117	0.48773	2.05030	1.11260	0.89879	60
1	0.43863	2.27981	0.48809	2.04879	1.11276	0.89867	59
2	0.43889	2.27845	0.48845	2.04728	1.11292	0.89854	58
3	0.43916	2.27710	0.48881	2.04577	1.11308	0.89841	57
4	0.43942	2.27574	0.48917	2.04426	1.11323	0.89828	56
5	0.43968	2.27439	0.48953	2.04276	1.11339	0.89816	55
6	0.43994	2.27304	0.48989	2.04125	1.11355	0.89803	54
7	0.44020	2.27169	0.49026	2.03975	1.11371	0.89790	53
8	0.44046	2.27035	0.49062	2.03825	1.11387	0.89777	52
9	0.44072	2.26900	0.49098	2.03675	1.11403	0.89764	51
10	0.44098	2.26766	0.49134	2.03526	1.11419	0.89752	50
11	0.44124	2.26632	0.49170	2.03376	1.11435	0.89739	49
12	0.44151	2.26498	0.49206	2.03227	1.11451	0.89726	48
13	0.44177	2.26364	0.49242	2.03078	1.11467	0.89713	47
14	0.44203	2.26230	0.49278	2.02929	1.11483	0.89700	46
15	0.44229	2.26097	0.49315	2.02780	1.11499	0.89687	45
16	0.44255	2.25963	0.49351	2.02631	1.11515	0.89674	44
17	0.44281	2.25830	0.49387	2.02483	1.11531	0.89662	43
18	0.44307	2.25697	0.49423	2.02335	1.11547	0.89649	42
19	0.44333	2.25565	0.49459	2.02187	1.11563	0.89636	41
20	0.44359	2.25432	0.49495	2.02039	1.11579	0.89623	40
21	0.44385	2.25300	0.49532	2.01891	1.11595	0.89610	39
22	0.44411	2.25167	0.49568	2.01743	1.11611	0.89597	38
23	0.44437	2.25035	0.49604	2.01596	1.11627	0.89584	37
24	0.44464	2.24903	0.49640	2.01449	1.11643	0.89571	36
25	0.44490	2.24772	0.49677	2.01302	1.11659	0.89558	35
26	0.44516	2.24640	0.49713	2.01155	1.11675	0.89545	34
27	0.44542	2.24509	0.49749	2.01008	1.11691	0.89532	33
28	0.44568	2.24378	0.49786	2.00862	1.11708	0.89519	32
29	0.44594	2.24247	0.49822	2.00715	1.11724	0.89506	31
30	0.44620	2.24116	0.49858	2.00569	1.11740	0.89493	30
31	0.44646	2.23985	0.49894	2.00423	1.11756	0.89480	29
32	0.44672	2.23855	0.49931	2.00277	1.11772	0.89467	28
33	0.44698	2.23724	0.49967	2.00131	1.11789	0.89454	27
34	0.44724	2.23594	0.50004	1.99986	1.11805	0.89441	26
35	0.44750	2.23464	0.50040	1.99841	1.11821	0.89428	25
36	0.44776	2.23334	0.50076	1.99695	1.11838	0.89415	24
37	0.44802	2.23205	0.50113	1.99550	1.11854	0.89402	23
38	0.44828	2.23075	0.50149	1.99406	1.11870	0.89389	22
39	0.44854	2.22946	0.50185	1.99261	1.11886	0.89376	21
40	0.44880	2.22817	0.50222	1.99116	1.11903	0.89363	20
41	0.44906	2.22688	0.50258	1.98972	1.11919	0.89350	19
42	0.44932	2.22559	0.50295	1.98828	1.11936	0.89337	18
43	0.44958	2.22430	0.50331	1.98684	1.11952	0.89324	17
44	0.44984	2.22302	0.50368	1.98540	1.11968	0.89311	16
45	0.45010	2.22174	0.50404	1.98396	1.11985	0.89298	15
46	0.45036	2.22045	0.50441	1.98253	1.12001	0.89285	14
47	0.45062	2.21918	0.50477	1.98110	1.12018	0.89272	13
48	0.45088	2.21790	0.50514	1.97966	1.12034	0.89259	12
49	0.45114	2.21662	0.50550	1.97823	1.12051	0.89245	11
50	0.45140	2.21535	0.50587	1.97681	1.12067	0.89232	10
51	0.45166	2.21407	0.50623	1.97538	1.12083	0.89219	9
52	0.45192	2.21280	0.50660	1.97395	1.12100	0.89206	8
53	0.45218	2.21153	0.50696	1.97253	1.12117	0.89193	7
54	0.45243	2.21026	0.50733	1.97111	1.12133	0.89180	6
55	0.45269	2.20900	0.50769	1.96969	1.12150	0.89167	5
56	0.45295	2.20773	0.50806	1.96827	1.12166	0.89153	4
57	0.45321	2.20647	0.50843	1.96685	1.12183	0.89140	3
58	0.45347	2.20521	0.50879	1.96544	1.12199	0.89127	2
59	0.45373	2.20395	0.50916	1.96402	1.12216	0.89114	1
60	0.45399	2.20269	0.50953	1.96261	1.12233	0.89101	0
↑ 116°→ cos	sec	cot	tan	csc	sin ←63° ↑		

27°→ ↓	sin	csc	tan	cot	sec	cos ←152° ↓	
0	0.45399	2.20269	0.50953	1.96261	1.12233	0.89101	60
1	0.45425	2.20143	0.50989	1.96120	1.12249	0.89087	59
2	0.45451	2.20018	0.51026	1.95979	1.12266	0.89074	58
3	0.45477	2.19892	0.51063	1.95838	1.12283	0.89061	57
4	0.45503	2.19767	0.51099	1.95698	1.12299	0.89048	56
5	0.45529	2.19642	0.51136	1.95557	1.12316	0.89035	55
6	0.45554	2.19517	0.51173	1.95417	1.12333	0.89021	54
7	0.45580	2.19393	0.51209	1.95277	1.12349	0.89008	53
8	0.45606	2.19268	0.51246	1.95137	1.12366	0.88995	52
9	0.45632	2.19144	0.51283	1.94997	1.12383	0.88981	51
10	0.45658	2.19019	0.51319	1.94858	1.12400	0.88968	50
11	0.45684	2.18895	0.51356	1.94718	1.12416	0.88955	49
12	0.45710	2.18772	0.51393	1.94579	1.12433	0.88942	48
13	0.45736	2.18648	0.51430	1.94440	1.12450	0.88928	47
14	0.45762	2.18524	0.51467	1.94301	1.12467	0.88915	46
15	0.45787	2.18401	0.51503	1.94162	1.12484	0.88902	45
16	0.45813	2.18277	0.51540	1.94023	1.12501	0.88888	44
17	0.45839	2.18154	0.51577	1.93885	1.12518	0.88875	43
18	0.45865	2.18031	0.51614	1.93746	1.12534	0.88862	42
19	0.45891	2.17909	0.51651	1.93608	1.12551	0.88848	41
20	0.45917	2.17786	0.51688	1.93470	1.12568	0.88835	40
21	0.45942	2.17663	0.51724	1.93332	1.12585	0.88822	39
22	0.45968	2.17541	0.51761	1.93195	1.12602	0.88808	38
23	0.45994	2.17419	0.51798	1.93057	1.12619	0.88795	37
24	0.46020	2.17297	0.51835	1.92920	1.12636	0.88782	36
25	0.46046	2.17175	0.51872	1.92782	1.12653	0.88768	35
26	0.46072	2.17053	0.51909	1.92645	1.12670	0.88755	34
27	0.46097	2.16932	0.51946	1.92508	1.12687	0.88741	33
28	0.46123	2.16810	0.51983	1.92371	1.12704	0.88728	32
29	0.46149	2.16689	0.52020	1.92235	1.12721	0.88715	31
30	0.46175	2.16568	0.52057	1.92098	1.12738	0.88701	30
31	0.46201	2.16447	0.52094	1.91962	1.12755	0.88688	29
32	0.46226	2.16326	0.52131	1.91826	1.12772	0.88674	28
33	0.46252	2.16206	0.52168	1.91690	1.12789	0.88661	27
34	0.46278	2.16085	0.52205	1.91554	1.12807	0.88647	26
35	0.46304	2.15965	0.52242	1.91418	1.12824	0.88634	25
36	0.46330	2.15845	0.52279	1.91282	1.12841	0.88620	24
37	0.46355	2.15725	0.52316	1.91147	1.12858	0.88607	23
38	0.46381	2.15605	0.52353	1.91012	1.12875	0.88593	22
39	0.46407	2.15485	0.52390	1.90876	1.12892	0.88580	21
40	0.46433	2.15366	0.52427	1.90741	1.12910	0.88566	20
41	0.46458	2.15246	0.52464	1.90607	1.12927	0.88553	19
42	0.46484	2.15127	0.52501	1.90472	1.12944	0.88539	18
43	0.46510	2.15008	0.52538	1.90337	1.12961	0.88526	17
44	0.46536	2.14889	0.52575	1.90203	1.12979	0.88512	16
45	0.46561	2.14770	0.52613	1.90069	1.12996	0.88499	15
46	0.46587	2.14651	0.52650	1.89935	1.13013	0.88485	14
47	0.46613	2.14533	0.52687	1.89801	1.13031	0.88472	13
48	0.46639	2.14414	0.52724	1.89667	1.13048	0.88458	12
49	0.46664	2.14296	0.52761	1.89533	1.13065	0.88445	11
50	0.46690	2.14178	0.52798	1.89400	1.13083	0.88431	10
51	0.46716	2.14060	0.52836	1.89266	1.13100	0.88417	9
52	0.46742	2.13942	0.52873	1.89133	1.13117	0.88404	8
53	0.46767	2.13825	0.52910	1.89000	1.13135	0.88390	7
54	0.46793	2.13707	0.52947	1.88867	1.13152	0.88377	6
55	0.46819	2.13590	0.52985	1.88734	1.13170	0.88363	5
56	0.46844	2.13473	0.53022	1.88602	1.13187	0.88349	4
57	0.46870	2.13356	0.53059	1.88469	1.13205	0.88336	3
58	0.46896	2.13239	0.53096	1.88337	1.13222	0.88322	2
59	0.46921	2.13122	0.53134	1.88205	1.13239	0.88308	1
60	0.46947	2.13005	0.53171	1.88073	1.13257	0.88295	0
↑ 117°→ cos	sec	cot	tan	csc	sin ←62° ↑		

28°→ ↓	sin	csc	tan	cot	sec	cos ←151° ↓	
0	0.46947	2.13005	0.53171	1.88073	1.13257	0.88295	60
1	0.46973	2.12889	0.53208	1.87941	1.13275	0.88281	59
2	0.46999	2.12773	0.53246	1.87809	1.13292	0.88267	58
3	0.47024	2.12657	0.53283	1.87677	1.13310	0.88254	57
4	0.47050	2.12540	0.53320	1.87546	1.13327	0.88240	56
5	0.47076	2.12425	0.53358	1.87415	1.13345	0.88226	55
6	0.47101	2.12309	0.53395	1.87283	1.13362	0.88213	54
7	0.47127	2.12193	0.53432	1.87152	1.13380	0.88199	53
8	0.47153	2.12078	0.53470	1.87021	1.13398	0.88185	52
9	0.47178	2.11963	0.53507	1.86891	1.13415	0.88172	51
10	0.47204	2.11847	0.53545	1.86760	1.13433	0.88158	50
11	0.47229	2.11732	0.53582	1.86630	1.13451	0.88144	49
12	0.47255	2.11617	0.53620	1.86499	1.13468	0.88130	48
13	0.47281	2.11503	0.53657	1.86369	1.13486	0.88117	47
14	0.47306	2.11388	0.53694	1.86239	1.13504	0.88103	46
15	0.47332	2.11274	0.53732	1.86109	1.13521	0.88089	45
16	0.47358	2.11159	0.53769	1.85979	1.13539	0.88075	44
17	0.47383	2.11045	0.53807	1.85850	1.13557	0.88062	43
18	0.47409	2.10931	0.53844	1.85720	1.13575	0.88048	42
19	0.47434	2.10817	0.53882	1.85591	1.13593	0.88034	41
20	0.47460	2.10704	0.53920	1.85462	1.13610	0.88020	40
21	0.47486	2.10590	0.53957	1.85333	1.13628	0.88006	39
22	0.47511	2.10477	0.53995	1.85204	1.13646	0.87993	38
23	0.47537	2.10363	0.54032	1.85075	1.13664	0.87979	37
24	0.47562	2.10250	0.54070	1.84946	1.13682	0.87965	36
25	0.47588	2.10137	0.54107	1.84818	1.13700	0.87951	35
26	0.47614	2.10024	0.54145	1.84689	1.13718	0.87937	34
27	0.47639	2.09911	0.54183	1.84561	1.13735	0.87923	33
28	0.47665	2.09799	0.54220	1.84433	1.13753	0.87909	32
29	0.47690	2.09686	0.54258	1.84305	1.13771	0.87896	31
30	0.47716	2.09574	0.54296	1.84177	1.13789	0.87882	30
31	0.47741	2.09462	0.54333	1.84049	1.13807	0.87868	29
32	0.47767	2.09350	0.54371	1.83922	1.13825	0.87854	28
33	0.47793	2.09238	0.54409	1.83794	1.13843	0.87840	27
34	0.47818	2.09126	0.54446	1.83667	1.13861	0.87826	26
35	0.47844	2.09014	0.54484	1.83540	1.13879	0.87812	25
36	0.47869	2.08903	0.54522	1.83413	1.13897	0.87798	24
37	0.47895	2.08791	0.54560	1.83286	1.13915	0.87784	23
38	0.47920	2.08680	0.54597	1.83159	1.13934	0.87770	22
39	0.47946	2.08569	0.54635	1.83033	1.13952	0.87756	21
40	0.47971	2.08458	0.54673	1.82906	1.13970	0.87743	20
41	0.47997	2.08347	0.54711	1.82780	1.13988	0.87729	19
42	0.48022	2.08236	0.54748	1.82654	1.14006	0.87715	18
43	0.48048	2.08126	0.54786	1.82528	1.14024	0.87701	17
44	0.48073	2.08015	0.54824	1.82402	1.14042	0.87687	16
45	0.48099	2.07905	0.54862	1.82276	1.14061	0.87673	15
46	0.48124	2.07795	0.54900	1.82150	1.14079	0.87659	14
47	0.48150	2.07685	0.54938	1.82025	1.14097	0.87645	13
48	0.48175	2.07575	0.54975	1.81899	1.14115	0.87631	12
49	0.48201	2.07465	0.55013	1.81774	1.14134	0.87617	11
50	0.48226	2.07356	0.55051	1.81649	1.14152	0.87603	10
51	0.48252	2.07246	0.55089	1.81524	1.14170	0.87589	9
52	0.48277	2.07137	0.55127	1.81399	1.14188	0.87575	8
53	0.48303	2.07027	0.55165	1.81274	1.14207	0.87561	7
54	0.48328	2.06918	0.55203	1.81150	1.14225	0.87546	6
55	0.48354	2.06809	0.55241	1.81025	1.14243	0.87532	5
56	0.48379	2.06701	0.55279	1.80901	1.14262	0.87518	4
57	0.48405	2.06592	0.55317	1.80777	1.14280	0.87504	3
58	0.48430	2.06483	0.55355	1.80653	1.14299	0.87490	2
59	0.48456	2.06375	0.55393	1.80529	1.14317	0.87476	1
60	0.48481	2.06267	0.55431	1.80405	1.14335	0.87462	0
↑ 118°cos →	sec	cot	tan	csc	sin ←61° ↑		

29°→ ↓	sin	csc	tan	cot	sec	cos ←150° ↓	
0	0.48481	2.06267	0.55431	1.80405	1.14335	0.87462	60
1	0.48506	2.06158	0.55469	1.80281	1.14354	0.87448	59
2	0.48532	2.06050	0.55507	1.80158	1.14372	0.87434	58
3	0.48557	2.05942	0.55545	1.80034	1.14391	0.87420	57
4	0.48583	2.05835	0.55583	1.79911	1.14409	0.87406	56
5	0.48608	2.05727	0.55621	1.79788	1.14428	0.87391	55
6	0.48634	2.05619	0.55659	1.79665	1.14446	0.87377	54
7	0.48659	2.05512	0.55697	1.79542	1.14465	0.87363	53
8	0.48684	2.05405	0.55736	1.79419	1.14483	0.87349	52
9	0.48710	2.05298	0.55774	1.79296	1.14502	0.87335	51
10	0.48735	2.05191	0.55812	1.79174	1.14521	0.87321	50
11	0.48761	2.05084	0.55850	1.79051	1.14539	0.87306	49
12	0.48786	2.04977	0.55888	1.78929	1.14558	0.87292	48
13	0.48811	2.04870	0.55926	1.78807	1.14576	0.87278	47
14	0.48837	2.04764	0.55964	1.78685	1.14595	0.87264	46
15	0.48862	2.04657	0.56003	1.78563	1.14614	0.87250	45
16	0.48888	2.04551	0.56041	1.78441	1.14632	0.87235	44
17	0.48913	2.04445	0.56079	1.78319	1.14651	0.87221	43
18	0.48938	2.04339	0.56117	1.78198	1.14670	0.87207	42
19	0.48964	2.04233	0.56156	1.78077	1.14689	0.87193	41
20	0.48989	2.04128	0.56194	1.77955	1.14707	0.87178	40
21	0.49014	2.04022	0.56232	1.77834	1.14726	0.87164	39
22	0.49040	2.03916	0.56270	1.77713	1.14745	0.87150	38
23	0.49065	2.03811	0.56309	1.77592	1.14764	0.87136	37
24	0.49090	2.03706	0.56347	1.77471	1.14782	0.87121	36
25	0.49116	2.03601	0.56385	1.77351	1.14801	0.87107	35
26	0.49141	2.03496	0.56424	1.77230	1.14820	0.87093	34
27	0.49166	2.03391	0.56462	1.77110	1.14839	0.87079	33
28	0.49192	2.03286	0.56501	1.76990	1.14858	0.87064	32
29	0.49217	2.03182	0.56539	1.76869	1.14877	0.87050	31
30	0.49242	2.03077	0.56577	1.76749	1.14896	0.87036	30
31	0.49268	2.02973	0.56616	1.76629	1.14914	0.87021	29
32	0.49293	2.02869	0.56654	1.76510	1.14933	0.87007	28
33	0.49318	2.02765	0.56693	1.76390	1.14952	0.86993	27
34	0.49344	2.02661	0.56731	1.76271	1.14971	0.86978	26
35	0.49369	2.02557	0.56769	1.76151	1.14990	0.86964	25
36	0.49394	2.02453	0.56808	1.76032	1.15009	0.86949	24
37	0.49419	2.02349	0.56846	1.75913	1.15028	0.86935	23
38	0.49445	2.02246	0.56885	1.75794	1.15047	0.86921	22
39	0.49470	2.02143	0.56923	1.75675	1.15066	0.86906	21
40	0.49495	2.02039	0.56962	1.75556	1.15085	0.86892	20
41	0.49521	2.01936	0.57000	1.75437	1.15105	0.86878	19
42	0.49546	2.01833	0.57039	1.75319	1.15124	0.86863	18
43	0.49571	2.01730	0.57078	1.75200	1.15143	0.86849	17
44	0.49596	2.01628	0.57116	1.75082	1.15162	0.86834	16
45	0.49622	2.01525	0.57155	1.74964	1.15181	0.86820	15
46	0.49647	2.01422	0.57193	1.74846	1.15200	0.86805	14
47	0.49672	2.01320	0.57232	1.74728	1.15219	0.86791	13
48	0.49697	2.01218	0.57271	1.74610	1.15239	0.86777	12
49	0.49723	2.01116	0.57309	1.74492	1.15258	0.86762	11
50	0.49748	2.01014	0.57348	1.74375	1.15277	0.86748	10
51	0.49773	2.00912	0.57386	1.74257	1.15296	0.86733	9
52	0.49798	2.00810	0.57425	1.74140	1.15315	0.86719	8
53	0.49824	2.00708	0.57464	1.74022	1.15335	0.86704	7
54	0.49849	2.00607	0.57503	1.73905	1.15354	0.86690	6
55	0.49874	2.00505	0.57541	1.73788	1.15373	0.86675	5
56	0.49899	2.00404	0.57580	1.73671	1.15393	0.86661	4
57	0.49924	2.00303	0.57619	1.73555	1.15412	0.86646	3
58	0.49950	2.00202	0.57657	1.73438	1.15431	0.86632	2
59	0.49975	2.00101	0.57696	1.73321	1.15451	0.86617	1
60	0.50000	2.00000	0.57735	1.73205	1.15470	0.86603	0
↑ 119°cos →	sec	cot	tan	csc	sin ←60° ↑		

	sin	csc	tan	cot	sec	cos	
0	0.50000	2.00000	0.57735	1.73205	1.15470	0.86603	60
1	0.50025	1.99899	0.57774	1.73089	1.15489	0.86588	59
2	0.50050	1.99799	0.57813	1.72973	1.15509	0.86573	58
3	0.50076	1.99698	0.57851	1.72857	1.15528	0.86559	57
4	0.50101	1.99598	0.57890	1.72741	1.15548	0.86544	56
5	0.50126	1.99498	0.57929	1.72625	1.15567	0.86530	55
6	0.50151	1.99398	0.57968	1.72509	1.15587	0.86515	54
7	0.50176	1.99299	0.58007	1.72393	1.15606	0.86501	53
8	0.50201	1.99198	0.58046	1.72278	1.15626	0.86486	52
9	0.50227	1.99098	0.58085	1.72163	1.15645	0.86471	51
10	0.50252	1.98998	0.58124	1.72047	1.15665	0.86457	50
11	0.50277	1.98899	0.58162	1.71932	1.15684	0.86442	49
12	0.50302	1.98799	0.58201	1.71817	1.15704	0.86427	48
13	0.50327	1.98700	0.58240	1.71702	1.15724	0.86413	47
14	0.50352	1.98601	0.58279	1.71588	1.15743	0.86398	46
15	0.50377	1.98502	0.58318	1.71473	1.15763	0.86384	45
16	0.50403	1.98403	0.58357	1.71358	1.15782	0.86369	44
17	0.50428	1.98304	0.58396	1.71244	1.15802	0.86354	43
18	0.50453	1.98205	0.58435	1.71129	1.15822	0.86340	42
19	0.50478	1.98107	0.58474	1.71015	1.15841	0.86325	41
20	0.50503	1.98008	0.58513	1.70901	1.15861	0.86310	40
21	0.50528	1.97910	0.58552	1.70787	1.15881	0.86295	39
22	0.50553	1.97811	0.58591	1.70673	1.15901	0.86281	38
23	0.50578	1.97713	0.58631	1.70560	1.15920	0.86266	37
24	0.50603	1.97615	0.58670	1.70446	1.15940	0.86251	36
25	0.50628	1.97517	0.58709	1.70332	1.15960	0.86237	35
26	0.50654	1.97420	0.58748	1.70219	1.15980	0.86222	34
27	0.50679	1.97322	0.58787	1.70106	1.16000	0.86207	33
28	0.50704	1.97224	0.58826	1.69992	1.16019	0.86192	32
29	0.50729	1.97127	0.58865	1.69879	1.16039	0.86178	31
30	0.50754	1.97029	0.58905	1.69766	1.16059	0.86163	30
31	0.50779	1.96932	0.58944	1.69653	1.16079	0.86148	29
32	0.50804	1.96835	0.58983	1.69541	1.16099	0.86133	28
33	0.50829	1.96738	0.59022	1.69428	1.16119	0.86119	27
34	0.50854	1.96641	0.59061	1.69316	1.16139	0.86104	26
35	0.50879	1.96544	0.59101	1.69203	1.16159	0.86089	25
36	0.50904	1.96448	0.59140	1.69091	1.16179	0.86074	24
37	0.50929	1.96351	0.59179	1.68979	1.16199	0.86059	23
38	0.50954	1.96255	0.59218	1.68866	1.16219	0.86045	22
39	0.50979	1.96158	0.59258	1.68754	1.16239	0.86030	21
40	0.51004	1.96062	0.59297	1.68643	1.16259	0.86015	20
41	0.51029	1.95966	0.59336	1.68531	1.16279	0.86000	19
42	0.51054	1.95870	0.59376	1.68419	1.16299	0.85985	18
43	0.51079	1.95774	0.59415	1.68308	1.16319	0.85970	17
44	0.51104	1.95678	0.59454	1.68196	1.16339	0.85956	16
45	0.51129	1.95583	0.59494	1.68085	1.16359	0.85941	15
46	0.51154	1.95487	0.59533	1.67974	1.16380	0.85926	14
47	0.51179	1.95392	0.59573	1.67863	1.16400	0.85911	13
48	0.51204	1.95296	0.59612	1.67752	1.16420	0.85896	12
49	0.51229	1.95201	0.59651	1.67641	1.16440	0.85881	11
50	0.51254	1.95106	0.59691	1.67530	1.16460	0.85866	10
51	0.51279	1.95011	0.59730	1.67419	1.16481	0.85851	9
52	0.51304	1.94916	0.59770	1.67309	1.16501	0.85836	8
53	0.51329	1.94821	0.59809	1.67198	1.16521	0.85821	7
54	0.51354	1.94726	0.59849	1.67088	1.16541	0.85806	6
55	0.51379	1.94632	0.59888	1.66978	1.16562	0.85792	5
56	0.51404	1.94537	0.59928	1.66867	1.16582	0.85777	4
57	0.51429	1.94443	0.59967	1.66757	1.16602	0.85762	3
58	0.51454	1.94349	0.60007	1.66647	1.16623	0.85747	2
59	0.51479	1.94254	0.60046	1.66538	1.16643	0.85732	1
60	0.51504	1.94160	0.60086	1.66428	1.16663	0.85717	0

	sin	csc	tan	cot	sec	cos	
0	0.51504	1.94160	0.60086	1.66428	1.16663	0.85717	60
1	0.51529	1.94066	0.60126	1.66318	1.16684	0.85702	59
2	0.51554	1.93973	0.60165	1.66209	1.16704	0.85687	58
3	0.51579	1.93879	0.60205	1.66099	1.16725	0.85672	57
4	0.51604	1.93785	0.60245	1.65990	1.16745	0.85657	56
5	0.51628	1.93692	0.60284	1.65881	1.16766	0.85642	55
6	0.51653	1.93598	0.60324	1.65772	1.16786	0.85627	54
7	0.51678	1.93505	0.60364	1.65663	1.16806	0.85612	53
8	0.51703	1.93412	0.60403	1.65554	1.16827	0.85597	52
9	0.51728	1.93319	0.60443	1.65445	1.16848	0.85582	51
10	0.51753	1.93226	0.60483	1.65337	1.16868	0.85567	50
11	0.51778	1.93133	0.60522	1.65228	1.16889	0.85551	49
12	0.51803	1.93040	0.60562	1.65120	1.16909	0.85536	48
13	0.51828	1.92947	0.60602	1.65011	1.16930	0.85521	47
14	0.51852	1.92855	0.60642	1.64903	1.16950	0.85506	46
15	0.51877	1.92762	0.60681	1.64795	1.16971	0.85491	45
16	0.51902	1.92670	0.60721	1.64687	1.16992	0.85476	44
17	0.51927	1.92578	0.60761	1.64579	1.17012	0.85461	43
18	0.51952	1.92486	0.60801	1.64471	1.17033	0.85446	42
19	0.51977	1.92394	0.60841	1.64363	1.17054	0.85431	41
20	0.52002	1.92302	0.60881	1.64256	1.17075	0.85416	40
21	0.52026	1.92210	0.60921	1.64148	1.17095	0.85401	39
22	0.52051	1.92118	0.60960	1.64041	1.17116	0.85385	38
23	0.52076	1.92027	0.61000	1.63934	1.17137	0.85370	37
24	0.52101	1.91935	0.61040	1.63826	1.17158	0.85355	36
25	0.52126	1.91844	0.61080	1.63719	1.17178	0.85340	35
26	0.52151	1.91752	0.61120	1.63612	1.17199	0.85325	34
27	0.52175	1.91661	0.61160	1.63505	1.17220	0.85310	33
28	0.52200	1.91570	0.61200	1.63398	1.17241	0.85294	32
29	0.52225	1.91479	0.61240	1.63292	1.17262	0.85279	31
30	0.52250	1.91388	0.61280	1.63185	1.17283	0.85264	30
31	0.52275	1.91297	0.61320	1.63079	1.17304	0.85249	29
32	0.52299	1.91207	0.61360	1.62972	1.17325	0.85234	28
33	0.52324	1.91116	0.61400	1.62866	1.17346	0.85218	27
34	0.52349	1.91026	0.61440	1.62760	1.17367	0.85203	26
35	0.52374	1.90935	0.61480	1.62654	1.17388	0.85188	25
36	0.52399	1.90845	0.61520	1.62548	1.17409	0.85173	24
37	0.52423	1.90755	0.61561	1.62442	1.17430	0.85157	23
38	0.52448	1.90665	0.61601	1.62336	1.17451	0.85142	22
39	0.52473	1.90575	0.61641	1.62230	1.17472	0.85127	21
40	0.52498	1.90485	0.61681	1.62125	1.17493	0.85112	20
41	0.52522	1.90395	0.61721	1.62019	1.17514	0.85096	19
42	0.52547	1.90305	0.61761	1.61914	1.17535	0.85081	18
43	0.52572	1.90216	0.61801	1.61808	1.17556	0.85066	17
44	0.52597	1.90126	0.61842	1.61703	1.17577	0.85051	16
45	0.52621	1.90037	0.61882	1.61598	1.17598	0.85035	15
46	0.52646	1.89948	0.61922	1.61493	1.17620	0.85020	14
47	0.52671	1.89858	0.61962	1.61388	1.17641	0.85005	13
48	0.52696	1.89769	0.62003	1.61283	1.17662	0.84989	12
49	0.52720	1.89680	0.62043	1.61179	1.17683	0.84974	11
50	0.52745	1.89591	0.62083	1.61074	1.17704	0.84959	10
51	0.52770	1.89503	0.62124	1.60970	1.17726	0.84943	9
52	0.52794	1.89414	0.62164	1.60865	1.17747	0.84928	8
53	0.52819	1.89325	0.62204	1.60761	1.17768	0.84913	7
54	0.52844	1.89237	0.62245	1.60657	1.17790	0.84897	6
55	0.52869	1.89148	0.62285	1.60553	1.17811	0.84882	5
56	0.52893	1.89060	0.62325	1.60449	1.17832	0.84866	4
57	0.52918	1.88972	0.62366	1.60345	1.17854	0.84851	3
58	0.52943	1.88884	0.62406	1.60241	1.17875	0.84836	2
59	0.52967	1.88796	0.62446	1.60137	1.17896	0.84820	1
60	0.52992	1.88708	0.62487	1.60033	1.17918	0.84805	0

32°→ ↓	sin	csc	tan	cot	sec	cos ←147° ↓	
0	0.52992	1.88708	0.62487	1.60033	1.17918	0.84805	60
1	0.53017	1.88620	0.62527	1.59930	1.17939	0.84789	59
2	0.53041	1.88532	0.62568	1.59826	1.17961	0.84774	58
3	0.53066	1.88445	0.62608	1.59723	1.17982	0.84759	57
4	0.53091	1.88357	0.62649	1.59620	1.18004	0.84743	56
5	0.53115	1.88270	0.62689	1.59517	1.18025	0.84728	55
6	0.53140	1.88183	0.62730	1.59414	1.18047	0.84712	54
7	0.53164	1.88095	0.62770	1.59311	1.18068	0.84697	53
8	0.53189	1.88008	0.62811	1.59208	1.18090	0.84681	52
9	0.53214	1.87921	0.62852	1.59105	1.18111	0.84666	51
10	0.53238	1.87834	0.62892	1.59002	1.18133	0.84650	50
11	0.53263	1.87748	0.62933	1.58900	1.18155	0.84635	49
12	0.53288	1.87661	0.62973	1.58797	1.18176	0.84619	48
13	0.53312	1.87574	0.63014	1.58695	1.18198	0.84604	47
14	0.53337	1.87488	0.63055	1.58593	1.18220	0.84588	46
15	0.53361	1.87401	0.63095	1.58490	1.18241	0.84573	45
16	0.53386	1.87315	0.63136	1.58388	1.18263	0.84557	44
17	0.53411	1.87229	0.63177	1.58286	1.18285	0.84542	43
18	0.53435	1.87142	0.63217	1.58184	1.18307	0.84526	42
19	0.53460	1.87056	0.63258	1.58083	1.18328	0.84511	41
20	0.53484	1.86970	0.63299	1.57981	1.18350	0.84495	40
21	0.53509	1.86885	0.63340	1.57879	1.18372	0.84480	39
22	0.53534	1.86799	0.63380	1.57778	1.18394	0.84464	38
23	0.53558	1.86713	0.63421	1.57676	1.18416	0.84448	37
24	0.53583	1.86627	0.63462	1.57575	1.18437	0.84433	36
25	0.53607	1.86542	0.63503	1.57474	1.18459	0.84417	35
26	0.53632	1.86457	0.63544	1.57372	1.18481	0.84402	34
27	0.53656	1.86371	0.63584	1.57271	1.18503	0.84386	33
28	0.53681	1.86286	0.63625	1.57170	1.18525	0.84370	32
29	0.53705	1.86201	0.63666	1.57069	1.18547	0.84355	31
30	0.53730	1.86116	0.63707	1.56969	1.18569	0.84339	30
31	0.53754	1.86031	0.63748	1.56868	1.18591	0.84324	29
32	0.53779	1.85946	0.63789	1.56767	1.18613	0.84308	28
33	0.53804	1.85861	0.63830	1.56667	1.18635	0.84292	27
34	0.53828	1.85777	0.63871	1.56566	1.18657	0.84277	26
35	0.53853	1.85692	0.63912	1.56466	1.18679	0.84261	25
36	0.53877	1.85608	0.63953	1.56366	1.18701	0.84245	24
37	0.53902	1.85523	0.63994	1.56265	1.18723	0.84230	23
38	0.53926	1.85439	0.64035	1.56165	1.18745	0.84214	22
39	0.53951	1.85355	0.64076	1.56065	1.18767	0.84198	21
40	0.53975	1.85271	0.64117	1.55966	1.18790	0.84182	20
41	0.54000	1.85187	0.64158	1.55866	1.18812	0.84167	19
42	0.54024	1.85103	0.64199	1.55766	1.18834	0.84151	18
43	0.54049	1.85019	0.64240	1.55666	1.18856	0.84135	17
44	0.54073	1.84935	0.64281	1.55567	1.18878	0.84120	16
45	0.54097	1.84852	0.64322	1.55467	1.18901	0.84104	15
46	0.54122	1.84768	0.64363	1.55368	1.18923	0.84088	14
47	0.54146	1.84685	0.64404	1.55269	1.18945	0.84072	13
48	0.54171	1.84601	0.64446	1.55170	1.18967	0.84057	12
49	0.54195	1.84518	0.64487	1.55071	1.18990	0.84041	11
50	0.54220	1.84435	0.64528	1.54972	1.19012	0.84025	10
51	0.54244	1.84352	0.64569	1.54873	1.19034	0.84009	9
52	0.54269	1.84269	0.64610	1.54774	1.19057	0.83994	8
53	0.54293	1.84186	0.64652	1.54675	1.19079	0.83978	7
54	0.54317	1.84103	0.64693	1.54576	1.19102	0.83962	6
55	0.54342	1.84020	0.64734	1.54478	1.19124	0.83946	5
56	0.54366	1.83938	0.64775	1.54379	1.19146	0.83930	4
57	0.54391	1.83855	0.64817	1.54281	1.19169	0.83915	3
58	0.54415	1.83773	0.64858	1.54183	1.19191	0.83899	2
59	0.54440	1.83690	0.64899	1.54085	1.19214	0.83883	1
60	0.54464	1.83608	0.64941	1.53986	1.19236	0.83867	0

33°→ ↓	sin	csc	tan	cot	sec	cos ←146° ↓	
0	0.54464	1.83608	0.64941	1.53986	1.19236	0.83867	60
1	0.54488	1.83526	0.64982	1.53888	1.19259	0.83851	59
2	0.54513	1.83444	0.65024	1.53791	1.19281	0.83835	58
3	0.54537	1.83362	0.65065	1.53693	1.19304	0.83819	57
4	0.54561	1.83280	0.65106	1.53595	1.19327	0.83804	56
5	0.54586	1.83198	0.65148	1.53497	1.19349	0.83788	55
6	0.54610	1.83116	0.65189	1.53400	1.19372	0.83772	54
7	0.54635	1.83034	0.65231	1.53302	1.19394	0.83756	53
8	0.54659	1.82953	0.65272	1.53205	1.19417	0.83740	52
9	0.54683	1.82871	0.65314	1.53107	1.19440	0.83724	51
10	0.54708	1.82790	0.65355	1.53010	1.19463	0.83708	50
11	0.54732	1.82709	0.65397	1.52913	1.19485	0.83692	49
12	0.54756	1.82627	0.65438	1.52816	1.19508	0.83676	48
13	0.54781	1.82546	0.65480	1.52719	1.19531	0.83660	47
14	0.54805	1.82465	0.65521	1.52622	1.19553	0.83645	46
15	0.54829	1.82384	0.65563	1.52525	1.19576	0.83629	45
16	0.54854	1.82303	0.65604	1.52429	1.19599	0.83613	44
17	0.54878	1.82222	0.65646	1.52332	1.19622	0.83597	43
18	0.54902	1.82142	0.65688	1.52235	1.19645	0.83581	42
19	0.54927	1.82061	0.65729	1.52139	1.19668	0.83565	41
20	0.54951	1.81981	0.65771	1.52043	1.19691	0.83549	40
21	0.54975	1.81900	0.65813	1.51946	1.19713	0.83533	39
22	0.54999	1.81820	0.65854	1.51850	1.19736	0.83517	38
23	0.55024	1.81740	0.65896	1.51754	1.19759	0.83501	37
24	0.55048	1.81659	0.65938	1.51658	1.19782	0.83485	36
25	0.55072	1.81579	0.65980	1.51562	1.19805	0.83469	35
26	0.55097	1.81499	0.66021	1.51466	1.19828	0.83453	34
27	0.55121	1.81419	0.66063	1.51370	1.19851	0.83437	33
28	0.55145	1.81340	0.66105	1.51275	1.19874	0.83421	32
29	0.55169	1.81260	0.66147	1.51179	1.19897	0.83405	31
30	0.55194	1.81180	0.66189	1.51084	1.19920	0.83389	30
31	0.55218	1.81101	0.66230	1.50988	1.19944	0.83373	29
32	0.55242	1.81021	0.66272	1.50893	1.19967	0.83356	28
33	0.55266	1.80942	0.66314	1.50797	1.19990	0.83340	27
34	0.55291	1.80862	0.66356	1.50702	1.20013	0.83324	26
35	0.55315	1.80783	0.66398	1.50607	1.20036	0.83308	25
36	0.55339	1.80704	0.66440	1.50512	1.20059	0.83292	24
37	0.55363	1.80625	0.66482	1.50417	1.20083	0.83276	23
38	0.55388	1.80546	0.66524	1.50322	1.20106	0.83260	22
39	0.55412	1.80467	0.66566	1.50228	1.20129	0.83244	21
40	0.55436	1.80388	0.66608	1.50133	1.20152	0.83228	20
41	0.55460	1.80309	0.66650	1.50038	1.20176	0.83212	19
42	0.55484	1.80231	0.66692	1.49944	1.20199	0.83195	18
43	0.55509	1.80152	0.66734	1.49849	1.20222	0.83179	17
44	0.55533	1.80074	0.66776	1.49755	1.20246	0.83163	16
45	0.55557	1.79995	0.66818	1.49661	1.20269	0.83147	15
46	0.55581	1.79917	0.66860	1.49566	1.20292	0.83131	14
47	0.55605	1.79839	0.66902	1.49472	1.20316	0.83115	13
48	0.55630	1.79761	0.66944	1.49378	1.20339	0.83098	12
49	0.55654	1.79682	0.66986	1.49284	1.20363	0.83082	11
50	0.55678	1.79604	0.67028	1.49190	1.20386	0.83066	10
51	0.55702	1.79527	0.67071	1.49097	1.20410	0.83050	9
52	0.55726	1.79449	0.67113	1.49003	1.20433	0.83034	8
53	0.55750	1.79371	0.67155	1.48909	1.20457	0.83017	7
54	0.55775	1.79293	0.67197	1.48816	1.20480	0.83001	6
55	0.55799	1.79216	0.67239	1.48722	1.20504	0.82985	5
56	0.55823	1.79138	0.67282	1.48629	1.20527	0.82969	4
57	0.55847	1.79061	0.67324	1.48536	1.20551	0.82953	3
58	0.55871	1.78984	0.67366	1.48442	1.20575	0.82936	2
59	0.55895	1.78906	0.67409	1.48349	1.20598	0.82920	1
60	0.55919	1.78829	0.67451	1.48256	1.20622	0.82904	0

34°→ ↓	sin	csc	tan	cot	sec	cos ←145° ↓	
0	0.55919	1.78829	0.67451	1.48256	1.20622	0.82904	60
1	0.55943	1.78752	0.67493	1.48163	1.20645	0.82887	59
2	0.55968	1.78675	0.67536	1.48070	1.20669	0.82871	58
3	0.55992	1.78598	0.67578	1.47977	1.20693	0.82855	57
4	0.56016	1.78521	0.67620	1.47885	1.20717	0.82839	56
5	0.56040	1.78445	0.67663	1.47792	1.20740	0.82822	55
6	0.56064	1.78368	0.67705	1.47699	1.20764	0.82806	54
7	0.56088	1.78291	0.67748	1.47607	1.20788	0.82790	53
8	0.56112	1.78215	0.67790	1.47514	1.20812	0.82773	52
9	0.56136	1.78138	0.67832	1.47422	1.20836	0.82757	51
10	0.56160	1.78062	0.67875	1.47330	1.20859	0.82741	50
11	0.56184	1.77986	0.67917	1.47238	1.20883	0.82724	49
12	0.56208	1.77910	0.67960	1.47146	1.20907	0.82708	48
13	0.56232	1.77833	0.68002	1.47053	1.20931	0.82692	47
14	0.56256	1.77757	0.68045	1.46962	1.20955	0.82675	46
15	0.56280	1.77681	0.68088	1.46870	1.20979	0.82659	45
16	0.56305	1.77606	0.68130	1.46778	1.21003	0.82643	44
17	0.56329	1.77530	0.68173	1.46686	1.21027	0.82626	43
18	0.56353	1.77454	0.68215	1.46595	1.21051	0.82610	42
19	0.56377	1.77378	0.68258	1.46503	1.21075	0.82593	41
20	0.56401	1.77303	0.68301	1.46411	1.21099	0.82577	40
21	0.56425	1.77227	0.68343	1.46320	1.21123	0.82561	39
22	0.56449	1.77152	0.68386	1.46229	1.21147	0.82544	38
23	0.56473	1.77077	0.68429	1.46137	1.21171	0.82528	37
24	0.56497	1.77001	0.68471	1.46046	1.21195	0.82511	36
25	0.56521	1.76926	0.68514	1.45955	1.21220	0.82495	35
26	0.56545	1.76851	0.68557	1.45864	1.21244	0.82478	34
27	0.56569	1.76776	0.68600	1.45773	1.21268	0.82462	33
28	0.56593	1.76701	0.68642	1.45682	1.21292	0.82446	32
29	0.56617	1.76626	0.68685	1.45592	1.21316	0.82429	31
30	0.56641	1.76552	0.68728	1.45501	1.21341	0.82413	30
31	0.56665	1.76477	0.68771	1.45410	1.21365	0.82396	29
32	0.56689	1.76402	0.68814	1.45320	1.21389	0.82380	28
33	0.56713	1.76328	0.68857	1.45229	1.21414	0.82363	27
34	0.56736	1.76253	0.68900	1.45139	1.21438	0.82347	26
35	0.56760	1.76179	0.68942	1.45049	1.21462	0.82330	25
36	0.56784	1.76105	0.68985	1.44958	1.21487	0.82314	24
37	0.56808	1.76031	0.69028	1.44868	1.21511	0.82297	23
38	0.56832	1.75956	0.69071	1.44778	1.21535	0.82281	22
39	0.56856	1.75882	0.69114	1.44688	1.21560	0.82264	21
40	0.56880	1.75808	0.69157	1.44598	1.21584	0.82248	20
41	0.56904	1.75734	0.69200	1.44508	1.21609	0.82231	19
42	0.56928	1.75661	0.69243	1.44418	1.21633	0.82214	18
43	0.56952	1.75587	0.69286	1.44329	1.21658	0.82198	17
44	0.56976	1.75513	0.69329	1.44239	1.21682	0.82181	16
45	0.57000	1.75440	0.69372	1.44149	1.21707	0.82165	15
46	0.57024	1.75366	0.69416	1.44060	1.21731	0.82148	14
47	0.57047	1.75293	0.69459	1.43970	1.21756	0.82132	13
48	0.57071	1.75219	0.69502	1.43881	1.21781	0.82115	12
49	0.57095	1.75146	0.69545	1.43792	1.21805	0.82098	11
50	0.57119	1.75073	0.69588	1.43703	1.21830	0.82082	10
51	0.57143	1.75000	0.69631	1.43614	1.21855	0.82065	9
52	0.57167	1.74927	0.69675	1.43525	1.21879	0.82048	8
53	0.57191	1.74854	0.69718	1.43436	1.21904	0.82032	7
54	0.57215	1.74781	0.69761	1.43347	1.21929	0.82015	6
55	0.57238	1.74708	0.69804	1.43258	1.21953	0.81999	5
56	0.57262	1.74635	0.69847	1.43169	1.21978	0.81982	4
57	0.57286	1.74562	0.69891	1.43080	1.22003	0.81965	3
58	0.57310	1.74490	0.69934	1.42992	1.22028	0.81949	2
59	0.57334	1.74417	0.69977	1.42903	1.22053	0.81932	1
60	0.57358	1.74345	0.70021	1.42815	1.22077	0.81915	0
124°→ cos	sec	cot	tan	csc	sin ←55° ↑		

35°→ ↓	sin	csc	tan	cot	sec	cos ←144° ↓	
0	0.57358	1.74345	0.70021	1.42815	1.22077	0.81915	60
1	0.57381	1.74272	0.70064	1.42726	1.22102	0.81899	59
2	0.57405	1.74200	0.70107	1.42638	1.22127	0.81882	58
3	0.57429	1.74128	0.70151	1.42550	1.22152	0.81865	57
4	0.57453	1.74056	0.70194	1.42462	1.22177	0.81848	56
5	0.57477	1.73983	0.70238	1.42374	1.22202	0.81832	55
6	0.57501	1.73911	0.70281	1.42286	1.22227	0.81815	54
7	0.57524	1.73840	0.70325	1.42198	1.22252	0.81798	53
8	0.57548	1.73768	0.70368	1.42110	1.22277	0.81782	52
9	0.57572	1.73696	0.70412	1.42022	1.22302	0.81765	51
10	0.57596	1.73624	0.70455	1.41934	1.22327	0.81748	50
11	0.57619	1.73552	0.70499	1.41847	1.22352	0.81731	49
12	0.57643	1.73481	0.70542	1.41759	1.22377	0.81714	48
13	0.57667	1.73409	0.70586	1.41672	1.22402	0.81698	47
14	0.57691	1.73338	0.70629	1.41584	1.22428	0.81681	46
15	0.57715	1.73267	0.70673	1.41497	1.22453	0.81664	45
16	0.57738	1.73195	0.70717	1.41409	1.22478	0.81647	44
17	0.57762	1.73124	0.70760	1.41322	1.22503	0.81631	43
18	0.57786	1.73053	0.70804	1.41235	1.22528	0.81614	42
19	0.57810	1.72982	0.70848	1.41148	1.22554	0.81597	41
20	0.57833	1.72911	0.70891	1.41061	1.22579	0.81580	40
21	0.57857	1.72840	0.70935	1.40974	1.22604	0.81563	39
22	0.57881	1.72769	0.70979	1.40887	1.22629	0.81546	38
23	0.57904	1.72698	0.71023	1.40800	1.22655	0.81530	37
24	0.57928	1.72628	0.71066	1.40714	1.22680	0.81513	36
25	0.57952	1.72557	0.71110	1.40627	1.22706	0.81496	35
26	0.57976	1.72487	0.71154	1.40540	1.22731	0.81479	34
27	0.57999	1.72416	0.71198	1.40454	1.22756	0.81462	33
28	0.58023	1.72346	0.71242	1.40367	1.22782	0.81445	32
29	0.58047	1.72275	0.71285	1.40281	1.22807	0.81428	31
30	0.58070	1.72205	0.71329	1.40195	1.22833	0.81412	30
31	0.58094	1.72135	0.71373	1.40109	1.22858	0.81395	29
32	0.58118	1.72065	0.71417	1.40022	1.22884	0.81378	28
33	0.58141	1.71995	0.71461	1.39936	1.22909	0.81361	27
34	0.58165	1.71925	0.71505	1.39850	1.22935	0.81344	26
35	0.58189	1.71855	0.71549	1.39764	1.22960	0.81327	25
36	0.58212	1.71785	0.71593	1.39679	1.22986	0.81310	24
37	0.58236	1.71715	0.71637	1.39593	1.23012	0.81293	23
38	0.58260	1.71646	0.71681	1.39507	1.23037	0.81276	22
39	0.58283	1.71576	0.71725	1.39421	1.23063	0.81259	21
40	0.58307	1.71506	0.71769	1.39336	1.23089	0.81242	20
41	0.58330	1.71437	0.71813	1.39250	1.23114	0.81225	19
42	0.58354	1.71368	0.71857	1.39165	1.23140	0.81208	18
43	0.58378	1.71298	0.71901	1.39079	1.23166	0.81191	17
44	0.58401	1.71229	0.71946	1.38994	1.23192	0.81174	16
45	0.58425	1.71160	0.71990	1.38909	1.23217	0.81157	15
46	0.58449	1.71091	0.72034	1.38824	1.23243	0.81140	14
47	0.58472	1.71022	0.72078	1.38738	1.23269	0.81123	13
48	0.58496	1.70953	0.72122	1.38653	1.23295	0.81106	12
49	0.58519	1.70884	0.72167	1.38568	1.23321	0.81089	11
50	0.58543	1.70815	0.72211	1.38484	1.23347	0.81072	10
51	0.58567	1.70746	0.72255	1.38399	1.23373	0.81055	9
52	0.58590	1.70677	0.72299	1.38314	1.23398	0.81038	8
53	0.58614	1.70609	0.72344	1.38229	1.23424	0.81021	7
54	0.58637	1.70540	0.72388	1.38145	1.23450	0.81004	6
55	0.58661	1.70472	0.72432	1.38060	1.23476	0.80987	5
56	0.58684	1.70403	0.72477	1.37976	1.23502	0.80970	4
57	0.58708	1.70335	0.72521	1.37891	1.23529	0.80953	3
58	0.58731	1.70267	0.72565	1.37807	1.23555	0.80936	2
59	0.58755	1.70198	0.72610	1.37722	1.23581	0.80919	1
60	0.58779	1.70130	0.72654	1.37638	1.23607	0.80902	0
125°→ cos	sec	cot	tan	csc	sin ←54° ↑		

36°↓ →	sin	csc	tan	cot	sec	cos ←143° ↓	
0	0.58779	1.70130	0.72654	1.37638	1.23607	0.80902	60
1	0.58802	1.70062	0.72699	1.37554	1.23633	0.80885	59
2	0.58826	1.69994	0.72743	1.37470	1.23659	0.80867	58
3	0.58849	1.69926	0.72788	1.37386	1.23685	0.80850	57
4	0.58873	1.69858	0.72832	1.37302	1.23711	0.80833	56
5	0.58896	1.69790	0.72877	1.37218	1.23738	0.80816	55
6	0.58920	1.69723	0.72921	1.37134	1.23764	0.80799	54
7	0.58943	1.69655	0.72966	1.37050	1.23790	0.80782	53
8	0.58967	1.69587	0.73010	1.36967	1.23816	0.80765	52
9	0.58990	1.69520	0.73055	1.36883	1.23843	0.80748	51
10	0.59014	1.69452	0.73100	1.36800	1.23869	0.80730	50
11	0.59037	1.69385	0.73144	1.36716	1.23895	0.80713	49
12	0.59061	1.69318	0.73189	1.36633	1.23922	0.80696	48
13	0.59084	1.69250	0.73234	1.36549	1.23948	0.80679	47
14	0.59108	1.69183	0.73278	1.36466	1.23975	0.80662	46
15	0.59131	1.69116	0.73323	1.36383	1.24001	0.80644	45
16	0.59154	1.69049	0.73368	1.36300	1.24028	0.80627	44
17	0.59178	1.68982	0.73413	1.36217	1.24054	0.80610	43
18	0.59201	1.68915	0.73457	1.36134	1.24081	0.80593	42
19	0.59225	1.68848	0.73502	1.36051	1.24107	0.80576	41
20	0.59248	1.68782	0.73547	1.35968	1.24134	0.80558	40
21	0.59272	1.68715	0.73592	1.35885	1.24160	0.80541	39
22	0.59295	1.68648	0.73637	1.35802	1.24187	0.80524	38
23	0.59318	1.68582	0.73681	1.35719	1.24213	0.80507	37
24	0.59342	1.68515	0.73726	1.35637	1.24240	0.80489	36
25	0.59365	1.68449	0.73771	1.35554	1.24267	0.80472	35
26	0.59389	1.68382	0.73816	1.35472	1.24293	0.80455	34
27	0.59412	1.68316	0.73861	1.35389	1.24320	0.80438	33
28	0.59436	1.68250	0.73906	1.35307	1.24347	0.80420	32
29	0.59459	1.68183	0.73951	1.35224	1.24373	0.80403	31
30	0.59482	1.68117	0.73996	1.35142	1.24400	0.80386	30
31	0.59506	1.68051	0.74041	1.35060	1.24427	0.80368	29
32	0.59529	1.67985	0.74086	1.34978	1.24454	0.80351	28
33	0.59552	1.67919	0.74131	1.34896	1.24481	0.80334	27
34	0.59576	1.67853	0.74176	1.34814	1.24508	0.80316	26
35	0.59599	1.67788	0.74221	1.34732	1.24534	0.80299	25
36	0.59622	1.67722	0.74267	1.34650	1.24561	0.80282	24
37	0.59646	1.67656	0.74312	1.34568	1.24588	0.80264	23
38	0.59669	1.67591	0.74357	1.34487	1.24615	0.80247	22
39	0.59693	1.67525	0.74402	1.34405	1.24642	0.80230	21
40	0.59716	1.67460	0.74447	1.34323	1.24669	0.80212	20
41	0.59739	1.67394	0.74492	1.34242	1.24696	0.80195	19
42	0.59763	1.67329	0.74538	1.34160	1.24723	0.80178	18
43	0.59786	1.67264	0.74583	1.34079	1.24750	0.80160	17
44	0.59809	1.67198	0.74628	1.33998	1.24777	0.80143	16
45	0.59832	1.67133	0.74674	1.33916	1.24804	0.80125	15
46	0.59856	1.67068	0.74719	1.33835	1.24832	0.80108	14
47	0.59879	1.67003	0.74764	1.33754	1.24859	0.80091	13
48	0.59902	1.66938	0.74810	1.33673	1.24886	0.80073	12
49	0.59926	1.66873	0.74855	1.33592	1.24913	0.80056	11
50	0.59949	1.66809	0.74900	1.33511	1.24940	0.80038	10
51	0.59972	1.66744	0.74946	1.33430	1.24967	0.80021	9
52	0.59995	1.66679	0.74991	1.33349	1.24995	0.80003	8
53	0.60019	1.66615	0.75037	1.33268	1.25022	0.79986	7
54	0.60042	1.66550	0.75082	1.33187	1.25049	0.79968	6
55	0.60065	1.66486	0.75128	1.33107	1.25077	0.79951	5
56	0.60089	1.66421	0.75173	1.33026	1.25104	0.79934	4
57	0.60112	1.66357	0.75219	1.32946	1.25131	0.79916	3
58	0.60135	1.66292	0.75264	1.32865	1.25159	0.79899	2
59	0.60158	1.66228	0.75310	1.32785	1.25186	0.79881	1
60	0.60182	1.66164	0.75355	1.32704	1.25214	0.79864	0

37°↓ →	sin	csc	tan	cot	sec	cos ←142° ↓	
0	0.60182	1.66164	0.75355	1.32704	1.25214	0.79864	60
1	0.60205	1.66100	0.75401	1.32624	1.25241	0.79846	59
2	0.60228	1.66036	0.75447	1.32544	1.25269	0.79829	58
3	0.60251	1.65972	0.75492	1.32464	1.25296	0.79811	57
4	0.60274	1.65908	0.75538	1.32384	1.25324	0.79793	56
5	0.60298	1.65844	0.75584	1.32304	1.25351	0.79776	55
6	0.60321	1.65780	0.75629	1.32224	1.25379	0.79758	54
7	0.60344	1.65717	0.75675	1.32144	1.25406	0.79741	53
8	0.60367	1.65653	0.75721	1.32064	1.25434	0.79723	52
9	0.60390	1.65589	0.75767	1.31984	1.25462	0.79706	51
10	0.60414	1.65526	0.75812	1.31904	1.25489	0.79688	50
11	0.60437	1.65462	0.75858	1.31825	1.25517	0.79671	49
12	0.60460	1.65399	0.75904	1.31745	1.25545	0.79653	48
13	0.60483	1.65335	0.75950	1.31666	1.25572	0.79635	47
14	0.60506	1.65272	0.75996	1.31586	1.25600	0.79618	46
15	0.60529	1.65209	0.76042	1.31507	1.25628	0.79600	45
16	0.60553	1.65146	0.76088	1.31427	1.25656	0.79583	44
17	0.60576	1.65083	0.76134	1.31348	1.25683	0.79565	43
18	0.60599	1.65020	0.76180	1.31269	1.25711	0.79547	42
19	0.60622	1.64957	0.76226	1.31190	1.25739	0.79530	41
20	0.60645	1.64894	0.76272	1.31110	1.25767	0.79512	40
21	0.60668	1.64831	0.76318	1.31031	1.25795	0.79494	39
22	0.60691	1.64768	0.76364	1.30952	1.25823	0.79477	38
23	0.60714	1.64705	0.76410	1.30873	1.25851	0.79459	37
24	0.60738	1.64643	0.76456	1.30795	1.25879	0.79441	36
25	0.60761	1.64580	0.76502	1.30716	1.25907	0.79424	35
26	0.60784	1.64518	0.76548	1.30637	1.25935	0.79406	34
27	0.60807	1.64455	0.76594	1.30558	1.25963	0.79388	33
28	0.60830	1.64393	0.76640	1.30480	1.25991	0.79371	32
29	0.60853	1.64330	0.76686	1.30401	1.26019	0.79353	31
30	0.60876	1.64268	0.76733	1.30323	1.26047	0.79335	30
31	0.60899	1.64206	0.76779	1.30244	1.26075	0.79318	29
32	0.60922	1.64144	0.76825	1.30166	1.26104	0.79300	28
33	0.60945	1.64081	0.76871	1.30087	1.26132	0.79282	27
34	0.60968	1.64019	0.76918	1.30009	1.26160	0.79264	26
35	0.60991	1.63957	0.76964	1.29931	1.26188	0.79247	25
36	0.61015	1.63895	0.77010	1.29853	1.26216	0.79229	24
37	0.61038	1.63834	0.77057	1.29775	1.26245	0.79211	23
38	0.61061	1.63772	0.77103	1.29696	1.26273	0.79193	22
39	0.61084	1.63710	0.77149	1.29618	1.26301	0.79176	21
40	0.61107	1.63648	0.77196	1.29541	1.26330	0.79158	20
41	0.61130	1.63587	0.77242	1.29463	1.26358	0.79140	19
42	0.61153	1.63525	0.77289	1.29385	1.26387	0.79122	18
43	0.61176	1.63464	0.77335	1.29307	1.26415	0.79105	17
44	0.61199	1.63402	0.77382	1.29229	1.26443	0.79087	16
45	0.61222	1.63341	0.77428	1.29152	1.26472	0.79069	15
46	0.61245	1.63279	0.77475	1.29074	1.26500	0.79051	14
47	0.61268	1.63218	0.77521	1.28997	1.26529	0.79033	13
48	0.61291	1.63157	0.77568	1.28919	1.26557	0.79016	12
49	0.61314	1.63096	0.77615	1.28842	1.26586	0.78998	11
50	0.61337	1.63035	0.77661	1.28764	1.26615	0.78980	10
51	0.61360	1.62974	0.77708	1.28687	1.26643	0.78962	9
52	0.61383	1.62913	0.77754	1.28610	1.26672	0.78944	8
53	0.61406	1.62852	0.77801	1.28533	1.26701	0.78926	7
54	0.61429	1.62791	0.77848	1.28456	1.26729	0.78908	6
55	0.61451	1.62730	0.77895	1.28379	1.26758	0.78891	5
56	0.61474	1.62669	0.77941	1.28302	1.26787	0.78873	4
57	0.61497	1.62609	0.77988	1.28225	1.26815	0.78855	3
58	0.61520	1.62548	0.78035	1.28148	1.26844	0.78837	2
59	0.61543	1.62487	0.78082	1.28071	1.26873	0.78819	1
60	0.61566	1.62427	0.78129	1.27994	1.26902	0.78801	0

38°→	sin	csc	tan	cot	sec	cos ←141°	
0	0.61566	1.62427	0.78129	1.27994	1.26902	0.78801	60
1	0.61589	1.62366	0.78175	1.27917	1.26931	0.78783	59
2	0.61612	1.62306	0.78222	1.27841	1.26960	0.78765	58
3	0.61635	1.62246	0.78269	1.27764	1.26988	0.78747	57
4	0.61658	1.62185	0.78316	1.27688	1.27017	0.78729	56
5	0.61681	1.62125	0.78363	1.27611	1.27046	0.78711	55
6	0.61704	1.62065	0.78410	1.27535	1.27075	0.78694	54
7	0.61726	1.62005	0.78457	1.27458	1.27104	0.78676	53
8	0.61749	1.61945	0.78504	1.27382	1.27133	0.78658	52
9	0.61772	1.61885	0.78551	1.27306	1.27162	0.78640	51
10	0.61795	1.61825	0.78598	1.27230	1.27191	0.78622	50
11	0.61818	1.61765	0.78645	1.27153	1.27221	0.78604	49
12	0.61841	1.61705	0.78692	1.27077	1.27250	0.78586	48
13	0.61864	1.61646	0.78739	1.27001	1.27279	0.78568	47
14	0.61887	1.61586	0.78786	1.26925	1.27308	0.78550	46
15	0.61909	1.61526	0.78834	1.26849	1.27337	0.78532	45
16	0.61932	1.61467	0.78881	1.26774	1.27366	0.78514	44
17	0.61955	1.61407	0.78928	1.26698	1.27396	0.78496	43
18	0.61978	1.61348	0.78975	1.26622	1.27425	0.78478	42
19	0.62001	1.61288	0.79022	1.26546	1.27454	0.78460	41
20	0.62024	1.61229	0.79070	1.26471	1.27483	0.78442	40
21	0.62046	1.61170	0.79117	1.26395	1.27513	0.78424	39
22	0.62069	1.61111	0.79164	1.26319	1.27542	0.78405	38
23	0.62092	1.61051	0.79212	1.26244	1.27572	0.78387	37
24	0.62115	1.60992	0.79259	1.26169	1.27601	0.78369	36
25	0.62138	1.60933	0.79306	1.26093	1.27630	0.78351	35
26	0.62160	1.60874	0.79354	1.26018	1.27660	0.78333	34
27	0.62183	1.60815	0.79401	1.25943	1.27689	0.78315	33
28	0.62206	1.60756	0.79449	1.25867	1.27719	0.78297	32
29	0.62229	1.60698	0.79496	1.25792	1.27748	0.78279	31
30	0.62251	1.60639	0.79544	1.25717	1.27778	0.78261	30
31	0.62274	1.60580	0.79591	1.25642	1.27807	0.78243	29
32	0.62297	1.60521	0.79639	1.25567	1.27837	0.78225	28
33	0.62320	1.60463	0.79686	1.25492	1.27867	0.78206	27
34	0.62342	1.60404	0.79734	1.25417	1.27896	0.78188	26
35	0.62365	1.60346	0.79781	1.25343	1.27926	0.78170	25
36	0.62388	1.60287	0.79829	1.25268	1.27956	0.78152	24
37	0.62411	1.60229	0.79877	1.25193	1.27985	0.78134	23
38	0.62433	1.60171	0.79924	1.25118	1.28015	0.78116	22
39	0.62456	1.60112	0.79972	1.25044	1.28045	0.78098	21
40	0.62479	1.60054	0.80020	1.24969	1.28075	0.78079	20
41	0.62502	1.59996	0.80067	1.24895	1.28105	0.78061	19
42	0.62524	1.59938	0.80115	1.24820	1.28134	0.78043	18
43	0.62547	1.59880	0.80163	1.24746	1.28164	0.78025	17
44	0.62570	1.59822	0.80211	1.24672	1.28194	0.78007	16
45	0.62592	1.59764	0.80258	1.24597	1.28224	0.77988	15
46	0.62615	1.59706	0.80306	1.24523	1.28254	0.77970	14
47	0.62638	1.59648	0.80354	1.24449	1.28284	0.77952	13
48	0.62660	1.59590	0.80402	1.24375	1.28314	0.77934	12
49	0.62683	1.59533	0.80450	1.24301	1.28344	0.77916	11
50	0.62706	1.59475	0.80498	1.24227	1.28374	0.77897	10
51	0.62728	1.59418	0.80546	1.24153	1.28404	0.77879	9
52	0.62751	1.59360	0.80594	1.24079	1.28434	0.77861	8
53	0.62774	1.59302	0.80642	1.24005	1.28464	0.77843	7
54	0.62796	1.59245	0.80690	1.23931	1.28495	0.77824	6
55	0.62819	1.59188	0.80738	1.23858	1.28525	0.77806	5
56	0.62842	1.59130	0.80786	1.23784	1.28555	0.77788	4
57	0.62864	1.59073	0.80834	1.23710	1.28585	0.77769	3
58	0.62887	1.59016	0.80882	1.23637	1.28615	0.77751	2
59	0.62909	1.58959	0.80930	1.23563	1.28646	0.77733	1
60	0.62932	1.58902	0.80978	1.23490	1.28676	0.77715	0
128°→cos	sec	cot	tan	csc	sin ←51°	

39°→	sin	csc	tan	cot	sec	cos ←140°	
0	0.62932	1.58902	0.80978	1.23490	1.28676	0.77715	60
1	0.62955	1.58845	0.81027	1.23416	1.28706	0.77696	59
2	0.62977	1.58788	0.81075	1.23343	1.28737	0.77678	58
3	0.63000	1.58731	0.81123	1.23270	1.28767	0.77660	57
4	0.63022	1.58674	0.81171	1.23196	1.28797	0.77641	56
5	0.63045	1.58617	0.81220	1.23123	1.28828	0.77623	55
6	0.63068	1.58560	0.81268	1.23050	1.28858	0.77605	54
7	0.63090	1.58503	0.81316	1.22977	1.28889	0.77586	53
8	0.63113	1.58447	0.81364	1.22904	1.28919	0.77568	52
9	0.63135	1.58390	0.81413	1.22831	1.28950	0.77550	51
10	0.63158	1.58333	0.81461	1.22758	1.28980	0.77531	50
11	0.63180	1.58277	0.81510	1.22685	1.29011	0.77513	49
12	0.63203	1.58221	0.81558	1.22612	1.29042	0.77494	48
13	0.63225	1.58164	0.81606	1.22539	1.29072	0.77476	47
14	0.63248	1.58108	0.81655	1.22467	1.29103	0.77458	46
15	0.63271	1.58051	0.81703	1.22394	1.29133	0.77439	45
16	0.63293	1.57995	0.81752	1.22321	1.29164	0.77421	44
17	0.63316	1.57939	0.81800	1.22249	1.29195	0.77402	43
18	0.63338	1.57883	0.81849	1.22176	1.29226	0.77384	42
19	0.63361	1.57827	0.81898	1.22104	1.29256	0.77366	41
20	0.63383	1.57771	0.81946	1.22031	1.29287	0.77347	40
21	0.63406	1.57715	0.81995	1.21959	1.29318	0.77329	39
22	0.63428	1.57659	0.82044	1.21886	1.29349	0.77310	38
23	0.63451	1.57603	0.82092	1.21814	1.29380	0.77292	37
24	0.63473	1.57547	0.82141	1.21742	1.29411	0.77273	36
25	0.63496	1.57491	0.82190	1.21670	1.29442	0.77255	35
26	0.63518	1.57436	0.82238	1.21598	1.29473	0.77236	34
27	0.63540	1.57380	0.82287	1.21526	1.29504	0.77218	33
28	0.63563	1.57324	0.82336	1.21454	1.29535	0.77199	32
29	0.63585	1.57269	0.82385	1.21382	1.29566	0.77181	31
30	0.63608	1.57213	0.82434	1.21310	1.29597	0.77162	30
31	0.63630	1.57158	0.82483	1.21238	1.29628	0.77144	29
32	0.63653	1.57103	0.82531	1.21166	1.29659	0.77125	28
33	0.63675	1.57047	0.82580	1.21094	1.29690	0.77107	27
34	0.63698	1.56992	0.82629	1.21023	1.29721	0.77088	26
35	0.63720	1.56937	0.82678	1.20951	1.29752	0.77070	25
36	0.63742	1.56881	0.82727	1.20879	1.29784	0.77051	24
37	0.63765	1.56826	0.82776	1.20808	1.29815	0.77033	23
38	0.63787	1.56771	0.82825	1.20736	1.29846	0.77014	22
39	0.63810	1.56716	0.82874	1.20665	1.29877	0.76996	21
40	0.63832	1.56661	0.82923	1.20593	1.29909	0.76977	20
41	0.63854	1.56606	0.82972	1.20522	1.29940	0.76959	19
42	0.63877	1.56551	0.83022	1.20451	1.29971	0.76940	18
43	0.63899	1.56497	0.83071	1.20379	1.30003	0.76921	17
44	0.63922	1.56442	0.83120	1.20308	1.30034	0.76903	16
45	0.63944	1.56387	0.83169	1.20237	1.30066	0.76884	15
46	0.63966	1.56332	0.83218	1.20166	1.30097	0.76866	14
47	0.63989	1.56278	0.83268	1.20095	1.30129	0.76847	13
48	0.64011	1.56223	0.83317	1.20024	1.30160	0.76828	12
49	0.64033	1.56169	0.83366	1.19953	1.30192	0.76810	11
50	0.64056	1.56114	0.83415	1.19882	1.30223	0.76791	10
51	0.64078	1.56060	0.83465	1.19811	1.30255	0.76772	9
52	0.64100	1.56005	0.83514	1.19740	1.30287	0.76754	8
53	0.64123	1.55951	0.83564	1.19669	1.30318	0.76735	7
54	0.64145	1.55897	0.83613	1.19599	1.30350	0.76717	6
55	0.64167	1.55843	0.83662	1.19528	1.30382	0.76698	5
56	0.64190	1.55789	0.83712	1.19457	1.30413	0.76679	4
57	0.64212	1.55734	0.83761	1.19387	1.30445	0.76661	3
58	0.64234	1.55680	0.83811	1.19316	1.30477	0.76642	2
59	0.64256	1.55626	0.83860	1.19246	1.30509	0.76623	1
60	0.64279	1.55572	0.83910	1.19175	1.30541	0.76604	0
129°→cos	sec	cot	tan	csc	sin ←50°	

40°↓→ sin	csc	tan	cot	sec	cos ←139°↓	
0	0.64279	1.55572	0.83910	1.19175	1.30541	0.76604	60
1	0.64301	1.55518	0.83960	1.19105	1.30573	0.76586	59
2	0.64323	1.55465	0.84009	1.19035	1.30605	0.76567	58
3	0.64346	1.55411	0.84059	1.18964	1.30636	0.76548	57
4	0.64368	1.55357	0.84108	1.18894	1.30668	0.76530	56
5	0.64390	1.55303	0.84158	1.18824	1.30700	0.76511	55
6	0.64412	1.55250	0.84208	1.18754	1.30732	0.76492	54
7	0.64435	1.55196	0.84258	1.18684	1.30764	0.76473	53
8	0.64457	1.55143	0.84307	1.18614	1.30796	0.76455	52
9	0.64479	1.55089	0.84357	1.18544	1.30829	0.76436	51
10	0.64501	1.55036	0.84407	1.18474	1.30861	0.76417	50
11	0.64524	1.54982	0.84457	1.18404	1.30893	0.76398	49
12	0.64546	1.54929	0.84507	1.18334	1.30925	0.76380	48
13	0.64568	1.54876	0.84556	1.18264	1.30957	0.76361	47
14	0.64590	1.54822	0.84606	1.18194	1.30989	0.76342	46
15	0.64612	1.54769	0.84656	1.18125	1.31022	0.76323	45
16	0.64635	1.54716	0.84706	1.18055	1.31054	0.76304	44
17	0.64657	1.54663	0.84756	1.17986	1.31086	0.76286	43
18	0.64679	1.54610	0.84806	1.17916	1.31119	0.76267	42
19	0.64701	1.54557	0.84856	1.17846	1.31151	0.76248	41
20	0.64723	1.54504	0.84906	1.17777	1.31183	0.76229	40
21	0.64746	1.54451	0.84956	1.17708	1.31216	0.76210	39
22	0.64768	1.54398	0.85006	1.17638	1.31248	0.76192	38
23	0.64790	1.54345	0.85057	1.17569	1.31281	0.76173	37
24	0.64812	1.54292	0.85107	1.17500	1.31313	0.76154	36
25	0.64834	1.54240	0.85157	1.17430	1.31346	0.76135	35
26	0.64856	1.54187	0.85207	1.17361	1.31378	0.76116	34
27	0.64878	1.54134	0.85257	1.17292	1.31411	0.76097	33
28	0.64901	1.54082	0.85308	1.17223	1.31443	0.76078	32
29	0.64923	1.54029	0.85358	1.17154	1.31476	0.76059	31
30	0.64945	1.53977	0.85408	1.17085	1.31509	0.76041	30
31	0.64967	1.53924	0.85458	1.17016	1.31541	0.76022	29
32	0.64989	1.53872	0.85509	1.16947	1.31574	0.76003	28
33	0.65011	1.53820	0.85559	1.16878	1.31607	0.75984	27
34	0.65033	1.53768	0.85609	1.16809	1.31640	0.75965	26
35	0.65055	1.53715	0.85660	1.16741	1.31672	0.75946	25
36	0.65077	1.53663	0.85710	1.16672	1.31705	0.75927	24
37	0.65100	1.53611	0.85761	1.16603	1.31738	0.75908	23
38	0.65122	1.53559	0.85811	1.16535	1.31771	0.75889	22
39	0.65144	1.53507	0.85862	1.16466	1.31804	0.75870	21
40	0.65166	1.53455	0.85912	1.16398	1.31837	0.75851	20
41	0.65188	1.53403	0.85963	1.16329	1.31870	0.75832	19
42	0.65210	1.53351	0.86014	1.16261	1.31903	0.75813	18
43	0.65232	1.53299	0.86064	1.16192	1.31936	0.75794	17
44	0.65254	1.53247	0.86115	1.16124	1.31969	0.75775	16
45	0.65276	1.53196	0.86166	1.16056	1.32002	0.75756	15
46	0.65298	1.53144	0.86216	1.15987	1.32035	0.75738	14
47	0.65320	1.53092	0.86267	1.15919	1.32068	0.75719	13
48	0.65342	1.53041	0.86318	1.15851	1.32101	0.75700	12
49	0.65364	1.52989	0.86368	1.15783	1.32134	0.75680	11
50	0.65386	1.52938	0.86419	1.15715	1.32168	0.75661	10
51	0.65408	1.52886	0.86470	1.15647	1.32201	0.75642	9
52	0.65430	1.52835	0.86521	1.15579	1.32234	0.75623	8
53	0.65452	1.52784	0.86572	1.15511	1.32267	0.75604	7
54	0.65474	1.52732	0.86623	1.15443	1.32301	0.75585	6
55	0.65496	1.52681	0.86674	1.15375	1.32334	0.75566	5
56	0.65518	1.52630	0.86725	1.15308	1.32368	0.75547	4
57	0.65540	1.52579	0.86776	1.15240	1.32401	0.75528	3
58	0.65562	1.52527	0.86827	1.15172	1.32434	0.75509	2
59	0.65584	1.52476	0.86878	1.15104	1.32468	0.75490	1
60	0.65606	1.52425	0.86929	1.15037	1.32501	0.75471	0
130°↑→ cos	sec	cot	tan	csc	sin ←49°↑	

41°↓→ sin	csc	tan	cot	sec	cos ←138°↓	
0	0.65606	1.52425	0.86929	1.15037	1.32501	0.75471	60
1	0.65628	1.52374	0.86980	1.14969	1.32535	0.75452	59
2	0.65650	1.52323	0.87031	1.14902	1.32568	0.75433	58
3	0.65672	1.52273	0.87082	1.14834	1.32602	0.75414	57
4	0.65694	1.52222	0.87133	1.14767	1.32636	0.75395	56
5	0.65716	1.52171	0.87184	1.14699	1.32669	0.75375	55
6	0.65738	1.52120	0.87236	1.14632	1.32703	0.75356	54
7	0.65759	1.52069	0.87287	1.14565	1.32737	0.75337	53
8	0.65781	1.52019	0.87338	1.14498	1.32770	0.75318	52
9	0.65803	1.51968	0.87389	1.14430	1.32804	0.75299	51
10	0.65825	1.51918	0.87441	1.14363	1.32838	0.75280	50
11	0.65847	1.51867	0.87492	1.14296	1.32872	0.75261	49
12	0.65869	1.51817	0.87543	1.14229	1.32905	0.75241	48
13	0.65891	1.51766	0.87595	1.14162	1.32939	0.75222	47
14	0.65913	1.51716	0.87646	1.14095	1.32973	0.75203	46
15	0.65935	1.51665	0.87698	1.14028	1.33007	0.75184	45
16	0.65956	1.51615	0.87749	1.13961	1.33041	0.75165	44
17	0.65978	1.51565	0.87801	1.13894	1.33075	0.75146	43
18	0.66000	1.51515	0.87852	1.13828	1.33109	0.75126	42
19	0.66022	1.51465	0.87904	1.13761	1.33143	0.75107	41
20	0.66044	1.51415	0.87955	1.13694	1.33177	0.75088	40
21	0.66066	1.51364	0.88007	1.13627	1.33211	0.75069	39
22	0.66088	1.51314	0.88059	1.13561	1.33245	0.75050	38
23	0.66109	1.51265	0.88110	1.13494	1.33279	0.75030	37
24	0.66131	1.51215	0.88162	1.13428	1.33314	0.75011	36
25	0.66153	1.51165	0.88214	1.13361	1.33348	0.74992	35
26	0.66175	1.51115	0.88265	1.13295	1.33382	0.74973	34
27	0.66197	1.51065	0.88317	1.13228	1.33416	0.74953	33
28	0.66218	1.51015	0.88369	1.13162	1.33451	0.74934	32
29	0.66240	1.50966	0.88421	1.13096	1.33485	0.74915	31
30	0.66262	1.50916	0.88473	1.13029	1.33519	0.74896	30
31	0.66284	1.50866	0.88524	1.12963	1.33554	0.74876	29
32	0.66306	1.50817	0.88576	1.12897	1.33588	0.74857	28
33	0.66327	1.50767	0.88628	1.12831	1.33622	0.74838	27
34	0.66349	1.50718	0.88680	1.12765	1.33657	0.74818	26
35	0.66371	1.50669	0.88732	1.12699	1.33691	0.74799	25
36	0.66393	1.50619	0.88784	1.12633	1.33726	0.74780	24
37	0.66414	1.50570	0.88836	1.12567	1.33760	0.74760	23
38	0.66436	1.50521	0.88888	1.12501	1.33795	0.74741	22
39	0.66458	1.50471	0.88940	1.12435	1.33830	0.74722	21
40	0.66480	1.50422	0.88992	1.12369	1.33864	0.74703	20
41	0.66501	1.50373	0.89045	1.12303	1.33899	0.74683	19
42	0.66523	1.50324	0.89097	1.12238	1.33934	0.74664	18
43	0.66545	1.50275	0.89149	1.12172	1.33968	0.74644	17
44	0.66566	1.50226	0.89201	1.12106	1.34003	0.74625	16
45	0.66588	1.50177	0.89253	1.12041	1.34038	0.74606	15
46	0.66610	1.50128	0.89306	1.11975	1.34073	0.74586	14
47	0.66632	1.50079	0.89358	1.11909	1.34108	0.74567	13
48	0.66653	1.50030	0.89410	1.11844	1.34142	0.74548	12
49	0.66675	1.49981	0.89463	1.11778	1.34177	0.74528	11
50	0.66697	1.49933	0.89515	1.11713	1.34212	0.74509	10
51	0.66718	1.49884	0.89567	1.11648	1.34247	0.74489	9
52	0.66740	1.49835	0.89620	1.11582	1.34282	0.74470	8
53	0.66762	1.49787	0.89672	1.11517	1.34317	0.74451	7
54	0.66783	1.49738	0.89725	1.11452	1.34352	0.74431	6
55	0.66805	1.49690	0.89777	1.11387	1.34387	0.74412	5
56	0.66827	1.49641	0.89830	1.11321	1.34423	0.74392	4
57	0.66848	1.49593	0.89883	1.11256	1.34458	0.74373	3
58	0.66870	1.49544	0.89935	1.11191	1.34493	0.74353	2
59	0.66891	1.49496	0.89988	1.11126	1.34528	0.74334	1
60	0.66913	1.49448	0.90040	1.11061	1.34563	0.74314	0
131°↑→ cos	sec	cot	tan	csc	sin ←48°↑	

42°→ sin	csc	tan	cot	sec	cos ←137°	
0	0.66913	1.49448	0.90040	1.11061	1.34563	0.74314	60
1	0.66935	1.49399	0.90093	1.10996	1.34599	0.74295	59
2	0.66956	1.49351	0.90146	1.10931	1.34634	0.74276	58
3	0.66978	1.49303	0.90199	1.10867	1.34669	0.74256	57
4	0.66999	1.49255	0.90251	1.10802	1.34704	0.74237	56
5	0.67021	1.49207	0.90304	1.10737	1.34740	0.74217	55
6	0.67043	1.49159	0.90357	1.10672	1.34775	0.74198	54
7	0.67064	1.49111	0.90410	1.10607	1.34811	0.74178	53
8	0.67086	1.49063	0.90463	1.10543	1.34846	0.74159	52
9	0.67107	1.49015	0.90516	1.10478	1.34882	0.74139	51
10	0.67129	1.48967	0.90569	1.10414	1.34917	0.74120	50
11	0.67151	1.48919	0.90621	1.10349	1.34953	0.74100	49
12	0.67172	1.48871	0.90674	1.10285	1.34988	0.74080	48
13	0.67194	1.48824	0.90727	1.10220	1.35024	0.74061	47
14	0.67215	1.48776	0.90781	1.10156	1.35060	0.74041	46
15	0.67237	1.48728	0.90834	1.10091	1.35095	0.74022	45
16	0.67258	1.48681	0.90887	1.10027	1.35131	0.74002	44
17	0.67280	1.48633	0.90940	1.09963	1.35167	0.73983	43
18	0.67301	1.48586	0.90993	1.09899	1.35203	0.73963	42
19	0.67323	1.48538	0.91046	1.09834	1.35238	0.73944	41
20	0.67344	1.48491	0.91099	1.09770	1.35274	0.73924	40
21	0.67366	1.48443	0.91153	1.09706	1.35310	0.73904	39
22	0.67387	1.48396	0.91206	1.09642	1.35346	0.73885	38
23	0.67409	1.48349	0.91259	1.09578	1.35382	0.73865	37
24	0.67430	1.48301	0.91313	1.09514	1.35418	0.73846	36
25	0.67452	1.48254	0.91366	1.09450	1.35454	0.73826	35
26	0.67473	1.48207	0.91419	1.09386	1.35490	0.73806	34
27	0.67495	1.48160	0.91473	1.09322	1.35526	0.73787	33
28	0.67516	1.48113	0.91526	1.09258	1.35562	0.73767	32
29	0.67538	1.48066	0.91580	1.09195	1.35598	0.73747	31
30	0.67559	1.48019	0.91633	1.09131	1.35634	0.73728	30
31	0.67580	1.47972	0.91687	1.09067	1.35670	0.73708	29
32	0.67602	1.47925	0.91740	1.09003	1.35707	0.73688	28
33	0.67623	1.47878	0.91794	1.08940	1.35743	0.73669	27
34	0.67645	1.47831	0.91847	1.08876	1.35779	0.73649	26
35	0.67666	1.47784	0.91901	1.08813	1.35815	0.73629	25
36	0.67688	1.47738	0.91955	1.08749	1.35852	0.73610	24
37	0.67709	1.47691	0.92008	1.08686	1.35888	0.73590	23
38	0.67730	1.47644	0.92062	1.08622	1.35924	0.73570	22
39	0.67752	1.47598	0.92116	1.08559	1.35961	0.73551	21
40	0.67773	1.47551	0.92170	1.08496	1.35997	0.73531	20
41	0.67795	1.47504	0.92224	1.08432	1.36034	0.73511	19
42	0.67816	1.47458	0.92277	1.08369	1.36070	0.73491	18
43	0.67837	1.47411	0.92331	1.08306	1.36107	0.73472	17
44	0.67859	1.47365	0.92385	1.08243	1.36143	0.73452	16
45	0.67880	1.47319	0.92439	1.08179	1.36180	0.73432	15
46	0.67901	1.47272	0.92493	1.08116	1.36217	0.73413	14
47	0.67923	1.47226	0.92547	1.08053	1.36253	0.73393	13
48	0.67944	1.47180	0.92601	1.07990	1.36290	0.73373	12
49	0.67965	1.47134	0.92655	1.07927	1.36327	0.73353	11
50	0.67987	1.47087	0.92709	1.07864	1.36363	0.73333	10
51	0.68008	1.47041	0.92763	1.07801	1.36400	0.73314	9
52	0.68029	1.46995	0.92817	1.07738	1.36437	0.73294	8
53	0.68051	1.46949	0.92872	1.07676	1.36474	0.73274	7
54	0.68072	1.46903	0.92926	1.07613	1.36511	0.73254	6
55	0.68093	1.46857	0.92980	1.07550	1.36548	0.73234	5
56	0.68115	1.46811	0.93034	1.07487	1.36585	0.73215	4
57	0.68136	1.46765	0.93088	1.07425	1.36622	0.73195	3
58	0.68157	1.46719	0.93143	1.07362	1.36659	0.73175	2
59	0.68179	1.46674	0.93197	1.07299	1.36696	0.73155	1
60	0.68200	1.46628	0.93252	1.07237	1.36733	0.73135	0

132°→ cos	sec	cot	tan	csc	sin ←47°	

43°→ sin	csc	tan	cot	sec	cos ←136°	
0	0.68200	1.46628	0.93252	1.07237	1.36733	0.73135	60
1	0.68221	1.46582	0.93306	1.07174	1.36770	0.73116	59
2	0.68242	1.46537	0.93360	1.07112	1.36807	0.73096	58
3	0.68264	1.46491	0.93415	1.07049	1.36844	0.73076	57
4	0.68285	1.46445	0.93469	1.06987	1.36881	0.73056	56
5	0.68306	1.46400	0.93524	1.06925	1.36919	0.73036	55
6	0.68327	1.46354	0.93578	1.06862	1.36956	0.73016	54
7	0.68349	1.46309	0.93633	1.06800	1.36993	0.72996	53
8	0.68370	1.46263	0.93688	1.06738	1.37030	0.72976	52
9	0.68391	1.46218	0.93742	1.06676	1.37068	0.72957	51
10	0.68412	1.46173	0.93797	1.06613	1.37105	0.72937	50
11	0.68434	1.46127	0.93852	1.06551	1.37143	0.72917	49
12	0.68455	1.46082	0.93906	1.06489	1.37180	0.72897	48
13	0.68476	1.46037	0.93961	1.06427	1.37218	0.72877	47
14	0.68497	1.45992	0.94016	1.06365	1.37255	0.72857	46
15	0.68518	1.45946	0.94071	1.06303	1.37293	0.72837	45
16	0.68539	1.45901	0.94125	1.06241	1.37330	0.72817	44
17	0.68561	1.45856	0.94180	1.06179	1.37368	0.72797	43
18	0.68582	1.45811	0.94235	1.06117	1.37406	0.72777	42
19	0.68603	1.45766	0.94290	1.06056	1.37443	0.72757	41
20	0.68624	1.45721	0.94345	1.05994	1.37481	0.72737	40
21	0.68645	1.45676	0.94400	1.05932	1.37519	0.72717	39
22	0.68666	1.45631	0.94455	1.05870	1.37556	0.72697	38
23	0.68688	1.45587	0.94510	1.05809	1.37594	0.72677	37
24	0.68709	1.45542	0.94565	1.05747	1.37632	0.72657	36
25	0.68730	1.45497	0.94620	1.05685	1.37670	0.72637	35
26	0.68751	1.45452	0.94676	1.05624	1.37708	0.72617	34
27	0.68772	1.45408	0.94731	1.05562	1.37746	0.72597	33
28	0.68793	1.45363	0.94786	1.05501	1.37784	0.72577	32
29	0.68814	1.45319	0.94841	1.05439	1.37822	0.72557	31
30	0.68835	1.45274	0.94896	1.05378	1.37860	0.72537	30
31	0.68857	1.45229	0.94952	1.05317	1.37898	0.72517	29
32	0.68878	1.45185	0.95007	1.05255	1.37936	0.72497	28
33	0.68899	1.45141	0.95062	1.05194	1.37974	0.72477	27
34	0.68920	1.45096	0.95118	1.05133	1.38012	0.72457	26
35	0.68941	1.45052	0.95173	1.05072	1.38051	0.72437	25
36	0.68962	1.45007	0.95229	1.05010	1.38089	0.72417	24
37	0.68983	1.44963	0.95284	1.04949	1.38127	0.72397	23
38	0.69004	1.44919	0.95340	1.04888	1.38165	0.72377	22
39	0.69025	1.44875	0.95395	1.04827	1.38204	0.72357	21
40	0.69046	1.44831	0.95451	1.04766	1.38242	0.72337	20
41	0.69067	1.44787	0.95506	1.04705	1.38280	0.72317	19
42	0.69088	1.44742	0.95562	1.04644	1.38319	0.72297	18
43	0.69109	1.44698	0.95618	1.04583	1.38357	0.72277	17
44	0.69130	1.44654	0.95673	1.04522	1.38396	0.72257	16
45	0.69151	1.44610	0.95729	1.04461	1.38434	0.72236	15
46	0.69172	1.44567	0.95785	1.04401	1.38473	0.72216	14
47	0.69193	1.44523	0.95841	1.04340	1.38512	0.72196	13
48	0.69214	1.44479	0.95897	1.04279	1.38550	0.72176	12
49	0.69235	1.44435	0.95952	1.04218	1.38589	0.72156	11
50	0.69256	1.44391	0.96008	1.04158	1.38628	0.72136	10
51	0.69277	1.44347	0.96064	1.04097	1.38666	0.72116	9
52	0.69298	1.44304	0.96120	1.04036	1.38705	0.72095	8
53	0.69319	1.44260	0.96176	1.03976	1.38744	0.72075	7
54	0.69340	1.44217	0.96232	1.03915	1.38783	0.72055	6
55	0.69361	1.44173	0.96288	1.03855	1.38822	0.72035	5
56	0.69382	1.44129	0.96344	1.03794	1.38860	0.72015	4
57	0.69403	1.44086	0.96400	1.03734	1.38899	0.71995	3
58	0.69424	1.44042	0.96457	1.03674	1.38938	0.71974	2
59	0.69445	1.43999	0.96513	1.03613	1.38977	0.71954	1
60	0.69466	1.43956	0.96569	1.03553	1.39016	0.71934	0

133°→ cos	sec	cot	tan	csc	sin ←46°	

44°→ sin	csc	tan	cot	sec	cos ←135°	
0 0.69466	1.43956	0.96569	1.03553	1.39016	0.71934	60
1 0.69487	1.43912	0.96625	1.03493	1.39055	0.71914	59
2 0.69508	1.43869	0.96681	1.03433	1.39095	0.71894	58
3 0.69529	1.43826	0.96738	1.03372	1.39134	0.71873	57
4 0.69549	1.43783	0.96794	1.03312	1.39173	0.71853	56
5 0.69570	1.43739	0.96850	1.03252	1.39212	0.71833	55
6 0.69591	1.43696	0.96907	1.03192	1.39251	0.71813	54
7 0.69612	1.43653	0.96963	1.03132	1.39291	0.71792	53
8 0.69633	1.43610	0.97020	1.03072	1.39330	0.71772	52
9 0.69654	1.43567	0.97076	1.03012	1.39369	0.71752	51
10 0.69675	1.43524	0.97133	1.02952	1.39409	0.71732	50
11 0.69696	1.43481	0.97189	1.02892	1.39448	0.71711	49
12 0.69717	1.43438	0.97246	1.02832	1.39487	0.71691	48
13 0.69737	1.43395	0.97302	1.02772	1.39527	0.71671	47
14 0.69758	1.43352	0.97359	1.02713	1.39566	0.71650	46
15 0.69779	1.43309	0.97416	1.02653	1.39606	0.71630	45
16 0.69800	1.43267	0.97472	1.02593	1.39646	0.71610	44
17 0.69821	1.43224	0.97529	1.02533	1.39685	0.71590	43
18 0.69842	1.43181	0.97586	1.02474	1.39725	0.71569	42
19 0.69862	1.43139	0.97643	1.02414	1.39764	0.71549	41
20 0.69883	1.43096	0.97700	1.02355	1.39804	0.71529	40
21 0.69904	1.43053	0.97756	1.02295	1.39844	0.71508	39
22 0.69925	1.43011	0.97813	1.02236	1.39884	0.71488	38
23 0.69946	1.42968	0.97870	1.02176	1.39924	0.71468	37
24 0.69966	1.42926	0.97927	1.02117	1.39963	0.71447	36
25 0.69987	1.42883	0.97984	1.02057	1.40003	0.71427	35
26 0.70008	1.42841	0.98041	1.01998	1.40043	0.71407	34
27 0.70029	1.42799	0.98098	1.01939	1.40083	0.71386	33
28 0.70049	1.42756	0.98155	1.01879	1.40123	0.71366	32
29 0.70070	1.42714	0.98213	1.01820	1.40163	0.71345	31
30 0.70091	1.42672	0.98270	1.01761	1.40203	0.71325	30
31 0.70112	1.42630	0.98327	1.01702	1.40243	0.71305	29
32 0.70132	1.42587	0.98384	1.01642	1.40283	0.71284	28
33 0.70153	1.42545	0.98441	1.01583	1.40324	0.71264	27
34 0.70174	1.42503	0.98499	1.01524	1.40364	0.71243	26
35 0.70195	1.42461	0.98556	1.01465	1.40404	0.71223	25
36 0.70215	1.42419	0.98613	1.01406	1.40444	0.71203	24
37 0.70236	1.42377	0.98671	1.01347	1.40485	0.71182	23
38 0.70257	1.42335	0.98728	1.01288	1.40525	0.71162	22
39 0.70277	1.42293	0.98786	1.01229	1.40565	0.71141	21
40 0.70298	1.42251	0.98843	1.01170	1.40606	0.71121	20
41 0.70319	1.42209	0.98901	1.01112	1.40646	0.71100	19
42 0.70339	1.42168	0.98958	1.01053	1.40687	0.71080	18
43 0.70360	1.42126	0.99016	1.00994	1.40727	0.71059	17
44 0.70381	1.42084	0.99073	1.00935	1.40768	0.71039	16
45 0.70401	1.42042	0.99131	1.00876	1.40808	0.71019	15
46 0.70422	1.42001	0.99189	1.00818	1.40849	0.70998	14
47 0.70443	1.41959	0.99247	1.00759	1.40890	0.70978	13
48 0.70463	1.41918	0.99304	1.00701	1.40930	0.70957	12
49 0.70484	1.41876	0.99362	1.00642	1.40971	0.70937	11
50 0.70505	1.41835	0.99420	1.00583	1.41012	0.70916	10
51 0.70525	1.41793	0.99478	1.00525	1.41053	0.70896	9
52 0.70546	1.41752	0.99536	1.00467	1.41093	0.70875	8
53 0.70567	1.41710	0.99594	1.00408	1.41134	0.70855	7
54 0.70587	1.41669	0.99652	1.00350	1.41175	0.70834	6
55 0.70608	1.41627	0.99710	1.00291	1.41216	0.70813	5
56 0.70628	1.41586	0.99768	1.00233	1.41257	0.70793	4
57 0.70649	1.41545	0.99826	1.00175	1.41298	0.70772	3
58 0.70670	1.41504	0.99884	1.00116	1.41339	0.70752	2
59 0.70690	1.41463	0.99942	1.00058	1.41380	0.70731	1
60 0.70711	1.41421	1.00000	1.00000	1.41421	0.70711	0
134° cos	sec	cot	tan	csc	sin ←45°	

TABLE OF SQUARES AND SQUARE ROOTS

n	n^2	$\sqrt{n}$	n	n^2	$\sqrt{n}$	n	n^2	$\sqrt{n}$
1	1	1.0000	51	2,601	7.1414	101	10,201	10.0499
2	4	1.4142	52	2,704	7.2111	102	10,404	10.0995
3	9	1.7321	53	2,809	7.2801	103	10,609	10.1489
4	16	2.0000	54	2,916	7.3485	104	10,816	10.1980
5	25	2.2361	55	3,025	7.4162	105	11,025	10.2470
6	36	2.4495	56	3,136	7.4833	106	11,236	10.2956
7	49	2.6458	57	3,249	7.5498	107	11,449	10.3441
8	64	2.8284	58	3,364	7.6158	108	11,664	10.3923
9	81	3.0000	59	3,481	7.6811	109	11,881	10.4403
10	100	3.1623	60	3,600	7.7460	110	12,100	10.4881
11	121	3.3166	61	3,721	7.8102	111	12,321	10.5357
12	144	3.4641	62	3,844	7.8740	112	12,544	10.5830
13	169	3.6056	63	3,969	7.9373	113	12,769	10.6301
14	196	3.7417	64	4,096	8.0000	114	12,996	10.6771
15	225	3.8730	65	4,225	8.0623	115	13,225	10.7238
16	256	4.0000	66	4,356	8.1240	116	13,456	10.7703
17	289	4.1231	67	4,489	8.1854	117	13,689	10.8167
18	324	4.2426	68	4,624	8.2462	118	13,924	10.8628
19	361	4.3589	69	4,761	8.3066	119	14,161	10.9087
20	400	4.4721	70	4,900	8.3666	120	14,400	10.9545
21	441	4.5826	71	5,041	8.4261	121	14,641	11.0000
22	484	4.6904	72	5,184	8.4853	122	14,884	11.0454
23	529	4.7958	73	5,329	8.5440	123	15,129	11.0905
24	576	4.8990	74	5,476	8.6023	124	15,376	11.1355
25	625	5.0000	75	5,625	8.6603	125	15,625	11.1803
26	676	5.0990	76	5,776	8.7178	126	15,876	11.2250
27	729	5.1962	77	5,929	8.7750	127	16,129	11.2694
28	784	5.2915	78	6,084	8.8318	128	16,384	11.3137
29	841	5.3852	79	6,241	8.8882	129	16,641	11.3578
30	900	5.4772	80	6,400	8.9443	130	16,900	11.4018
31	961	5.5678	81	6,561	9.0000	131	17,161	11.4455
32	1,024	5.6569	82	6,724	9.0554	132	17,424	11.4891
33	1,089	5.7446	83	6,889	9.1104	133	17,689	11.5326
34	1,156	5.8310	84	7,056	9.1652	134	17,956	11.5758
35	1,225	5.9161	85	7,225	9.2195	135	18,225	11.6190
36	1,296	6.0000	86	7,396	9.2736	136	18,496	11.6619
37	1,369	6.0828	87	7,569	9.3274	137	18,769	11.7047
38	1,444	6.1644	88	7,744	9.3808	138	19,044	11.7473
39	1,521	6.2450	89	7,921	9.4340	139	19,321	11.7898
40	1,600	6.3246	90	8,100	9.4868	140	19,600	11.8322
41	1,681	6.4031	91	8,281	9.5394	141	19,881	11.8743
42	1,764	6.4807	92	8,464	9.5917	142	20,164	11.9164
43	1,849	6.5574	93	8,649	9.6437	143	20,449	11.9583
44	1,936	6.6332	94	8,836	9.6954	144	20,736	12.0000
45	2,025	6.7082	95	9,025	9.7468	145	21,025	12.0416
46	2,116	6.7823	96	9,216	9.7980	146	21,316	12.0830
47	2,209	6.8557	97	9,409	9.8489	147	21,609	12.1244
48	2,304	6.9282	98	9,604	9.8995	148	21,904	12.1655
49	2,401	7.0000	99	9,801	9.9499	149	22,201	12.2066
50	2,500	7.0711	100	10,000	10.0000	150	22,500	12.2474

n	n²	√n	n	n²	√n	n	n²	√n
151	22,801	12.2882	201	40,401	14.1774	251	63,001	15.8430
152	23,104	12.3288	202	40,804	14.2127	252	63,504	15.8745
153	23,409	12.3693	203	41,209	14.2478	253	64,009	15.9060
154	23,716	12.4097	204	41,616	14.2829	254	64,516	15.9374
155	24,025	12.4499	205	42,025	14.3178	255	65,025	15.9687
156	24,336	12.4900	206	42,436	14.3527	256	65,536	16.0000
157	24,649	12.5300	207	42,849	14.3875	257	66,049	16.0312
158	24,964	12.5698	208	43,264	14.4222	258	66,564	16.0624
159	25,281	12.6095	209	43,681	14.4568	259	67,081	16.0935
160	25,600	12.6491	210	44,100	14.4914	260	67,600	16.1245
161	25,921	12.6886	211	44,521	14.5258	261	68,121	16.1555
162	26,244	12.7279	212	44,944	14.5602	262	68,644	16.1864
163	26,569	12.7671	213	45,369	14.5945	263	69,169	16.2173
164	26,896	12.8062	214	45,796	14.6287	264	69,696	16.2481
165	27,225	12.8452	215	46,225	14.6629	265	70,225	16.2788
166	27,556	12.8841	216	46,656	14.6969	266	70,756	16.3095
167	27,889	12.9228	217	47,089	14.7309	267	71,289	16.3401
168	28,224	12.9615	218	47,524	14.7648	268	71,824	16.3707
169	28,561	13.0000	219	47,961	14.7986	269	72,361	16.4012
170	28,900	13.0384	220	48,400	14.8324	270	72,900	16.4317
171	29,241	13.0767	221	48,841	14.8661	271	73,441	16.4621
172	29,584	13.1149	222	49,284	14.8997	272	73,984	16.4924
173	29,929	13.1529	223	49,729	14.9332	273	74,529	16.5227
174	30,276	13.1909	224	50,176	14.9666	274	75,076	16.5529
175	30,625	13.2288	225	50,625	15.0000	275	75,625	16.5831
176	30,976	13.2665	226	51,076	15.0333	276	76,176	16.6132
177	31,329	13.3041	227	51,529	15.0665	277	76,729	16.6433
178	31,684	13.3417	228	51,984	15.0997	278	77,284	16.6733
179	32,041	13.3791	229	52,441	15.1327	279	77,841	16.7033
180	32,400	13.4164	230	52,900	15.1658	280	78,400	16.7332
181	32,761	13.4536	231	53,361	15.1987	281	78,961	16.7631
182	33,124	13.4907	232	53,824	15.2315	282	79,524	16.7929
183	33,489	13.5277	233	54,289	15.2643	283	80,089	16.8226
184	33,856	13.5647	234	54,756	15.2971	284	80,656	16.8523
185	34,225	13.6015	235	55,225	15.3297	285	81,225	16.8819
186	34,596	13.6382	236	55,696	15.3623	286	81,796	16.9115
187	34,969	13.6748	237	56,169	15.3948	287	82,369	16.9411
188	35,344	13.7113	238	56,644	15.4272	288	82,944	16.9706
189	35,721	13.7477	239	57,121	15.4596	289	83,521	17.0000
190	36,100	13.7840	240	57,600	15.4919	290	84,100	17.0294
191	36,481	13.8203	241	58,081	15.5242	291	84,681	17.0587
192	36,864	13.8564	242	58,564	15.5563	292	85,264	17.0880
193	37,249	13.8924	243	59,049	15.5885	293	85,849	17.1172
194	37,636	13.9284	244	59,536	15.6205	294	86,436	17.1464
195	38,025	13.9642	245	60,025	15.6525	295	87,025	17.1756
196	38,416	14.0000	246	60,516	15.6844	296	87,616	17.2047
197	38,809	14.0357	247	61,009	15.7162	297	88,209	17.2337
198	39,204	14.0712	248	61,504	15.7480	298	88,804	17.2627
199	39,601	14.1067	249	62,001	15.7797	299	89,401	17.2916
200	40,000	14.1421	250	62,500	15.8114	300	90,000	17.3205

n	n²	√n	n	n²	√n	n	n²	√n
301	90,601	17.3494	351	123,201	18.7350	401	160,801	20.0250
302	91,204	17.3781	352	123,904	18.7617	402	161,604	20.0499
303	91,809	17.4069	353	124,609	18.7883	403	162,409	20.0749
304	92,416	17.4356	354	125,316	18.8149	404	163,216	20.0998
305	93,025	17.4642	355	126,025	18.8414	405	164,025	20.1246
306	93,636	17.4929	356	126,736	18.8680	406	164,836	20.1494
307	94,249	17.5214	357	127,449	18.8944	407	165,649	20.1742
308	94,864	17.5499	358	128,164	18.9209	408	166,464	20.1990
309	95,481	17.5784	359	128,881	18.9473	409	167,281	20.2237
310	96,100	17.6068	360	129,600	18.9737	410	168,100	20.2485
311	96,721	17.6352	361	130,321	19.0000	411	168,921	20.2731
312	97,344	17.6635	362	131,044	19.0263	412	169,744	20.2978
313	97,969	17.6918	363	131,769	19.0526	413	170,569	20.3224
314	98,596	17.7200	364	132,496	19.0788	414	171,396	20.3470
315	99,225	17.7482	365	133,225	19.1050	415	172,225	20.3715
316	99,856	17.7764	366	133,956	19.1311	416	173,056	20.3961
317	100,489	17.8045	367	134,689	19.1572	417	173,889	20.4206
318	101,124	17.8326	368	135,424	19.1833	418	174,724	20.4450
319	101,761	17.8606	369	136,161	19.2094	419	175,561	20.4695
320	102,400	17.8885	370	136,900	19.2354	420	176,400	20.4939
321	103,041	17.9165	371	137,641	19.2614	421	177,241	20.5183
322	103,684	17.9444	372	138,384	19.2873	422	178,084	20.5426
323	104,329	17.9722	373	139,129	19.3132	423	178,929	20.5670
324	104,976	18.0000	374	139,876	19.3391	424	179,776	20.5913
325	105,625	18.0278	375	140,625	19.3649	425	180,625	20.6155
326	106,276	18.0555	376	141,376	19.3907	426	181,476	20.6398
327	106,929	18.0831	377	142,129	19.4165	427	182,329	20.6640
328	107,584	18.1108	378	142,884	19.4422	428	183,184	20.6882
329	108,241	18.1384	379	143,641	19.4679	429	184,041	20.7123
330	108,900	18.1659	380	144,400	19.4936	430	184,900	20.7364
331	109,561	18.1934	381	145,161	19.5192	431	185,761	20.7605
332	110,224	18.2209	382	145,924	19.5448	432	186,624	20.7846
333	110,889	18.2483	383	146,689	19.5704	433	187,489	20.8087
334	111,556	18.2757	384	147,456	19.5959	434	188,356	20.8327
335	112,225	18.3030	385	148,225	19.6214	435	189,225	20.8567
336	112,896	18.3303	386	148,996	19.6469	436	190,096	20.8806
337	113,569	18.3576	387	149,769	19.6723	437	190,969	20.9045
338	114,244	18.3848	388	150,544	19.6977	438	191,844	20.9284
339	114,921	18.4120	389	151,321	19.7231	439	192,721	20.9523
340	115,600	18.4391	390	152,100	19.7484	440	193,600	20.9762
341	116,281	18.4662	391	152,881	19.7737	441	194,481	21.0000
342	116,964	18.4932	392	153,664	19.7990	442	195,364	21.0238
343	117,649	18.5203	393	154,449	19.8242	443	196,249	21.0476
344	118,336	18.5472	394	155,236	19.8494	444	197,136	21.0713
345	119,025	18.5742	395	156,025	19.8746	445	198,025	21.0950
346	119,716	18.6011	396	156,816	19.8997	446	198,916	21.1187
347	120,409	18.6279	397	157,609	19.9249	447	199,809	21.1424
348	121,104	18.6548	398	158,404	19.9499	448	200,704	21.1660
349	121,801	18.6815	399	159,201	19.9750	449	201,601	21.1896
350	122,500	18.7083	400	160,000	20.0000	450	202,500	21.2132

n	n²	√n	n	n²	√n	n	n²	√n
451	203,401	21.2368	501	251,001	22.3830	551	303,601	23.4734
452	204,304	21.2603	502	252,004	22.4054	552	304,704	23.4947
453	205,209	21.2838	503	253,009	22.4277	553	305,809	23.5160
454	206,116	21.3073	504	254,016	22.4499	554	306,916	23.5372
455	207,025	21.3307	505	255,025	22.4722	555	308,025	23.5584
456	207,936	21.3542	506	256,036	22.4944	556	309,136	23.5797
457	208,849	21.3776	507	257,049	22.5167	557	310,249	23.6008
458	209,764	21.4009	508	258,064	22.5389	558	311,364	23.6220
459	210,681	21.4243	509	259,081	22.5610	559	312,481	23.6432
460	211,600	21.4476	510	260,100	22.5832	560	313,600	23.6643
461	212,521	21.4709	511	261,121	22.6053	561	314,721	23.6854
462	213,444	21.4942	512	262,144	22.6274	562	315,844	23.7065
463	214,369	21.5174	513	263,169	22.6495	563	316,969	23.7276
464	215,296	21.5407	514	264,196	22.6716	564	318,096	23.7487
465	216,225	21.5639	515	265,225	22.6936	565	319,225	23.7697
466	217,156	21.5870	516	266,256	22.7156	566	320,356	23.7908
467	218,089	21.6102	517	267,289	22.7376	567	321,489	23.8118
468	219,024	21.6333	518	268,324	22.7596	568	322,624	23.8328
469	219,961	21.6564	519	269,361	22.7816	569	323,761	23.8537
470	220,900	21.6795	520	270,400	22.8035	570	324,900	23.8747
471	221,841	21.7025	521	271,441	22.8254	571	326,041	23.8956
472	222,784	21.7256	522	272,484	22.8473	572	327,184	23.9165
473	223,729	21.7486	523	273,529	22.8692	573	328,329	23.9374
474	224,676	21.7715	524	274,576	22.8910	574	329,476	23.9583
475	225,625	21.7945	525	275,625	22.9129	575	330,625	23.9792
476	226,576	21.8174	526	276,676	22.9347	576	331,776	24.0000
477	227,529	21.8403	527	277,729	22.9565	577	332,929	24.0208
478	228,484	21.8632	528	278,784	22.9783	578	334,084	24.0416
479	229,441	21.8861	529	279,841	23.0000	579	335,241	24.0624
480	230,400	21.9089	530	280,900	23.0217	580	336,400	24.0832
481	231,361	21.9317	531	281,961	23.0434	581	337,561	24.1039
482	232,324	21.9545	532	283,024	23.0651	582	338,724	24.1247
483	233,289	21.9773	533	284,089	23.0868	583	339,889	24.1454
484	234,256	22.0000	534	285,156	23.1084	584	341,056	24.1661
485	235,225	22.0227	535	286,225	23.1301	585	342,225	24.1868
486	236,196	22.0454	536	287,296	23.1517	586	343,396	24.2074
487	237,169	22.0681	537	288,369	23.1733	587	344,569	24.2281
488	238,144	22.0907	538	289,444	23.1948	588	345,744	24.2487
489	239,121	22.1133	539	290,521	23.2164	589	346,921	24.2693
490	240,100	22.1359	540	291,600	23.2379	590	348,100	24.2899
491	241,081	22.1585	541	292,681	23.2594	591	349,281	24.3105
492	242,064	22.1811	542	293,764	23.2809	592	350,464	24.3311
493	243,049	22.2036	543	294,849	23.3024	593	351,649	24.3516
494	244,036	22.2261	544	295,936	23.3238	594	352,836	24.3721
495	245,025	22.2486	545	297,025	23.3452	595	354,025	24.3926
496	246,016	22.2711	546	298,116	23.3666	596	355,216	24.4131
497	247,009	22.2935	547	299,209	23.3880	597	356,409	24.4336
498	248,004	22.3159	548	300,304	23.4094	598	357,604	24.4540
499	249,001	22.3383	549	301,401	23.4307	599	358,801	24.4745
500	250,000	22.3607	550	302,500	23.4521	600	360,000	24.4949

n	n²	√n	n	n²	√n	n	n²	√n
601	361,201	24.5153	651	423,801	25.5147	701	491,401	26.4764
602	362,404	24.5357	652	425,104	25.5343	702	492,804	26.4953
603	363,609	24.5561	653	426,409	25.5539	703	494,209	26.5141
604	364,816	24.5764	654	427,716	25.5734	704	495,616	26.5330
605	366,025	24.5967	655	429,025	25.5930	705	497,025	26.5518
606	367,236	24.6171	656	430,336	25.6125	706	498,436	26.5707
607	368,449	24.6374	657	431,649	25.6320	707	499,849	26.5895
608	369,664	24.6577	658	432,964	25.6515	708	501,264	26.6083
609	370,881	24.6779	659	434,281	25.6710	709	502,681	26.6271
610	372,100	24.6982	660	435,600	25.6905	710	504,100	26.6458
611	373,321	24.7184	661	436,921	25.7099	711	505,521	26.6646
612	374,544	24.7386	662	438,244	25.7294	712	506,944	26.6833
613	375,769	24.7588	663	439,569	25.7488	713	508,369	26.7021
614	376,996	24.7790	664	440,896	25.7682	714	509,796	26.7208
615	378,225	24.7992	665	442,225	25.7876	715	511,225	26.7395
616	379,456	24.8193	666	443,556	25.8070	716	512,656	26.7582
617	380,689	24.8395	667	444,889	25.8263	717	514,089	26.7769
618	381,924	24.8596	668	446,224	25.8457	718	515,524	26.7955
619	383,161	24.8797	669	447,561	25.8650	719	516,961	26.8142
620	384,400	24.8998	670	448,900	25.8844	720	518,400	26.8328
621	385,641	24.9199	671	450,241	25.9037	721	519,841	26.8514
622	386,884	24.9399	672	451,584	25.9230	722	521,284	26.8701
623	388,129	24.9600	673	452,929	25.9422	723	522,729	26.8887
624	389,376	24.9800	674	454,276	25.9615	724	524,176	26.9072
625	390,625	25.0000	675	455,625	25.9808	725	525,625	26.9258
626	391,876	25.0200	676	456,976	26.0000	726	527,076	26.9444
627	393,129	25.0400	677	458,329	26.0192	727	528,529	26.9629
628	394,384	25.0599	678	459,684	26.0384	728	529,984	26.9815
629	395,641	25.0799	679	461,041	26.0576	729	531,441	27.0000
630	396,900	25.0998	680	462,400	26.0768	730	532,900	27.0185
631	398,161	25.1197	681	463,761	26.0960	731	534,361	27.0370
632	399,424	25.1396	682	465,124	26.1151	732	535,824	27.0555
633	400,689	25.1595	683	466,489	26.1343	733	537,289	27.0740
634	401,956	25.1794	684	467,856	26.1534	734	538,756	27.0924
635	403,225	25.1992	685	469,225	26.1725	735	540,225	27.1109
636	404,496	25.2190	686	470,596	26.1916	736	541,696	27.1293
637	405,769	25.2389	687	471,969	26.2107	737	543,169	27.1477
638	407,044	25.2587	688	473,344	26.2298	738	544,644	27.1662
639	408,321	25.2784	689	474,721	26.2488	739	546,121	27.1846
640	409,600	25.2982	690	476,100	26.2679	740	547,600	27.2029
641	410,881	25.3180	691	477,481	26.2869	741	549,081	27.2213
642	412,164	25.3377	692	478,864	26.3059	742	550,564	27.2397
643	413,449	25.3574	693	480,249	26.3249	743	552,049	27.2580
644	414,736	25.3772	694	481,636	26.3439	744	553,536	27.2764
645	416,025	25.3969	695	483,025	26.3629	745	555,025	27.2947
646	417,316	25.4165	696	484,416	26.3818	746	556,516	27.3130
647	418,609	25.4362	697	485,809	26.4008	747	558,009	27.3313
648	419,904	25.4558	698	487,204	26.4197	748	559,504	27.3496
649	421,201	25.4755	699	488,601	26.4386	749	561,001	27.3679
650	422,500	25.4951	700	490,000	26.4575	750	562,500	27.3861

n	n²	√n	n	n²	√n	n	n²	√n
751	564,001	27.4044	801	641,601	28.3019	851	724,201	29.1719
752	565,504	27.4226	802	643,204	28.3196	852	725,904	29.1890
753	567,009	27.4408	803	644,809	28.3373	853	727,609	29.2062
754	568,516	27.4591	804	646,416	28.3549	854	729,316	29.2233
755	570,025	27.4773	805	648,025	28.3725	855	731,025	29.2404
756	571,536	27.4955	806	649,636	28.3901	856	732,736	29.2575
757	573,049	27.5136	807	651,249	28.4077	857	734,449	29.2746
758	574,564	27.5318	808	652,864	28.4253	858	736,164	29.2916
759	576,081	27.5500	809	654,481	28.4429	859	737,881	29.3087
760	577,600	27.5681	810	656,100	28.4605	860	739,600	29.3258
761	579,121	27.5862	811	657,721	28.4781	861	741,321	29.3428
762	580,644	27.6043	812	659,344	28.4956	862	743,044	29.3598
763	582,169	27.6225	813	660,969	28.5132	863	744,769	29.3769
764	583,696	27.6405	814	662,596	28.5307	864	746,496	29.3939
765	585,225	27.6586	815	664,225	28.5482	865	748,225	29.4109
766	586,756	27.6767	816	665,856	28.5657	866	749,956	29.4279
767	588,289	27.6948	817	667,489	28.5832	867	751,689	29.4449
768	589,824	27.7128	818	669,124	28.6007	868	753,424	29.4618
769	591,361	27.7308	819	670,761	28.6182	869	755,161	29.4788
770	592,900	27.7489	820	672,400	28.6356	870	756,900	29.4958
771	594,441	27.7669	821	674,041	28.6531	871	758,641	29.5127
772	595,984	27.7849	822	675,684	28.6705	872	760,384	29.5296
773	597,529	27.8029	823	677,329	28.6880	873	762,129	29.5466
774	599,076	27.8209	824	678,976	28.7054	874	763,876	29.5635
775	600,625	27.8388	825	680,625	28.7228	875	765,625	29.5804
776	602,176	27.8568	826	682,276	28.7402	876	767,376	29.5973
777	603,729	27.8747	827	683,929	28.7576	877	769,129	29.6142
778	605,284	27.8927	828	685,584	28.7750	878	770,884	29.6311
779	606,841	27.9106	829	687,241	28.7924	879	772,641	29.6479
780	608,400	27.9285	830	688,900	28.8097	880	774,400	29.6648
781	609,961	27.9464	831	690,561	28.8271	881	776,161	29.6816
782	611,524	27.9643	832	692,224	28.8444	882	777,924	29.6985
783	613,089	27.9821	833	693,889	28.8617	883	779,689	29.7153
784	614,656	28.0000	834	695,556	28.8791	884	781,456	29.7321
785	616,225	28.0179	835	697,225	28.8964	885	783,225	29.7489
786	617,796	28.0357	836	698,896	28.9137	886	784,996	29.7658
787	619,369	28.0535	837	700,569	28.9310	887	786,769	29.7825
788	620,944	28.0713	838	702,244	28.9482	888	788,544	29.7993
789	622,521	28.0891	839	703,921	28.9655	889	790,321	29.8161
790	624,100	28.1069	840	705,600	28.9828	890	792,100	29.8329
791	625,681	28.1247	841	707,281	29.0000	891	793,881	29.8496
792	627,264	28.1425	842	708,964	29.0172	892	795,664	29.8664
793	628,849	28.1603	843	710,649	29.0345	893	797,449	29.8831
794	630,436	28.1780	844	712,336	29.0517	894	799,236	29.8998
795	632,025	28.1957	845	714,025	29.0689	895	801,025	29.9166
796	633,616	28.2135	846	715,716	29.0861	896	802,816	29.9333
797	635,209	28.2312	847	717,409	29.1033	897	804,609	29.9500
798	636,804	28.2489	848	719,104	29.1204	898	806,404	29.9666
799	638,401	28.2666	849	720,801	29.1376	899	808,201	29.9833
800	640,000	28.2843	850	722,500	29.1548	900	810,000	30.0000